SOIL SCIENCE

WITH

34 YEARS GOVT JOBS PYQ'S

FOR

UPSC (IAS, IFS)/ State PCS/ IBPS/ IFFCO/ ADO/ RAEO/ AO/ ARO/ ARS/NET /SRF/ JRF, Pre PG & Ph.D. Entrance Examinations, UPSC, PSCs and Interviews of all Agriculture Services

Dr P D Chaudhary
Agriculture Officer, GOR

Published By

SURAHEE PUBLICATIONS

JAIPUR, Rajasthan

First Edition :June, 2024

Publication & Distributers

Surahee Publications ,
Bobas,Jaipur-303338
(Rajasthan)

Contacts for supply:

Dr. P D Chaudhary+91-9784243509
Mr R N Rundla +91-9782087701
Plot No. 132,Shyampuri , Gali No. 6, Near Pani Ki Tanki,
Kanta Chouraha, Jhotwara
Jaipur,Rajasthan-302012
Email.-prabhu.surahee@gmail.com

SURAHEE PUBLICATIONS, JAIPUR (RAJ), INDIA
SP
Since: 2010

ISBN 978-81-952412-8-6

9 788195 241286

Price: ₹ 325/- (Three Hundred and Twenty Five only)

INDEX

Unit: 1 Soils, Terms, Fathers

Soil Science is the study of soil as a natural resource on the surface of the earth including soil formation, classification and mapping; physical, biological and fertility properties of soils; and these properties in relation to the use and management of soils.

Soil is a natural body of mineral and natural constituents differentiated into horizons usually unconsolidated , of variable depth which differs among themselves as well as from the underlying parent material in morphology , physical makeup, chemical properties and composition and biological characteristics **(Whitney, 1982; Hilgard,18992; Dokuchaiev,1900 and Joffe, 1936).**

According to **Soil Science Society of America (SSSA,1970) soil** is the unconsolidated mineral matter on the surface of the earth that has been subjected to and influenced by genetic and environmental factors of parent material, climate (including moisture and temperature effects0, macro and micro organisms and topography, all affecting over a period of time and producing a product , that is "SOIL" that differs from the material from which it is derived in physical , chemical, biological and morphological properties and characteristics. The unconsolidated mineral material on the immediate surface of the earth, that serves as a natural medium for the growth of plants.

Soil is the fine earth covering land surface that has the important function of serving as a substratum of plant, animal and human life and acts as a reservoir of nutrients and water.

- According to **Buckman and Brady,** " Soil is a dynamic natural body on the surface of the earth in which plants grow, composed of mineral and organic material and living form.
- Soil as natural body composed of mineral and organic constituents, having a definite genesis and a distinct nature of its own.
- **SOIL** is **Latin** word *'Solum'* means **Floor/ ground.**
- Father of **soil science** and modern soil science in world is : **V.V. Dokuchaiev.**
- Father of **pedology : V.V. Dokuchaiev.**
- Father of **Indian Soil Science** : **W. Laerther.**
- Father of modern **Organic farming : Sir Albert Howard**
- Father of **soil Taxonomy is Guy Smith.**
- Father of **soil testing: M.L. Troug**
- Father of **microbiology: S.N. Winogradsky**
- Father of Field Plot Experiment: **Jean-Baptiste Bossingault**
- Father of **GIS – Tomlinson.**
- Law of minimum was proposed by : **J.V. Liebig, 1840.**
- Law of optima and limiting factor: **Blackman, 1905.**
- Law of diminishing returns: **Mitscherlich, 1909.**
- Inverse yield N law / Agro-biology: **Wilcox, 1929.**
- **Zonality concept** was developed by **Dokuchaiev.**
- The term **remote sensing** given by **Evelyn Pruitt (1960).**
- **Alluvial** soils **most recently** formed soils.
- **Red soils** are **best suitable** for **agriculture.**
- Many **pedon** within defined limit is called **soil series** that is **basic unit** of classification.
- **International year of Soil, 2015** (Theme- 'Healthy soil for healthy life')

- **Organic matter** is the **store house of nutrient** in the soil, **source of energy** for micro organism in the soil and **act as chelate.**

Unit-2 : History of Soil Science

Justus Von Liebig: Father of Agriculture Chemistry.(German Chemist); In **1862** he proposed **"Law of Minimum"** may be stated that the level allowed by the most limiting of the essential plant growth factors. It is a simple but logical guide for predicting crop response to fertilization. The united states Department of Agriculture **(USDA)** was established in **1862** and the **first Agricultural Experiment Station in 1886**.

Jean-Baptiste Bossingault (1834): Father of Field Plot Experiment proved that air and water were the primary source of C,H and O in plants.

John Woodward (1699): Earth is sole mineral for plant growth (from his water ulture experiments in spearmint) which is later disproved when hydroponics was proposed by Gericke (1929).

Albrecht Thaer (1809): Proposed 'HUMUS THEORY' which states that humus was regarded as the chief nutrient for plant.

V.V.Dokuchaev: The concept of soil as natural bodies.

Theophrastus (372-287 B.C.) : Recommended manuring of thin soils but suggested that rich soils be manured sparingly. Plants with high nutrient requirement also had a high water requirements. Also recognized the value of green manure crops, particularly legumes.

Virgil (70-19 B.C.) : Advocated the application of legumes. He wrote on soil characteristics known today as **bulk density**.

Pietro de Crescenzi (1230-1307) ➤ *Opus Ruralium Commodorum* a collection of local agricultural practices .Also considered the **founder of modern agronomy**.

Jethro Tull (1674-1741): Father of **tillage** .Soil should be finely pulverized to provide the "proper pabulum" for growing plants. According to him the soil particles were actually ingested through opening in the plant roots.Invented the **grain drill and the horse drawn cultivator** . Wrote the **"Horse Hoeing Husbandry"**

Jan Igenhousz(1730-1799) : Showed that air was purified in the presence of light.

Theodore de Saussre: Worked on the effect of air on plants and the origin of salts in plants. Carbon (C) contained by plantswas derived from the air.

J.B.Lawes & J.H.Gilbert (1843) : Agricultural Experiment Station ,Rothamsted , England was established .

S.Winogradsky: Isolated the organisms responsible for nitrification.

Hellriegel & Wilforth(1886): German scientists gave first specific information regarding N fixation by legumes.

M.W.Beijerink: Isolated *Bacillus radicicola* (now rhizobium) the organism responsible for N fixation.

R.Bray: Nutrient mobility concept. A modification of Mitscherlich's equation was proposed by R.Bray. Crop yield obey the percentage sufficiency law of mitscherlich for such elements P and K which are relatively immobile in soil. Bray has modified the mitscherlich equation to

$Log(A-Y)=LogA-C_1b-CX$

Unit-3: Soil Scientist & their contribution

S.N.	Soil Scientist	→	Their contribution
1.	Atterberg	→	Soil consistency limit

		→	Plasticity limits
2.	Baule	→	Percent yield concept & nutrient sufficiency concept
3.	Beaufils	→	DRIS concept
4.	Beckett	→	Phosphate equilibrium potential
		→	Q /1 (Quantity / Intensity)
5.	Beijerink	→	Isolate *Rhizobium* from root nodules
6.	Blackman	→	Law of limiting factor
7.	Bothe & Becker	→	First Found neutron
8.	Bousingault	→	Father of field plot technique
9.	Bragg	→	X ray diffraction
10.	Bray & Kurtz	→	Phosphate estimation in Acid soil
11.	Buchanan	→	Laterite word
12.	Cameroon	→	Soil is an inexhaustible source of nutrients
13.	Cate & Nelson	→	Critical soil test level approach
14.	Chadwick	→	Coined the term neutron
15.	Chapman	→	Diagnostic technique for soil and plants
16.	Chepil	→	Dry sieving method
17.	Chepil & Wood	→	Wind erosion equation
18.	Colwell	→	Integrated soil test approach
19.	Curie & Joliot	→	Artificial radioactivity
20.	Dachaufour	→	Lessivage term
21.	Dalton	→	Atomic hypothesis
22.	Daniel Hillel	→	Father of Soil physics
23.	Das	→	Phosphate estimation in calcareous soil
24.	De broglie	→	Quantum mechanical model of atom
25.	Debierne	→	Actinium
26.	Devaux	→	Root CEC
27.	Dockuchaev & Sibirtzev	→	Law of adaptability
28.	Dokuchaev	→	Father of Soil Science
		→	Father of Modern Pedology
		→	Genetic system of classification
		→	Zonality concept
		→	Factors of soil formation
		→	Normal and extra-normal soil
29.	E.J. Russel	→	Theory of bonding of clay- clay particle
30.	Epstein	→	Carrier theory
31.	Fallov	→	Residual and transported soil
32.	Ficks law	→	Gaseous exchange between soil & atmosphere
33.	Fried & Dean	→	A value
34.	G.D. Smith	→	Seventh apprximation
35.	Glauber	→	Growth of plants to saltpeter (KNO3)
36.	Goldstein	→	Discovered positive rays
37.	Gris	→	Iron

38.	Guy Smith	→	Father of Soil Taxonomy
39.	Heisenberg	→	Ortho & Para hydrogen
40.	Helmont	→	Increase weight of willow shoot to water
		→	Water is sole nutrient for plant
41.	Henry Becquerel	→	Radioactivity
42.	Hevesy & Hoffer	→	Isotopic dilution
43.	Hole	→	Horizonaion
44.	Holmes	→	Total micronutrient
45.	J.B.Lawes	→	Super phosphate
46.	J.J. Thompson	→	Found e/m value
47.	J.W. Leather	→	Father of Soil Science in India
		→	Father of Agricultural Chemistry in India
48.	Jackson et al	→	Weathering Index
49.	Jenny	→	Parent material is initial stage of soil system
		→	S = f (cl, b, r, p, t) equation for soil formation
		→	Oscillation volume
		→	Classified the factors of soil formation as active & passive factors
		→	Expressed soil age in terms of time
50.	Jenny & Overstreet	→	Root exchange
51.	Joffe	→	Divided soil forming factors into active and passive
52.	John Dalton	→	All matter was composed of atoms
53.	Kappan	→	Total acidity
54.	Kellner & Dyer	→	Fixation of potassium
55.	Kellog	→	Latosols
56.	Kononova	→	Work on organic matter
57.	Kossel & Lewis	→	Octet rule
58.	Kostiakov	→	Equation on infiltration
59.	Krishnamoorthy, Davis, Overstreet	→	Nearest Neighbour Model
60.	La cassageue	→	Auto-radiogaphy
61.	Larsen	→	Y or L value
62.	Lawrence	→	Cyclotron
63.	Leather	→	First imperial agricultural chemist & Father of Soil Science & Agri.Chemistry in India
64.	Lewis & Randol	→	Ionic strength
65.	Libby	→	Carbon dating
		→	Radio carbon dating
66.	Liebig	→	Law of minimum
		→	Law of restitution
		→	Disproved humus theory
		→	Law of limiting nutrient
		→	Father of Agricultural chemistry

		→	Father of fertilizer chemistry
67.	Lindsay & Norvell	→	DTPA extractable micronutrients
		→	Available micronutrients
68.	Lorentz	→	Coined the term electron
69.	Ma Hargue	→	Manganese
70.	Marbut	→	Morphogenetic system of classification
71.	Marshall	→	CEC is next to photosynthesis & pH is physical phenomenon
72.	Mehlich	→	*Aspergillus niger* method
73.	Milne	→	Catena word
74.	Mohr & Van Baren	→	5 Weathering stages (Initial, Juvenile, Virile, Senile and Final)
75.	Mohr & Vanbaren	→	Five stages of soil formation
76.	Mosley	→	Determined atomic number or proton No.
77.	Murhty	→	Benchmark soils of India
78.	Murthy	→	Benchmark soil
79.	Neils bohr	→	Atomic structure for hydrogen
80.	Nernst	→	Third law of thermodynamics
81.	Newlands	→	Law of octaves
82.	Nicholas(1963)	→	Increase weight of plant during growth
		→	Functional nutrient term (or)
		→	Metabolic nutrient term
83.	Russel & Martin	→	Y index
84.	Silen	→	pE concept
85.	Simonson	→	Basic pedogenic processes (Additions or gains, Losses, Transformation and Translocation)
86.	Sorenson (1909)	→	pH term
87.	Thomas Graham	→	Colloid term (1861)
88.	Thompson and Thomas way	→	CEC (Cation Exchange Capacity) concept
89.	Warrington	→	Essentiality of B
90.	Whitney	→	Nutrient bin
91.	Palissy(1563)	→	The ash content of plants represented the material they have removed from the soil.
92.	J.B.Van Helmont	→	Water
93.	John woodward	→	Earth/ Terrestrial matter
94.	Arthur Young	→	Annals of Agriculture
95.	Priestley	→	Oxygen
96.	Cavendish	→	Hydrogen
97.	Briggs(1894)	→	Classification of soil water
98.	Hilgard(1906)	→	Moisture holding capacity
99.	Buckinghum (1907)	→	Capillary Potential
100.	Always (1913)	→	Hygroscopic coefficient
101.	Israelson & West (1922)	→	Field capacity

102.	Briggs & Santz (1912)	→	PWP
103.	Taylor et al. (1934)	→	Ultimate wilting percentage
104.	Schofield (1935)	→	pF
105.	SPL Sorenson (1909)	→	pH
106.	Wadleigh and Ayres (1945)	→	Total soil moisrure stress (TSMS) TSMS=Soil moisture tension + Osmotic pressure of the soil solution
107.	Richard & Gardner (1936)	→	Tensiometer
108.	Bouyoucous and Mick (1940)	→	Gypsum block
109.	Richards (1941)	→	Pressure membrane apparatus
110.	Fireman	→	Pressure plate apparatus
111.	Parshall (1941)	→	Parshall flume

Unit-4: Important events in soil water relationship

S.No.	Scientific contribution	➤	Associated scientist
1.	Classification of soil water	➤	Briggs, 1894
2.	Moisture holding capacity	➤	Hilgard, 1896
3.	Capillary potential	➤	Buckingham, 1907
4.	Moisture equivalent	➤	Briggs and McLane, 1910
5.	Permanent wilting point (PWP)	➤	Briggs and Shantz, 1912
6.	Hygroscopic coefficient	➤	Alway, 1913
7.	Field capacity (FC)	➤	Israelsen and West, 1922
8.	Ultimate wilting point	➤	Taylor et al., 1934
9.	pF, Ratio law	➤	Schofield, 1935
10.	Tensiometer or irrometer	➤	Richards and Gardner, 1936
11.	Gypsum block/ Electrical resistance	➤	Bouyoucos and Mick, 1940
12.	Permanent membrane apparatus (PMA)	➤	Richards, 1941
13.	Parshall flume	➤	Parshall, 1941
14.	Pressure plate apparatus (PPA)	➤	Richards and Fireman, 1941
15.	Total soil moisture stress (TSMS)	➤	Wadeigh and Aiyer, 1945
16.	Available water	➤	Veihmeyer and Hendrickson
17.	Darcy law	➤	Henry Darcy
18.	PET	➤	Thornthwaite, 1948
19.	Term 'Effective rainfall'	➤	N. G. Dastane
20.	Modified Penman method	➤	Doorenbos and Prutt, 1977
21.	Term 'water harvesting.'	➤	Myors
22.	Water expense efficiency	➤	Parihar et al., 1976
23.	Combination approach' of irrigation scheduling	➤	Doorenbos and Kassam, 1979
24.	Surge irrigation system	➤	Stringham and Keller, 1979
25.	Drip irrigation system	➤	Simcha Blass, 1964
26.	RSC (Residual Sodium Carbonate)	➤	Eaton, 1950
27.	Leaching requirement	➤	Richards, 1954

28.	SPAC concept	➤	Huber, 1924
29.	Water balance concept	➤	Thornthwaite
30.	ET first time used for calculation by	➤	Thornthwaite
31.	Author of book 'Irrigation Agronomy.'	➤	N. G. Dastane
32.	Author of book 'Irrigation Engineering.'	➤	A.M. Michael

Unit-5 : Different Laws of soil science

S.No.	Name of law	➤	Scientist
1.	Law of Minimum	➤	Liebig
2.	Law of Maximum	➤	Wallace and Wallace
3.	Law of Tolerance	➤	Schofiled
4.	Law of Limiting Nutrient	➤	Liebig
5.	Law of Limiting Factor	➤	Blackman
6.	Law of Optimum	➤	Velayutham
7.	Law of Diminishing Returns	➤	Mitscherlich
8.	Law of Restitution	➤	Liebig

Unit-6: Facts of soil science (highest)

S. NO	Particular	➤	Highest For
1	Category for soil classification	➤	Order
2	AEC	➤	Kaolinite
3	CEC	➤	Vermiculite
4	Total surface area	➤	Vermiculite
5	Internal surface area	➤	Smectite (Montmorillonite)
6	C : N ratio	➤	Saw dust (600 : 1)
7	Porosity	➤	Clay soil
8	Saturated flow	➤	Sandy soil
9	Unsaturated flow	➤	Clay soil
10	Bulk density	➤	Sandy soil
11	Thermal conductivity	➤	Sandy soil
12	Hydraulic conductivity	➤	Sandy soil
13	Electro negativity	➤	F (Flourine)
14	Ionic potential	➤	Li (Lithium)
15	Dielectric constant	➤	Water (81)
16	Layer charge	➤	Mica and Chlorite
17	Surface Charge Density	➤	Kaolinite
18	Radiation use Efficiency	➤	Maize

Unit-7: Dominants in soils

S. NO	Particular	➤	Dominant

1	Order in India	➤	Inceptisol
2	Silicates in soil system	➤	Phyllo silicates
3	Moisture regime in India	➤	Ustic
4	Exchangeable cation in soil	➤	Ca^{+2}
5	Mineral in Earth crust	➤	Feldspar
6	Metal in Earth crust	➤	Al
7	Element in Earth crust	➤	O_2
8	Organism in soil	➤	Bacteria
9	Potential in soil system	➤	Matric potential

Unit- 8 : Sequences in soils

1	**Chronosequence**	:	A group of soils that differ, one from the other, primarily as a result of **differences in time or age** as a soil forming factor.
2	**Clinosequence**	:	A group of related soils that differ from one another in certain properties primarily as a result of the effect of the **degree of slope** on which they were formed.
3	**Biosequence**	:	A group of related soils that differ, one from other, primarily because of differences in kinds and numbers of **plants and soil organisms** as soil forming factor.
4	**Lithosequence**	:	A group of related soils that differ, one from other, in certain properties primarily as a result of **differences in the parent material** as a soil forming factor.
5	**Toposequence**	:	A sequence of related soils that differ one from the other, primarily **because of topography** as a soil-formation factor

Unit-9 : Approaches of soil study

1. Pedological Approach

- **Pedology**: From **Greek** word *pedon* means **soil** or **earth** and *Logos* means **Study**.
- **Pedology (Natural Body of soil)** is the study of soil as a **natural body** and does not focus on the soils immediate practical use.
- The origin of the soil, its classification and description are examined in **pedology**.
- Father of oedology is known as : **V. Dokuchaiev**.

2. Edaphological Approach:

- **Edaphology**: It derived from two **Greek** words *Edaphos* means **soil** and *Logos* means **Discourse**.
- **Edaphology (Natural habitat of soil for plants)**: Study of various properties of soil in relation to growth, nutrition & yield of crops.

Unit-10 : Branches of soil science:

1. **Soil Chemistry:** study of chemical constituents, chemical properties and the chemical reactions in the soil.

2. **Soil Physics:** Study of physical properties in relation to plant growth.
3. **Soil fertility:** Inherent capacity of soil to supply the plant nutrients in adequate amount without any toxicity to crop plants.
4. **Soil microbiology:** It deals with micro organisms, its population, classification and its role in transformations of nutrients and plant growth.
5. **Soil conservation:** Dealing with protection of soil against physical loss by erosion or against chemical deterioration i.e. excessive loss of nutrients either natural or artificial.
6. **Pedology:** Study of soil genesis, survey and classification.

Unit-11: Soil comparison with human body system

Human body system		**Soil system**
Digestive	→	Matter decomposition
Respiratory	→	Air circulation & exchange of gases
Circulatory	→	Water movement within the soil system
Excretory	→	Leaching out of excessive salts
Brain	→	Soil Clay
Colour	→	Soil colour
Height	→	Soil Depth

Unit-12: Components of soil on volume basis & Weight basis

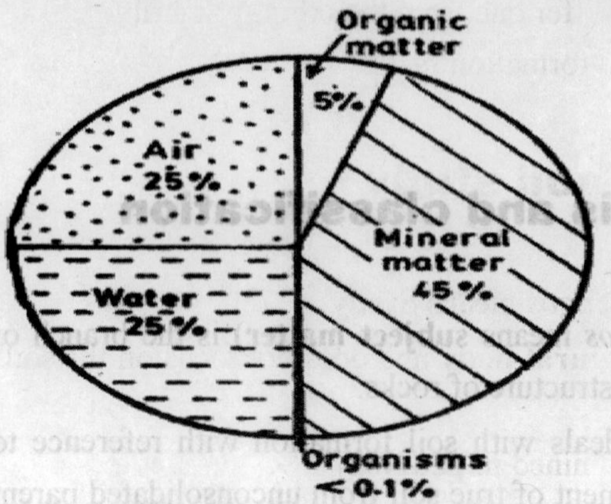

VOLUME COMPOSITION

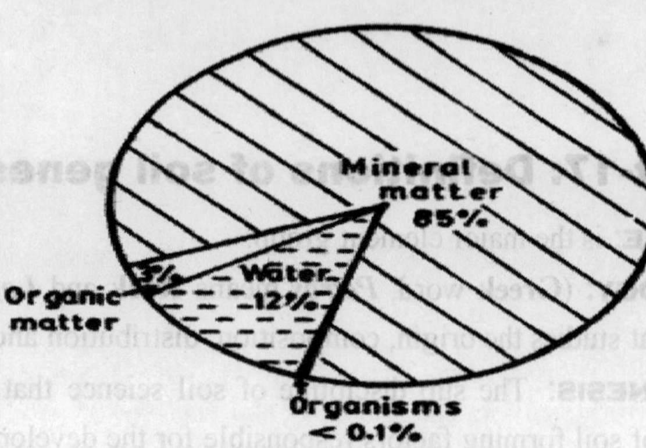

WEIGHT COMPOSITION

Unit-13: Soil Genesis and classification

- **Earth Crust:** Consists of 106 elements and out of which 08 elements makes composition 99% earth crust. Oxygen>silicon>aluminum > iron etc. , in the decreasing order of their amount.
- Earth crust is upto **16 km.**

Unit-14: Mineral percentage in earth crust and soil:

Mineral	In earth crust	In soil
Feldspar	61	2.5
Ferro-magnesium/Amphibol	16	3

Quartz (SiO_2)	13	44.5
Mica	4	0.5
Clay	1	21.5

Unit-15: Classification composition of earth crust

	Element	➤	Earth crust (By Weight %)
1.	Oxygen	➤	46.60%
2.	Si (Silicon)	➤	27.70%
3.	Al (Aluminium)	➤	8.13%
4.	Fe (Iron)	➤	5.00%
5.	Ca (Calcium)	➤	3.63%
6.	Na (Sodium)	➤	2.83%
7.	K (Potassium)	➤	2.59%
8.	Mg (Magnesium)	➤	2.09%
9.	Other	➤	1.41%

Unit-16: Composition of soil air

	Gases	➤	Soil air
1.	Nitrogen (N)	➤	79.2%
2.	Oxygen (O_2)	➤	20.6%
3.	Carbon dioxide (CO_2)	➤	0.25%

Unit-17: Definitions of soil genesis and classification

- **LITHOPILE:** is the major element group.
- **PETROLOGY: (Greek word, *Petros* means Rock and *Logos* means subject matter)** is the branch of geology that studies the origin, composition, distribution and structure of rocks.
- **SOIL GENESIS:** The sub discipline of soil science that deals with soil formation with reference to processes of soil forming factors responsible for the development of true soil from unconsolidated parent material and it is also known as pedogenesis.
- **SOIL CLASSIFICATION:** It is systematic categorization of soils based on distinguishing characteristics as well as choices of use.
- **SOIL SURVEY:** It is systematic examination , description and a mapping of soil in suitable scale is called soil survey.
- **ROCKS:** It is naturally occurring solid aggregate of minerals and mineraloides.
- **PETROGRAPHY:** Deals with the description of rocks and petrogenesis.
- **PETROGENESIS:** Is a study of origin of rocks.
- **MINERALS:** It is naturally occurring inorganic compound that has a definite chemical composition and characteristic geometric form.
  a. **Lithophile elements:** which ionize or form stable oxyanions

b. **Chalcophile elements:** which twnd to form covalent bond with sulphide.
c. **Siderophile elements:** which readily form metallic bonds.
d. **Atmosphile elements:** which tend to remain in atmospheric gases.
e. **Biophile elements:** which tend to associated with living organisms.

Unit-18: Soil Rocks

ROCKS ARE THREE TYPES: 1.Igneous rocks 2. Sedimentary rocks 3. Metamorphic rocks

ROCKS & MINERALS

Sedimentary (stratified) rocks		Igneous rocks	
Shale→52%	74%	Granite→ 15%	18%
Sand stone → 15%		Basalt → 3%	
Lime stone & dolomite →7%		Other rocks →8%	

1. IGNEOUS ROCKS

Based on ≤ mode of origin		Based on chemical composition		
Instrusive or plutonic (Solidification takes place at moderate depths)	**Extrusive or volcanic** (Solidification takes place at surface of depths)	**Acid** (67-75% silica)	**Neutral or intermediate** (55-65% silica)	**Basic** (40-55% silica)
Eg. **Granite**	Eg. **Basalt**	**Eg.Granite, Sandstone**	Eg. **Andesite, Deorite**	**Eg. Basalt, Limestone, Gabbro**

IGNEOUS ROCKS CONTAINS

Feldspar	→	60%
Pyroxene	→	18%
Quartz	→	12%
Mica	→	4%
Others	→	6%

2. SEDIMENTARY ROCKS:

1. Mechanically formed rocks: **Sand stone and shale**
2. Inorganically formed rocks: **Halite and Gypsum** are formed by evaporation.
3. Precipitation and flocculation: **Limestone and Dolomite**
4. Organically formed rocks: **Lignite and Anorthite**

3. METAMORPHIC ROCKS

- Are formed from Igneous and Sedimentary rocks e.g. **Marble, Gneiss, Schist, graphite and slate.**
- **Important conversions:**
    - **Gneiss** ← Granite
    - **Marble** ← Lime stone
    - **Graphite** ← Coal
    - **Slate** ← shale
    - **Quarts** ← sandstone
- **74 per cent sedimentary rock** is found in earth crust while **igneous** rocks present is only **18 per cent**.
- **Granite** is **83 per cent** part of **igneous** rock.
- **Granite** and **Sandstone** are **acidic** nature of rocks.
- Pyroxens , olivine, biotite and amphiboles are called *ferromagnesiam minerals*. These groups are easily weatherable and **main source** of **micro nutrients** in soil.
- Non-ferromagnesian mineral groups are plagioclase feldspar, orthoclase feldspar and quartz.

CLASSIFICATION OF ROCKS (ACCORDING TO THEIR ORIGIN/ MODE OF ACTION)

	Rocks		**Examples**
1.	Acid rocks	➢	Granite , Rhyolite
2.	Sub Acid rock	➢	Syenite and Trachika
3.	Sub basic rocks	➢	Andesite
4.	Basic rocks	➢	Gabbro and Basalt
5.	Ultra basic Rocks	➢	Lime stone
	2. Sedimentary Rocks		
1.	Aranaceous	➢	Sandstone
2.	Agrillaceous	➢	Mudstone
3.	Calcareous	➢	Limestone
4.	Carbonaceous	➢	Calpet
5.	Silicious	➢	Diatomecious
6.	Precipited	➢	Gypsum
	3. Metamorphic Rock		
1.	Hydro metamorphic rocks	➢	Quartzite, Laterite
2.	Dynamo metamorphic rocks	➢	Schist, Gnesis
3.	By Heat (Thermometamorphic)	➢	Marble

IGNEOUS ROCKS CLASSIFIED ON THE BASIS OF CHEMICAL COMPOSITION

	Igneous rocks		**Silica %**
1.	Acid rocks	➢	> 65%
2.	Sub Acid rock	➢	60-65%
3.	Sub basic rocks	➢	55-60%
4.	Basic Rocks	➢	45-55%
5.	Ultra Basic Rocks	➢	< 50-45%

Unit: 19: Soil origin,Weathering, morphology, factors and processes of soil formation:

- Rocks are are the chief source of soil parent material over which soils are formed.
- Soil is formed from weathering of rocks.
- **WEATHERING= Disintegration + Decomposition**
- Disintegration breaks consolidated rocks into unconsolidated parent materials, which on further breaking and chemical decomposition form soil.
- **Weathering** is the process of disintegration and decomposition of rocks , soil and minerals through contact with the Earth's atmosphere , water and biological organisms.

DIFFERENT TYPE OF WEATHERING AND WEATHERING AGENTS:

Physical	Chemical	Biological
Physical condition of rocks	Hydration	Man and animals
Change in temperature	Hydrolysis	Higher plants & their roots
Action of water, action of freezing of glaciers	Solution	
Action of wind and sand	Carbonation	Microbes
Atmospheric electric phenomenon	Oxidation & Reduction	

- **Physical weathering**: Involves agents such as temperature , water, wind, plant and animals and processes such as exfoliation (surface peeling off of rocks), alternate wetting and drying, freezing and thawing.
- **Chemical weathering reactions**: Solution hydration, hydrolysis, carbonation, Oxidation and reduction.
- **Biological weathering**: Due to man, animals, micro organism and roots of higher plants etc.
- **Geo-chemical weathering**: Is the weathering taking place at the layers down below whereas pedo-chemical or pedogenic weathering is the one taking place at the surface and sub surface layers.
- Chemical weathering is not possible without water **(hydrolysis)**
- Soil found at the site of formation is called- **Sedentary soils**
- Soil found far away from the site of formation is called- **Cumulous** or **transported** soils
- **Parent material** is an **end product** of weathering.
- Most resistance mineral to weathering is **quartz** while least resistant is **Gypsum > Calcite > Dolomite.**

Granite —(Weathering)→ Quatz sand → Deposition → (Sand stone)

Quatz sand → Recementation → (Shale)

Weathering minerals:

Most resistant ➤ Quartz

Moderate resistant ➤ Feldspar

Least resistant ➤ Calcite

❖ **Very low→** Quartz, Zircon, Rutile, Magnetite and Illmenite

- **Low** → Orthoclase, Albite, Muscovite and Tourmaline (Boron bearing mineral)
- **Soluble** → Calcite
- **Very High**→ Anorthite, Olivine and Biotite

☛ **Quartz>Muscovite>Feldspar>Biotite>Calcite**

Examples of hydration:

1. Lime stone from Hematite
2. Serpentine from Olivine
3. Gypsum from calcium sulphate

Examples of hydrolysis:

1. Kaolinite from potash feldspar
2. Kaolinite from Biotite
3.

Unit-20: Agent of transportation name of soil formed

S. NO	Name of soil/ Parent material	➤	Agent of transportation
1	Colluvium	➤	Sediments transported and deposited by gravity
2	Alluvium	➤	Sediments transported and deposited by water
3	Aeolian	➤	Sediments transported and deposited by air (common in sand dunes)
4	Lacustrine	➤	Sediments transported and deposited lake by water
5	Marine	➤	Sediments transported and deposited by sea and oceans
6	Organic	➤	Organic materials accumulated as several maters in thickness and common in deep forests
7	Outwash	➤	Sediments transported and deposited by flowing water
8	Residuum	➤	Material deposited due to weathering of Hard Rock in place
9	Till/Moraine	➤	Sediments transported and deposited by glacial till (Ice)
10	Loess	➤	If wind Blown material comprised by primarily silt or silt with some fine sand and clay.

Unit-21: Earth Minerals:

1. Quartz: Silica or SiO_2

- **Chief** constituent of **sandy** fraction.
- Constitute **36% of earth's** crust.
- Rocks containing free silica in abundance , which is not combined with bases, are called **acid rocks**.
- **In granite (acid rocks),** quartz is present in a pure form as a prominent constituent.
- **In basic** rocks like **basalt** contain only a little if any of free silica.

2.Feldspars : ($K_2O.AlO_3.6SiO_2$)

- Such mineral constitutes about **48% earth's crust**.
- Feldspar weather easily and give rise to clay on hydrolysis.

Feldspar

↓ Potash feldspar
- ↓ Orthoclase feldspar $(K,Na)AlSi_3O_8$
- ↓ Microcline $KAlSi_3O_8$

↓ Plagiclase feldspar
- ↓ Albite (Sodium mineral) $NaAlSi_3O_8$
- ↓ Anorthite (Calcium Mineral) $CaAl_2Si_2O_8$

3. Micas:

- White mica is more resistant to weathering than black mica.
- Micas are more resistant to weathering than feldspar and other silicates.
- Micas constitute 10 ^{0}A of earth's crust.
- **Muscovite (Also known as common mica, insinglass or Potash mica) is white clear and transparent.**
- **Biotite mica** is called **black mica**.
-

Essential minerals are classified based on oxygen atom shared between the silica tetrahedrons:

1. **Neso silicates:** None of the oxygen is shared e.g. Olivine, Garnet and Zicon.
2. **Soro silicates:** One oxygen is shared e.g. Epidote, Hemimorphite
3. **Ino silicates**: **Single chain-** Two oxygen is shared e.g. Pyroxene.; **Double chain-** 2.5 oxygen is shared e.g. Amphiboles.
4. **Phyllosilicates:** Three oxygen is shared e.g. Biotite, Serpentine, clay minerals, Talc.
5. **Tecto silicates:** All oxygen are shared e.g. Feldspar and Quartz.
6. **Cyclo silicates:** e.g. Tourmaline, Bentonite.

MINERALS CLASSIFICATION BASED ON MODE OF ORIGIN

(A.) Primary minerals: Formation of minerals by crystallization of molten magma.

1. Silicate minerals

a. Orthosilicates → Olivine

b. Inosilicate → Single chained - Pyroxene; Double chained – Amphoboles

c. Phyllosilicate → Biotite, muscovite

d. Tecto silicate → Quartz, feldspar

2. Ferro magnesium minerals

a. Ferro magnesium mineral → Olivines, pyroxenes, amphiboles, biotite

b. Non-ferro magnesium mineral → Feldspar, albite, anorthite, orthoclase, quartz.

(B) Secondary minerals: Formed due to weathering of primary minerals

1. Silicate minerals

a. 1:1 type minerals: Kaolinite (one Si tetrahedral and One Al octahedral sheets)

b. 2:1 type minerals : Montmorillonite (expanding), Vermicultite (limited expansion) and illite (non expanding).

c. 2:1:1 type minerals: Chlorites

2. **Non silicate minerals**
   a. **Oxides** ------------------ Hematite, limonite, Geothite, Gibbsite
   b. **Carbonates**--------------Calcite, dolomite
   c. **Sulphates**----------------Gypsum
   d. **Phosphates**--------------Apatite
   e. **Boron**--------------------Tourmaline
   f. **Iron**-----------------------Limonite, siderite, pyrite, hematite, magnetite
   g. **Zinc**----------------------Sphalerite
   h. **Magnesium**------------ Dolomite, Epsomite
   i. **Copper**--------------------Chalcopyrite, Chalcorite, Covellite
   j. **Molybdenum**-----------Olivine

Unit-22: Basic properties of major silicate minerals:

SN	Property	Kaolinite	Illite	Montmorillonite	Vermiculate	Humus
1	Type of silicate clays	1:1type non expanding	2:1 non expanding	2:1 expanding type	2:1 limited expanding	
1	Total surface area m^2/g	37-45	120-170	580-750	**780-900** (highest **among silicates)**	1200
2	External surface area	Very low	Low	Medium	High	-
3	Internal surface area	None	Low	High	High	
4	Cohesion, plasticity, swelling	Very low	Low	High	medium	Low
5	CEC (meq/100 g soil)	2-15	30-40	60-150	100-150	>200
6	Size (in μ)	0.1-5.0	0.1-2.0	0.01-1.0	-	
7	P fixing	Highest	Low		Medium	-

Unit-23: CEC [(C.mol (P^+) kg^{-1}) or meq/100 g of Soil]

1	**Highest For**	➤	Vermiculite (volume base) Humus (weight base)
2	**Lowest For**	➤	Kaolinite
3	Kaolinite	➤	3 – 15
4	Montmorillonite	➤	80 – 100
5	Illite	➤	15 – 40
6	Humus	➤	150 – 300
7	Vermiculite	➤	80 – 150

Unit-24: [C – Axis Spacing (A^0)] of clay minerals

S. NO	Name of the mineral		Spacing
1	Kaolinite	➤	7.2 A°
2	Montmorillonite	➤	14 A°
3	Halloysite	➤	10.25 A°
4	Illite (or) Mica	➤	10 A°
5	Vermicultie	➤	10 – 15 A°
6	Chlorite	➤	14 A°

Note: 1 nm = 10 A°

Unit-25: Typed of soil formed in different climatic zones

1. **Podzol** → Temperate humid
2. **Chernozem** → Semi arid & sub humid
3. **Laterite** → Sub tropics and Tropics
4. **Desert** → Arid & Semi arid

Unit-26: Soil Formation factors

- Soils wherein there is continuous deposition of materials always remains **young** e.g. **Desert soils and alluvial deposits**.
- It is formed from **weathering of rocks and minerals**.
- It is a slow process , formation of one –**inch soil needs >1000 years.**
- Surface soil is called as **furrow slice layer (0-15 cm depth)**
- According to Jenny 1949, Soil property is determined by the relative influence of these factor.

Passive factors:

1. Parent material: it is the unconsolidated mass from which the solum develops.
2. Relief/ topography
3. Time

Active factors:

1. Climate
2. Organisms (biosphere)

FACTORS OF SOIL FORMATION {S=F(CL, O, R, P, T,........)}			
1.	S	➤	Soil formation
2.	O	➤	Organism
3.	T	➤	Time
4.	F	➤	Function
5.	Cl	➤	Climate
6.	R	➤	Relief of topography
7.	P	➤	Parent material

- **Dokuchaev (1889)** was the first to show that soil forms a definite pattern on the landscape and establish that they develop distinct horizons under the influence of parent material, climate and organism which put as S=f(p,cl,o). Latter on **Jenny (1941)** added two more factors i.e. relief and time. These are further classified into two group's i.e. active andpassive soil forming factors by **J.S. Joffe (1949).**
- The term"**CATENA**" was introduced by **G. Milne (1935)** which is the sequence of topographically related soils which have comparable parent material, climate and age but show different soil characteristics because of the variation in relief.
- If the soil are developed mainly under the influence of parent material such type of soils are called **"Endodynamomorphic soils"** (calcimorphic and hydromorphic soils) while if the soils are formed mainly due to climate such type of soils are called **"Ectodynamomorphic soils"** (Podzol and Laterite soils).
- The period of time devoted by the nature from the stage ofparent material to the stage of soil formation is considered as "Pedologic time".
- Rate of soil development is called aging.
- Humification is the process of transformation of raw organic matter into humus.

Unit-27: Soil profile

- A vertical section of the soil through all its horizon and extending into the parent material and the individual layers are regarded as horizons.
- A pedon is the smallest volume that can be recognized as a soil individual and it is 3- dimensional.
- The horizontal layers in a soil profile are called horizons, grouped into O,A,B and C horizons.
- The entire soil profile is categorized in three zones. The upper zone is known as Soil Water Zone / Root Zone extends from the soil surface to the lower boundary of the root zone. Below the soil water zone , there is an unsaturated zone is called **"Vadose zone"** which extends upto upper boundary of the next zone which is called "Capillary fringe zone' and is a near saturated zone occurring over the water table. The recharging of ground water depends on the water flow through this unsaturated "Vadose zone".
- **"Clay Migration" or "Lessivage":** Removal of clay , particularly of fine clay in suspension from the upper part of soil profile and its accumulation in lower part.
- **Pedon:** The term "Pedon" has been proposed for small basic soil entity that is a part of continuum mantling over the land surface. It is smallest volume that can be classified as a "soil".
- **Master Horizons:** The capital letters used to represents the master horizons. Earlier there were only six (6) master horizons (O,A,E,B,C and R), later on soil survey staff added three more (L,M and W) horizons.
- The horizon which is dominated by properties of one master horizon but having subordinate properties of another is called **Transitional horizon**. E.g. **AB, EB, and BE etc**. For example , an AB horizon has characteristics of both A and B horizons, but it is more like the A horizon than the B horizon. The first symbol indicates horizon with the greater volume than another.

S.No.	Name of horizon		Characteristics
1.	'O' horizon	:	Higher mineral soil, occurs commonly in forest areas , absent in arable land.
2.	"A'	:	Topmost mineral horizon

3. 'E' or 'A_2'	:	Horizon of maximum **eluviations** of clay, Fe and Al, maximum leaching take place so also called as **wash-out**.
4. 'AB' and 'EB'	:	---
5. 'B'	:	Absent in black soil, maximum accumulation **(Illuviation)** so also called as **wash-in.**
6. 'C'	:	Rock, Regolith
7. 'R'	:	Tied rock / bed rock

- **Solum = A+B horizons**
- **Regolith = A+B+C horizons**

- **Eluviation (Emigration):** Process of **removal (wash out)** of soil constituents in suspension or solution by the percolating water from the upper to lower layers , resulting textural differences which leads to horizon differentiation or development of soil. This process occurs in **E-horizon** or **A_2** horizon of soil profile.

- **Illuviation (Immigration):** Process of **deposition** of simpler soil constituents removed from upper layer (Eluvial) in to the lower layer **(zone of accumulation)** is termed as Illuviation. This process occurs in **B-horizon** of soil profile.

Unit-28: Type of soils

1. **Zonal Soils:** Fully developed soil profile , which are in equilibrium with the environmental conditions such as climate and vegetation (Ex: Lateritic, Sierozem, Chestnut, Podzol and Red soils).
2. **Azonal Soils:** The soils , where time has been a limiting factor to develop horizons are termed as azonal soils (ex.: Regosols, Alluvial soils and Lithosols).
3. **Intrazonal Soils:** If soil characteristics are modified by local conditions like topography, specific parent material etc such soils are termed as Intrazonal soils.[Ex. Halomorphic (saline and alkali soils), Hydromorphic and Calcimorphic].

- **Pedogenic process:**
  1. **Zonal soil forming process:** Calcification, Decalcification, Podzolization and Laterization
  2. **Intra zonal soil forming process:** Gleization, Salinization, Alkalization and Pedoturbation

- **Podzolization (Acid hydrolysis):** The term podzol is derived from Russian word- Pod means under, Zola means ash like. Podzolization is the process of accumulation of silica and removal sesquioxides (Fe and Al oxides). It is als called "Acid hydrolysis"
- **Laterization (Alkali hydrolysis):** The term laterite derived from Latin word later means brick or tile. It is the process of accumulation of sesquioxides and removal of silica.
- **Humification:** It is process of decomposition of organic matter and synthesis f new organic substances .
- **Calcification & Gypsification:** Formation and accumulation of $CaCO_3$ and $CaSO_4$, respectively.

- **Argillation:** It is the process by which the dispersed clay particles are migrated fro upper to the lower horizons result a textural horizon.
- **Lessivage:** Removal of clay particularly the fine clay in suspension from the upper part of soil profile and accumulate in the lower part.
- **Braunification or Ferruginisation (Brunisolic soils):** It is process of release of iron from primary minerals and their dispersal as coating on soil particles or as complexes with organic matter or as discrete aggregates to impart a brown to red colour to the soil.
- **Gleization:** The reduction of iron under anaerobic condition with the production of bluish to greenish grey colour with or without mottles.
- **Rubification:** In dried soils precipitates of iron and organic matter content cannot accumulate and even organic matter disappears by decay, causing formation of irreversibly dehydrated iron sesquioxides. Process is known as **rubification**, and the resulting soils, called **cinnamonic** , are rich in fine crystallites of dehydrated iron sesquioxides.
- **Salinization:** It is the process of accumulation of soluble salts in soil.
- **Alkalization:** It is the process of accumulation of sodium in exchange complex.
- **Solonization:** There is accumulation of Na^+ ions on the exchange site of the soil.
- **Solodization/ Dealkalization:** This process involves the movement of Al from A horizon to B horizon under the influence of Na.
- **Hydromorphic soils developed due to Gleizatio process.**

Unit-29: Epipedons: 9 types

The epipedons are uppermost soil horizons and include the upper part of the soil darkened by organic matter. The are not synonymous with A- horizon.

1. **Folistic Epipedon**: Newer saturated with water for more than 30 days in normal years.
2. **Histic Epipedon**: >20-30% organic matter.
3. **Melanic Epipedon**: A thick black colour horizon t or near, but with in 30 cm of the soil surface and having **andic** properties.
4. **Mollic Epipedon**: A thick dark colour , soft mineral horizon with high (>50%) base saturation. It contains less than 1500 mg citric acid soluble P_2O_5 per kg soil.
5. **Umbric Epipedon**: A surface horizon like mollic, but is low (<50%) in base saturation (dominantly saturated with H^+) with high C:N ratio.
6. **Ochric Epipedon**: A surface horizon that is light in colour.
7. **Anthropic Epipedon**: A surface horizon , like the millic, but formed due to under continued system of farming or cultivation that involves large addition of organic matter (compost). It contains 1500 mg or more citric acid soluble P_2O_5 per kg soil.
8. **Plaggen Epipedon**: A thick (>50 cm) man-made surface horzon produced by long and continued manuring with sod. It can be easily identified by artefacts , such as bits of bricks, pottery etc. It also shows spade marks.
9. **Grossarenic Epipedon**: A sandy horizon , 100 cm or more thick over an agrillic horizon.

❖ **Argillic horizon:** A silicate clay enriched B horizon with clay skin or clay films formed by Illuviation of clay is called Argillic horizon.

- **Natric horizon:** A high sodium clay enriched horizon with columnar and prismatic structure.
- **Cambic horizon:** is altered or structural B horizon.
- **Kandic horizon:** Low activity of clay related.

Unit-30: Major soil orders and their area

	Soil order		Region state
1.	Entisol	➢	Rajasthan, Gujarat, Haryana
2.	Inceptisols	➢	Uttar Pradesh
3.	Vertisols	➢	Kovilpatti (T.N.), Rajasthan, Gujarat, Maharashtra, Madhya Pradesh, Karnataka, Andhra Pradesh
4.	Aridisols	➢	Haryana, West Rajasthan, Gujarat, Anantpur (AP)
5.	Alfisols	➢	Andhra Pradesh, Jhansi (UP), Tamil Nadu, Karnataka
6.	Oxisols	➢	Ranchi (Jharkhand), Bhubaneswar (Orissa)

Unit-31: Classification of rainfall zones in India

S.No.	Rainfall (mm)	Zone	Rainfall %
1.	<500	Arid	Very low
2.	500-750	Semi-arid	Low
3.	750-1100	Dry sub-humid	Medium
4.	1100-1400	Moist sub-humid	High
5.	>1400	Humid mountain	Very high

Unit-32: Area of soils groups of India

S.No.	Group	→	Area in Mha
1.	Alluvial	→	78 Mha
2.	Black soil	→	51.8 Mha
3.	Red Soil	→	51 Mha
4.	Laterite soil	→	12.6 Mha
5.	Desert soil	→	37 Mha

Unit-33: Problematic soils Area in India

1. Acid soil → 49 Mha (in which 26 Mha <5.6 pH and 23 Mha (5.6 – 6.5 pH)
2. Saline soil → 7 Mha
3. Alkali soil → 2.8 Mha
4. Acid sulphate soil →50000 ha
5. Tarai soil → 56000 m^2
6. Coastal Alluvium → 85000 m^2

7.	Deltaic alluvium	→	18000 m^2

Unit-34: Soil orders (as per soil Taxonomy) representing different soil groups

S.No.	Genetic System	➢	Soil Taxonomy
1.	Alluvial soils	➢	Entisol, Inceptisol
2.	Black (Cotton) soils	➢	Vertisols
3.	Red Soils	➢	Alfisol, Ultisols
4.	Laterite and Lateritic soils	➢	Ultisols
5.	Desert soils	➢	Aridisol
6.	Forest and Hill soils	➢	Alfisols
7.	Salt affected soils	➢	Aridisols, Inceptisols

Unit-35: Six categories were adopted for soil order groups

	Categories	➢	Features
1.	Order	➢	It is highest category, there are 12 soil order
2.	Sub-Order	➢	63 sub order in this classification
3.	Great group	➢	>240
4.	Sub-Group	➢	>1000
5.	Family	➢	
6.	Series	➢	> 12000 It is most specific and lowest category (>200 in India)

7. **Note:** The smallest unit of soil classification is the soil series . Soil order is the 7th approximation and their deviation.

Unit-36: Soil Orders with characters

	Soil Order	Word	Deviation	Pronunciation
1.	Entisol	-	Nonsense symbol	Recent
2.	Inceptisol	Latin	Inceptum means beginning	Inception
3.	Gelisols	Greek	Gel means Ice	Frost churning
4.	Histosols	Greek	Histos means tissue	Histology
5.	Spodosols	Greek	Spodos means ash / Podzol	Odd
6.	Andisols	Japanese	And	Ando
7.	Oxisols	French	Oxide	Oxide
8.	Vertisols	Latin	Verto means turn	Invert
9.	Aridisols	Latin	Aridus	Arid
10.	Ultisols	Latin	Ultimus means last	Ultimate
11.	Mollisols	Latin	Mollis means soft	Mollify
12.	Alfisols	-	Nonsense symbol	Pedalfer

Unit-37: Soil Orders and soil characteristics:

	Soil order		Soil characteristics
1.	Entisol	➢	Soils with little horizon development or beginning of soil formation
2.	Inceptisol	➢	Soils with altered horizons, but no illuvial horizon containing clay or Fe, Al oxides, may have umbric , ochric or cambic horizon
3.	Gelisols	➢	Soils that have permafrost within 100 cm or gellic material with permanent frost within 2 m of the surface.
4.	Histosols	➢	Soils containing >30% organic matter to a depth of 40 cm.
5.	Spodosols	➢	Soils with spodic horizon with in 2 m.
6.	Andisols	➢	Soils that have andic soil properties in 60% or more of the thickness between the soil surface and 60 cm or lithic, paralithic contact.
7.	Oxisols	➢	Oxide highly weathered soils or tropical and subtropical regions with oxic horizon.
8.	Vertisols	➢	Soils with more than 30% clay in all horizons and crack when dry.
9.	Aridisols	➢	Dry soils , ochric epipedon, Some have argillic ,nitric or salic horizon
10.	Ultisols	➢	Soils in warm humid regions with argillic horizon and low base saturation (<35% at 2 m depth below the surface)
11.	Mollisols	➢	Dark coloured, base rich soils of grass land areas , mollic epipedon , many with argillic , nitric or calcic horizon
12.	Alfisols	➢	High base status (>35%) soils of humid and sub humid regions with an ochric epipedon and argillic (or nitric) horizon.

❖ **India has 10 soil orders .**

Unit-38: Soil Orders with special features

S.No.	Special features		Name of soil order
1.	Volcanic ash order	➢	Andisol
2.	Allophone minerals order	➢	Andisol
3.	Recently formed or developed	➢	Entisol
4.	Without diagnostic horizons	➢	Entisol
5.	Not reported in India (may found in snow falling Himalayas)	➢	Gelisol
6.	Recently introduced order	➢	Gelisol
7.	Permafrost and Cryoturbation order	➢	Gelisol
8.	Permafrost absent	➢	Histosol
9.	Negligible area in India	➢	Histosol
10.	Bogs, moors, peat and muck	➢	Histosol
11.	High Organic matter	➢	Histosol
12.	Dominant order in India	➢	Inceptisol
13.	Early stage in formation	➢	Inceptisol
14.	Absent of Fe and Al oxide	➢	Inceptisol
15.	Base rich order	➢	Mollisol
16.	Chemically degraded Uniform profile distribution, highly weathered	➢	Oxisol

	soils in world, Poor fertility	
17.	Bleached and wood ash A_2 horizon	➢ Spodosol
18.	Black cotton soils or Regurs	➢ Vertisol
19.	Gilgai micro relief ,Swell shrink and Slickensides	➢ Vertisol

- **Fragipan**: It is sub soil layer (s) of high bulk density. It is brittle when moist, and very hard when dry. It does not soften on wetting, but can be broken by the hands. The air dry fragments slake in water.
- **Duripan**: It is a subsurface horzon at least half cemented by SiO_2 . The air dry peds do not slake in water or HCl, but are destroyed by hot KOH after acid washing.

Unit-39: Soil Moisture regimes

1. Aquic regime
2. Aridic & torric regime
3. Udic regime (humid)
4. Ustic regime
5. Xeric regime

Unit-40: Soil temperature with Regimes

1. **Pergilic** regime: Mean annual temperature (MAT) is $< 0\ ^oC$
2. **Cryic** regime: MAT is 0 to 8 ^oC
3. **Frigid** regime: MAT is 8 ^oC
4. **Mesic** regime : 8 -15 ^oC
5. **Thermic** regime –MAT is 15- 22 ^oC
6. **Hyperthermic** regime : MAT is $> 22\ ^oC$

Unit-41: Soil Physics

Soil Physics is the study of soil physical properties and processes. It applied to management and prediction under natural and managed ecosystem. Soil physics deals with the dynamics of physical soil components and their phases as solids, liquids and gases.

Soil texture: Relative proportion of the different particle size fraction specifically referred to as sand, silt and clay.

Unit-42: Textural Classes of soils

COMPOSITION OF SAND SILT & CLAY RELATED TO TEXTURED CLASS

	Textural Class	Ranges of soil separates		
		Sand	**Silt**	**Clay**
1.	Sand	85-100	0-15	0-10
2.	Loamy sand	70-90	0.30	0.15
3.	Sandy loam	40-80	0-50	0-20
4.	Loam	23-52	28-50	7-27
5.	Silt loam	0-50	50-88	0-27

6.	Silt	0-20	80-100	0-12
7.	Sandy clay loam	45-80	0-28	20-35
8.	Clay loam	20-45	15-53	27-40
9.	Silty clay loam	0-20	40-73	27-40
10.	Sandy Clay	45-65	0-20	35-45
11.	Silty Clay	0-20	40-60	40-60
12.	Clay	0-45	0-40	40-100

- **Soil is three (3)-phase** , oarticulate, disperse, porous, open and heterogeneous system.
- Ideal soil Ideal soil contains **50% solid matter** (45% mineral matter and 5% organic matter) and **50 % pore space** (25% air and 25% water).
- Out of three phases , **Solid phase is the constant phase** in terms of composition.
- There are basically 3 soil separates viz. ,Sand, silt and clay.

Unit-43: Classification of soil particle size

S.No.	Classification	Diameter (mm)	
		ISSS given by Atterberg	USDA
1.	Gravel	>2.0	>2.0
2.	Very course sand	---	1-2
3.	Coarse Sand	0.2 – 2.0	0.5 – 1.0
4.	Medium sand	-----	0.25- 0.50
5.	Fine Sand	0.02 – 0.2	0.10- 0.25
6.	Very fine sand	----	0.05 – 0.10
7.	Silt	0.002 – 0.02	0.002 – 0.05
8.	Clay	<0.002	<0.002

- Size of soil separates >2 mm indicate as gravel in both USDA and ISSS category.

Unit -44: Soil texture determination Methods

1. Feel method

1. Smooth , talc like and no grittiness --------------- Silt
2. Smooth and talc like and gritty---------------------- Loam and silt loam
3. No smoothness and gritty------------------------------ Sand

2. Elutriation method

3. Pipette method

4. Hydrometric method

5. Beaker method

6.Test tube shaking method

Unit-45: Stokes Law (1851)

Terminal Velocity of a spherical particles settling under the influence of gravity in a fluid of a given density and viscosity is proportional to the square of its radius.

$$V = \frac{2}{9\eta} g r^2 (ps\text{-}pf)$$

Where, V- Settling velocity, r- Radius, ή- Fluid viscosity, g- Acceleration due to gravity, ps- Density of solid and pf- Density od liquid.

Sedimentation velocity

Clay- 347 x 10^{-6}

Silt- 347 x 10^{-4}

Fine sand- 347 x 10^{-2}

Coarse sand- 347

- ❖ Rate of sedimentation is directly proportional to the square of the diameter of the particle.
- ❖ Soil texture determination by hydrometer method- rapid but less accurate and also give erroneous results under conditions of high CaCO3, OM and high salinity.
- ❖ Hydrometer works based on principle of continues decreases in the density of soil suspension over time at the particles fall below the level of the hydrometer.

Unit-46: Specific surface area of soil particles

S.No.	Soil separates	➤	Specific surface area (Cm^2/g)
1.	Coarse sand	➤	45
2.	Fine sand	➤	446
3.	Silt	➤	4458
4.	Ultra clay	➤	9.8 millions
5.	Loam soil	➤	50-100 m^2/g
6.	Clay	➤	150-200 m^2/g
7.	Sandy loam	➤	10-40 m^2/g

Unit-47: Specific surface area of Clay minerals

S.No.	Clay minerals	➤	Specific surface area (Cm^2/g)
1.	Kaolinite	➤	37-45
2.	Illite	➤	120-170
3.	Chlorite	➤	130-180
4.	Montmorillonite	➤	580-750
5.	Vermiculite	➤	780-900

Unit-48: Cation exchange capacity (CEC) of soils

S.No.	Soil texture	➤	CEC (meq/100g)
1.	Sand (light colour)	➤	3-5
2.	Sand dark colour	➤	10-20

3.	Loam	➢	10-15
4.	Silt loam	➢	15-25
5.	Clay and clay loam	➢	20-50
6.	Organic soil	➢	50-100

Unit-49: Soil Structure

The arrangement of primary and secondary particles into a certain structural pattern is called as structure. It is a **changeable property** (change due to tillage) of soil.

Classification of structure

1. **Type**: shape and arrangement of peds
2. **Class** : Size of peds
3. **Grade** : Distinctiveness and durability

Types of soil structure

1. **Prism like**: Vertical axis is more developed than horizontal axis. Structure having flat tops are called as **prismatic**. Rounded top are called as **columnar**. Found in sub horizons 'B' of clayey soils in arid and semi arid regions. Prism like structure are associated with swelling type clay and also occur in poor drained soils of humid region. **Mostly occur** in sub soils of **salt affected / sodic** soils.
2. **Plate like**: Horizontal axis is well developed than vertical axis. If it is thick it is called **platy**. If it is thin it is called laminar. The structure is inherited from parent material. This soil structure formed due to compaction by heavy tractor on clayey soils.
3. **Blocky**: Structure having angular corners are called as angular blocky and rounded corners are called as sub angular blocky. Blocky structures are called nutty or nuci form. It is found in soils which is poorly drained. Ped size ranging from 1-10 cm .Commonly found in humid regions and upper part of 'B' horizon.
4. **Spheroidal**:
   1. **Crumb**: It is found in pasture land and more porous in nature.
   2. **Granular**: It is found in cultivated soil and less porous in nature.
   3. **Crumb & Granular** structure found in surface soil high in OM,, respectively.

Classes of structure:

- ❖ Very fine, fine, medium, coarse and very coarse.
- ❖ **Grade**: Moderate, strong, and **structure less** (single grain, **massive-puddled soil**)

Important exam points:

- Natural aggregates are called as **ped**.
- Artificial aggregates are called as **clod**.
- Broken peds are called as **fragment**.
- Salt dissolved in water precipitate is called as **concretion**.
- **Type of structure** is characterized by shape and arrangement.
- **Class of structure** is characterized by size of peds.
- **Grade of structure** is characterized by degree of distinctness and durability of the visible aggregates or peds.

- Outside of aggregate is dark and called as clay skin.

Unit-50: Types of soil

1. **Sandy soil:** are typically comprised of approximately **80-100 per cent sand, 0-10 per cent silt** and **0-10 per cent clay** by **volume** . Sandy soils are light and typically very free draining, usually holding water very poorly.
2. **Loam soil:** are typically comprised of approximately **25-50 per cent sand, 30-50 per cent silt** and **10-30 per cent clay** by **volume**. Loam soils are somewhat heavier than sandy soils, but also tend to be fairly free draining again , due to typically low organic matter.
3. **Clay soil:** are typically comprised of approximately **0-45 per cent sand, 0-45 per cent silt and 50-100 per cent clay** by **volume.** Clay soil are not typically free draining, and water tend to take a long time to infiltrate . When wet, such soil tend to alow water to runn-off. Clay soils tend to be heavy and difficult to work when dry.

Soil classification	Clay soil	Loam soil	Sandy soil
Clay %	40-100%	7-27 %	1-10 %
Silt %	0-40%	28-50%	1-15%
San %	0-45%	23-52%	85-100%

Important points:

- Gravel is neither a soil separate nor one of the soil texture.
- Particles greater than 2 mm are not considered as soil.
- Texture is determined by International pipette and Bouycous Hydrometer method.
- Stoke's law is applied in the determination of soil texture.
- Silt has intermediate characteristics between sand and clay.
- Loamy texture and granular or crumb structure (Sandy loam) is the **best soil for agriculture cultivation** whereas especially **black cotton soil for cotton** and light soil for groundnut , tubers and roots and bulb crops.
- Clay is called the active fraction of the soil. It is made up of alumino-silicates
- Soil texture is a **static/ natural property** of soil which **can't be changed**.

Unit-51: Soil Colour with Muncell colour chart

1. The colour of soil is a result of the light reflected from the soil . It is an easily observable soil property and gives an immediate indication of soil condition.
2. Soil colour is inherited from its parent material and that is referred to as **litho-chromic** , e.g. red soils developed from red sand stone.
3. Soil colour if developed by soil froming process is called **"Pedo-chromic"** soil colour .
4. Pure blue colour and pure green colour is practically not seen . If two or three colours occurs in patches at a same place this condition is called **"mottling"**.

It is find out by using **Munsell Colour Chart**. Three variables are used to denote soil colour

Components of soil colour

1.	HUE	➢	Denotes the dominant spectral colour (yellow, red, blue, brown etc.
2.	VALUE	➢	Denotes the lightness and darkness of colour
3.	CHROMA	➢	Denotes purity of colour

Factors influencing soil colour

1. Mineralogy and soil chemical constituent
2. Organic matter , moisture content , soil structure

Different soil and responsible minerals

Soil colour		Mineral responsible of soil colour
Red colour	➢	Unhydrated ferric oxide
Yellow colour	➢	Goethite & limonite
Red colour	➢	Hematite
Brown colour	➢	Maghemite.
Green colour	➢	**Glauconite**
Black colour	➢	Manganese oxide
White colour	➢	**Calcite ($CaCO_3$)**

SOIL COLOUR RESPONSIBLE FACTORS

S.No.	Colour of soil		Due to (Responsible factors)
1.	Red	➢	Warm humid
2.	Grey	➢	Cool humid
3.	Black to dark brown	➢	High organic matter
4.	Red (if ferric oxides occur as haematite) and yellow (if ferric oxides occur as limonite)	➢	Iron oxides
5.	Brown	➢	Mixing of organic matter and Fe oxides
6.	White or light	➢	Silica and lime
7.	Mottle or variegated	➢	Alternate wetting and drying
8.	Bluish and greenish	➢	Oxidation and reduction
9.	Black	➢	Titanium and Manganese

- Under prolonged anaerobic conditions , soil colour changed into **gray / bluish** due to coating of **reduced iron oxide.**
- High de-nitrification risk and **methane emission hazard** is problem of grey and green colour of soil.

MUNSELL COLOUR CHART

- Munsell colour chart contains 175 different colour papers/ chips.
- Musell colour chart consists of with 7 cards, each has constant hue.
- In each card value is constant with in horizontal row and increase towards top.

- In each card chroma is constant with in vertical colomn and increase to th right.
- Value of 0 indicates Black colour .
- Value of 10 indicates white colour.
- Chroma increases with decreasing greyness.
- Chroma 0 for neutral grey and 20 for high purity.
- Normally hroma above 8 is rarely found in soil.
- Achromatic colour have neutral hue and zero chroma and differ only in value.

Unit-52: Density of soils

- It is defined as **mass per unit volume**.
- It is measured by **Pycnometer**.

TWO TYPES OF DENSITY

1.Particle density/true density/ real density (P.D.)

- Weight of per unit volume of soil solids and no pore space is considered.

$$\text{P.D. (g/cc)} = \frac{\text{Mass of soil solids}}{\text{Volume of soil solids}}$$

- Particle density of normal soils is **2.65 g/cc..**
- Particle density is lower when organic matter added in soil.
- In coarse sand the particle density is less because of larger volume of soil solids and it will be more in clay because of lesser volume of soil solids.
- **When volume of soil solids increases, particle density decreases.**

2. Bulk Density (B.D.)

- Oven dry weight of soil solids per unit volume of soil solids along with volume of its pore space.

$$\text{B.D. (g/cc)} = \frac{\text{Weight of oven dry soil}}{\text{Volume of soil (Vol.of soil solids+vol.of pore space)}}$$

- Bulk density of normal soils is about **1.33 g/cc.**
- Tillage operation increases pore space , hence reduces bulk dencity.

Unit-53: Porosity of soils

- Porosity is the percentage of soil volume occupied by pores.
- It is that portion of soil nor occupied by soil solids.
- There are two types of pores :
  1. Macro pores (>0.006 mm)
  2. Micro pores (<0.006mm)

CALCULATION OF POROSITY:

$$\%\text{ solid space} = \frac{\text{Bulk density}}{\text{Particle density}} \times 100$$

% pore space = 100 - % Solid space

$$\% \text{ pore space} = (100 - \frac{B.D.}{P.D.}) \times 100$$

$$= [1 - \frac{B.D.}{P.D.}] \times 100$$

SOIL TEXTURE CLASSES , BULK DENSITY AND PORE SPACE

S.No.	Texture class	Bulk density	Pore space (%)
1.	Sandy soil	1.6	40
2.	Loam	1.4	47
3.	Silt loam	1.3	50
4.	Clay	1.1	58

COMPARISON BETWEEN PD & BD OF SOIL

S.No.	Soil	Particle density (cm/cc)	Bulk density (cm/cc)
1.	Normal soil	2.65	1-1.6
2.	Sandy Soil	2.6	1.6
3.	Silty soil	2.7	1.3
4.	Clay soil	2.8	1.1

Total pore space of soils

Soils	Pore space (%)
Sandy	20-30
Loamy	30-50
Clay	50-60

☛ **In sandy** soils, there are **25000 pores/m^2** where as in **clay, 25X10^6 pores /m^2**.

Unit-54: Soil consistency

❖ Resistance of soil at various moisture content to mechanical stress.

❖ Soil consistency order Dry soil> Moist soil > Wet soil.

Unit-55: Atterberg limits (1911)

Atterberg a Swedish agricultural scientist (1911) developed a method to describe the consistency of fine-grained soils with varying moisture content, and he proposed five "limits" for fine-grained soils with varying water content. The water contents at which the soil changes from one state to another are known as consistency limits or Atterberg's limits.

1. **Liquid Limit (LL, WL):** It is the water content at which the soil on a verge (border) to become viscous fluid.
2. **Plastic Limit (PL, WP):** It is the water content at which the soil just fails to behave plastically.
3. **Shrinkage Limit (SL,WS):** It is the water content at which the soil stops shrinking further and attains a constant volume.
4. **Sticky Limit:** It is that moisture content which soil crumbles just stick together.

5. **Cohesion Limit:** It is that moisture content which soil just sticks metal surface such as spatula blade.

- Soils containing >15% clay exhibit plasticity.
- **Plasticity index** given by **Atterberg, 1911** also gave limits of soil.
- Soil plasticity determined by **Liquid limit devices**.

Unit-56: Soil Plasticity and cohesion

- **Plasticity** is the capacity of the soil to change its shape under moist conditions. It exhibits **more in clay soil.**
- **Cohesion** is the capacity to **stick together**.
- Plastic soils are **cohesive**.
- **Redox potential:** Is regulated by the concentration of reduced and oxidized substance. **Eh=E_0**
- **Redox potential (Eh):** The redox potential is a measure (in volts) of the affinity of a substance for electron. Its electronegativity compared with hydrogen (which is set at 0).
- **Eh = E_0 +RT/nF** in (Oxidation)/(Reduction)
- **Eh of well drained soil** (400-700mv) and **water logging** (-250 to 350 mv).

Unit-57: Soil colloids

- Soil collids are inorganic (clay) and organic (humus) , which have very small particles size (0.001 mm or smaller 1 micron) containing large surface area per unit mass.
- Soil colloids have high exchange capacity , which increases with silica sesquioxides ratio.
- The two phases are dispersed phase (clay and humus) and dispersion medium/ water).
- Soil colloids also carry electrostatic charges (- and +). Most of organic and inorganic soil colloids carry a negative charge.

TYPES OF SOIL COLLOIDS

1. **Crystalline silicate** clays – Phylosiicates (tetrahedral and octahedral crystal sheets)
2. **Non- crystalline silicate** clays – Dominantly amorphous clays (allophone and imogolite)
3. **Iron and aluminum oxides** – Dominantly gibbsite (Al-oxide) and goethite (Fe-oxide).
4. **Organic (humus) colloids** – Non crystalline colloids dominated by long C-chain molecules.

- **Colloidal property increases** with **decrease in diameter**.
- When colloidal particles are coagulated by adding oppositely charged ions called **flocculation.** Maximum flocculation cation mineral are Al^{+3} > Ca^{2+} whereas minimum flocculation of **Na^+ > K^+**
- Colloids exhibit the property of sacrificial activity such as the capacity to hold solid, gases, salts and ions.
- Soil colloids have high exchange capacity, which increases with silica sesquioxides ratio.

Unit-58: Silicate clay minerals

Group	Layer type	Cation to anion exchange capacity	Remarks

		(EEC/AEC)	
Kaolinite	1:1	0.5	Mineral clay
Illite	2:1	2.3	Non expanding
Vermicultite	2:1	-	Limited expanding
Smectite / Montmorillonite	2:1	6.7	Most prominent expanding type clay minerals with swelling & shrinking characteristics
Chlorite	2:1:1	-	-

Basic Properties of Major Silicate Minerals

		Kaolinite	Illite	Mobtmorillonite
1.	Type of silicate clays	1:1 non expanding type	2:1 Non expanding type	2:1 expanding type
2.	Total surface area (M^2/g)	37-45	120-170	580-750
3.	External surface	Very low	Low	Medium
4.	Internal surface	None	Low	High
5.	Cohesion, Plasticity, Swelling	Very low	Low	High
6.	CEC (meq/100 g soil)	2-15	30-40	60-150
7.	Size (in micron)	0.1-5.0	0.1-2.0	0.01-1.0
8.	P fixing	Highest	Low	----

Basic Properties of Major Silicate Minerals

			Vermiculite	Humus
1.	Type of silicate clays	➢	2:1 Limited expanding	------
2.	Total surface area (M^2/g)	➢	780-900 (Highest among silicates)	1200
3.	External surface	➢	High	----
4.	Internal surface	➢	High	----
5.	Cohesion, Plasticity, Swelling	➢	Medium	Low
6.	CEC (meq/100 g soil)	➢	100-150	>200
7.	P fixing	➢	Medium	----

Unit-59: Soil Air

It is **gaseous phase** of soil. Can be defined as the air that fills the soil pore spaces not occupied by water whereas soil aeration is exchange of CO_2 and O_2 gases between the soil pore space and aerial atmosphere. Under moist field conditions macropores generally constitute the air space. Ordinarily , the occupation of nearly **one-third** of the pore space in the soil **by air** and **two-third by water** constitute the **most favourable condition** for **plant growth**.

- **Oxygen Diffusion rate (ODR):**It is best and most reliable measurement of aeration capacity. It determines the rate at which O_2 in soil air is replenished.ODR decrease with soil depth.

- **Pant growth suffers** when oxygen diffusion rate (**ODR**) below **40 X 10^{-8} g/cm^2/minute**.
- The **growth of root is ceased at 20 X 10^{-8}** g/cm^2/minute **ODR**.

GASEOUS COMPOSITION OF SOIL AIR

1. Oxygen (O_2): Once the supply of oxygen is virtually exhausted, the soil environment become **anaerobic**. Typically **wet soils** have **very low oxygen.** Drastic reduction in the oxygen content of soil air may occur following a **heavy rain**.

2. Carbon dioxide (CO_2): Carbon dioxide typically increases in soil air (around **10 times of atmosphere). When it is as high as 10% in soil air it** may become **toxic to plants**.

3. Other gases: soil air is usually higher in water vapour than in the atmosphere. Under water logged conditions, the concentration of **methane (CH_4), and hydrogen sulphide (H_2S)** is particularly higher in soil air.

COMPOSITION OF GASES IN ATMOSPHERE AND SOIL

S.No.	Name of gas	Atmosphere (%)	Soil (%0
1.	Nitrogen (N_2)	78.03	78.60
2.	Oxygen (O_2)	20.97	20.60
3.	Argon	0.94	0.90
4.	**Carbon dioxide (CO_2)**	**0.03**	**0.25-0.3(10 times than atm.)**
5.	Hydrogen	0.01	----

Unit-60: Soil Water

Water has maximum density at 4 ^{0}C. The diameter of water molecule is 3°A **(3x10^{-10}m).** Water has high dielectric constant of 80. Its surface tension is **7.2x10^{-2} N/m**. Structure of water molecule is **hexagonal lattice** and the angle is **104^0 5'** or (105^0) . One molecule of water is attached to four molecules in the neighborhood.

- **Adhesive**: An attraction between **two unlike/dissimilar** molecules. e.g. **(water + soil).**
- **Cohesive**: An attraction /bonding between **two similar** molecules **e.g.(water + water)** .
- **Heat of solution**: when ions are hydrated a large amount of energy to released is known as heat of solution
- **Heat of wetting**: when clay particles are hydrated in a certain amount of energy to release is called heat of wetting.
- **Adsorbed water**: always less free energy than water in the pool **(zero potential)**. Free energy of soil water potential is measured by **pF Scale**.
- **pF Scale (Schofield, 1935)**: The logarithm of centimeter height of a water column to give the necessary suction is called pF scale. **p** means **logarithm** and **F** means **free energy.**

Unit-61: pF value:

- P means potenz its meaning power at 10.
- pF is the scale like pH through which measure the force with which water is retained in capillary or soil.

	Soil condition	Pressure (atm/bars)	pF Value
1.	Saturated soil	0.001	0
2.	Field capacity	1/3	2.53
3.	PWP	15	4.18
4.	Hygroscopic point	31	4.5
5.	Oven dry soil	10,000	7

pF value

Pressure (bar)	=	pF value
0 – 0.001 (Maximum water holding capacity)	=	Zero
- 0.3 (FC)	=	2.53
- 15 (PWP)	=	4.18
- 31	=	4.50
-60(UWP)	=	4.75
- 100	=	5
- 1000	=	6
- 10000 (oven dry soil)	=	7

- **Saturated** soil having **pF** value lowest **(0)** and height (1.00 cm).
- If water is allowed to **drain by gravity** after supplying water , some water remains even after drainage due to gravity.
- **Darcy's law** in soil deals to **hydraulic gradient**.

Unit-62: Soil water potential

The amount of work done to convert the water to pure water by acting against the forces acting on it.

S.No.	Type of potential		Force due to
1.	Gravitational potential (g)	➤	Force of gravity on water
2.	Matric potential (m)	➤	Force of attraction of soil or ions in it on water.
3.	Osmotic potential (o)	➤	Force due to solutes in water.
4.	Pressure potential (p)	➤	Force due to air pressure if air above the water table is considered (negative) but if capillarity i.e. below the water table (positive)
5.	Total (g+m+o+p)		Soil water potential

POTENTIALS

S. No	Condition	➤	Potential
1	Field Capacity	➤	-1/3 bar (or) 33kPa
2	PWP (Permanent Wilting Point)	➤	-15 bar
3	Saturation	➤	Zero
4	Hygroscopic Coefficient	➤	> -31 bar
5	Gravitational water	➤	> -1/3 bar
6	Capillary water	➤	-1/3 bar to -31 bar
7	Available water	➤	-1/3 bar to -15 bar

8	Pressure plate apparatus measure moisture upto	➤	-15 bar
9	Pressure membrane apparatus measure moisture upto	➤	-100 bar
10	Gypsum block method measure moisture from	➤	PC to PWP
11	Air dry soil	➤	-1000 bar
12	Oven dry soil	➤	- 10000 bar
13	Saturate flow	➤	> -1/3 bar
14	Unsaturated flow	➤	Lower than -1/3 bar

Unit-63: Physical classification of soil water

1. Gravitational water (free water):

- It has a suction of **less than 1/3 atmosphere**.
- The drainage or deep percolation loss of water results from downward movement of this gravity water.
- The **plants can't absorb it** as it drains out of root zone in short period of time.
- This form of water is **loosely held in soil (in macro pores)** and move downwards freely under the influence of gravity.
- Water in **excess of the field capacity** is termed **gravitational water**.

2. Capillary water:

- Capillary water is held in the capillary pores **(micro pores)** with a suction ranging from **1/3 and 31 atmospheres.** Capillary water is retained on the soil particles by surface **forces (PF value -2.54 to 4.50).**
- It is held so **strongly that gravity cannot remove it** from the soil particles.
- The availability of capillary water to plant roots depends on pore diameter which controls the pressure of water. The narrower the capillary pore, lesser is the availability.

3. Hygroscopic water:

- Generally, it includes first two molecular layers of water on soil particle. Only **microorganism uses this form of water**.
- This form of soil water is held with a **high suction** ranging from **31 to 10000 atmospheres**. It is held tightly on the surface of soil colloidal particles.

Physical	**Pressure**
Gravitational water	>1/3 atm
Capillary Water	1/3 – 31 atm
• Field Capacity	1/3 atn
• Wilting Point	15 atm
Hygroscopic Coefficient	>31 atm

Unit-64: Biological classification of water

1. **Available water**- it is held between field capacity (-1/3) to permanent wilting coefficient (-15)
2. **Unavailable water**- it is held at > -15 bar and it include whole hygroscopic water plus a part of capillary water below the wilting point.
3. **Superfluous water**- it is retained in the soil beyond the field capacity of soil moisture tension.

Biological	Pressure
Superfluous water	1/3 atmosphere or less
Available water	1/3 to 15 atmosphere
Unavailable water	15 and above atmosphere

Unit-65: Soil moisture constants

These are of practical importance for irrigation and drainage management. These are also used to compare water retention capacity of different soils.

1. **Field Capacity**

- If a soil is saturated, gravity water starts moving downwards. When all the gravitational water is drained away, and then the wet soil are almost uniformly moist.
- The amount of water held by the soil at this stage is known as the field capacity of that soil. It is the capacity of the soil to retain water against the downward pull of the force of gravity.
- At this stage only micro/capillary pores are filled with water and plants absorb water for their use.
- At field capacity water is held with a suction of **1/3 atmosphere and pF 2.54.**

2. **Wilting coefficient** also called **Permanent wilting point (Briggs and Shantz, 1912.)**

- Although plants root not dead, but they are now in a permanently wilted condition and will die if water is not added.
- As the soil water content decreases, a point is reached when the water is so firmly held by the soil particles that plant roots are unable to extract water at a rate sufficient to meet the transpiration needs.
- The plant begins to wilt. At this stage even if the plant is kept in a saturated atmosphere it does not regain its turgidity and wilt unless water is applied to the soil.
- The stage at which this occurs is termed the wilting point and the percentage amount of water held by the soil at this stage is known as the wilting coefficient.
- Water at wilting coefficient is held with a force of **15 atmospheres (pF=4.2).**

3. **Ultimate Permanent wilting point (UPWP)**

- "Ultimate permanent wilting point,", at which the apical leaves do not recover. The permanent WP depends upon plant osmotic adjustment. Therefore, we recognize that there is a range of values for permanent WP, and it is not a unique value.
- It is usually estimated to be the water content at a soil matric potential of **1.5 MPa or 1500 kPa (15 bars).** However, plants can absorb water from soil at potentials much lower than this; **creosote bush** (*Larrea divaricata*) can absorb water to 6.0 MPa .

4. **Hygroscopic Coefficient:**

- The hygroscopic coefficient is the maximum amount of hygroscopic water absorbed by 100 g of dry soil under standard conditions of humidity (50% relative humidity) and temperature (15°C).
- This tension is equal to a force of **31 atmospheres (pF=4.5). varies from 31 -10000 atm.**
- Water at this tension is not available to plant but may be available to certain bacteria.

Moisture equivalent (Brigg's and Mc. Lane, 1907)

- The **weight percentage of water retained** by a previously saturated sample of soil **1 cm in thickness** after it has been subjected to a **centrifugal force of 1000 time gravity** for 30 minutes.
- **Brigg's and Shantz (1912)** used the moisture equivalent as an indirect measure of wilting point W.P.)

$$\text{Wilting Point} = \frac{\text{Moisture Equivalent}}{1.84}$$

However this factor i.e. can't be used for all soils. Moisture equivalent is assumed to represent moisture held under field conditions or the field capacity.

Maximum capillary Capacity (MCC)= Water holding capacity – Hygroscopic Coefficient

Unit-66: Energy concept of Soil water

- The energy related phenomenon is retention and movement of water in soils, its **uptake** and **translocation** in plants and its **loss** to the atmosphere etc.
- The **more strongly water is held in the soil, the greater is the heat (energy)** required. In other words, if water is to be removed from a moist Soil, work has to be done against adsorptive forces.
- Conversely, **when water is absorbed by the soil, a negative amount of work is done**. The movement is from a zone where the free energy of water is high (standing water table) to one where the free energy is low (a dry Soil). This is called **energy concept of soil water**.
- The difference between the energy status of soil water and pure free water is known as soil **water potential.**
- Soil moisture is measured **by gravimetric method**. And its drying temperature is **105-110 °C.**

$$\textbf{Formula moisture (\%)} = \frac{\textbf{weight of wet soil - weight of dry soil x 100}}{\textbf{Weight of dry soil}}$$

Unit-67: Tensiometer

- **Tensiometer** is used to measure in **situ soil moisture**. And its range is **0.0 to 0.85 bars.**

TENSIOMETER READING & ITS INDICATIONS

S.No.	Tensiometer reading		Indications
1.	0-8 Kpa	➤	Soil Very wet
2.	8 kpa	➤	Field capacity
3.	8-35 Kpa	➤	Best condition for crop growth
4.	35-50 Kpa	➤	Mild stress on well drained soil

5. >50 Kpa ➤ Very dry soil

- **More water means less tension and less water is held at more tension.** So **WATER MOVES FROM LOW TENSION TO HIGH TENSION.**
- Darcy's law in soil deals to hydraulic gradient.

Height of water column (cm)	P_F Value	Atmospheric pressure
1	0 (Saturated soil)	1/1000
10	1.0	1/100
100	2.0	1/10
346	2.53 (field Capacity)	1/3
1000	3.0	1
10000	4.0	10
15849	4.2 (Wilting point)	15
31623	4.5 (Hygroscopic point)	31
100000	5.0	100
10000000	7 (Oven dry soil)	10000

Unit-68: Soil Water Movement

mainly through saturated flow, unsaturated flow and water vapour.

1. **Saturated flow**: This occurs when the soil pores are **completely filled with water**. This water moves at water potentials **larger than - 33 kPa.** Hydraulic conductivity can be expressed as **V = kf.** Where, V = Total volume of water moved per unit time f= Water moving force, k = Hydraulic conductivity of soil.
2. **Unsaturated Flow**: It is flow of water held with water potentials **lower than 1/3 bar.** Water will move toward the region of lower potential (towards the greater pulling force).
3. **Water Vapour Movement**: The movement of water vapour from soils take place in two ways:

(a) **Internal movement**: The change from the liquid to the vapour state takes place within the soil, that is, in the soil pores

(b) **External movement**: The phenomenon occurs at the land surface resulting vapour is lost to the atmosphere by diffusion and convection.

ENTRY OF WATER INTO SOIL

1. **Infiltration**: Infiltration refers to the **downward entry or movement of water into the soil** profile. Vegetative covered soil surface has more infiltration rate than bare soil. It occurs in upper layers of soil.
2. **Percolation**: The **downward movement of water through a column of soil** is called percolation. Sandy soils have greater percolation than clayey soil, and it in lower layers of soil.
3. **Permeability**: It indicates the **relative ease of movement of water with in the soil**. The characteristics that determine how fast air and water move through the soil are known as permeability.
4. **Drainage**: Water moving below the root zone of the plant is unavailable to plant and move the chemical deeper into the profile and to recharge the underlying aquifer.

5. **Hysteresis**: It is difference in energy status of soil when soil are alternately wetted and dried is called hysteresis. **Desorption** is upper solid line developed curve due to drying of saturated soil whereas lower dotted line developed curve due to wetting an initially dry soils called **Sorption.**

- **Consumptive water use**: quantity of water lost by evapotranspiration (ET) plus that contained in plant tissue is called consumptive water use.
- **Water use efficiency (WUE)**: amount of water (evapotranspiration, plant tissue and drainage loss) required to produce a unit of dry weight material is known as WUE. It is mathematically define as **WUE=DW/ET**
- **Maximum water movement** occurred in **single grain structure** and **lowest in massive soil** structure.

FINAL INFILTRATION RATE:

Soil Type	:	Final Infiltration rate (mm/hr)
Sand	:	> 20
Silt/Loam	:	5 – 10
Clay	:	1 – 5
Sodic clay soil	:	< 1

Unit-69: Soil Temperature

- The temperature measured **near the surface of the soil.**
- **Favourable** temperature for **nutrient absorption** is **27 – 32 ^{0}C.**
- **Speed of chemical reaction** is **doubled** by **every 10 ^{0}C** rise in temperature.
- The soil temperature on **south slope** is **higher** than that on North slope.
- For every **900 feet of height** atmospheric temperature falls by **1 ^{0}C.**
- Soil temperature is used at family level **categorization in soil taxonomy**.
- **Fourier's law** deals with heat conduction in soils.

Specific heat (Cal/g): It is defined as the amount of heat in calories required to rise in temperature of 1 g of soil solid by 1 ^{0}C.

SPECIFIC HEAT

S. NO	Material	➤	Specific heat (cal/g/^{0}C)
1	Organic Matter	➤	0.46
2	Air	➤	0.25
3	Mineral matter	➤	0.18
4	Water	➤	1
5	Clay	➤	0.22
6	Ice (0^0)	➤	0.5
7	Quartz	➤	0.19

Heat capacity (Cal/cm^3):The ratio of heat supplied to its corresponding rise in temperature is the heat capacity of the soil.

S.No.	Heat capacity	➤	Specific heat X Specific gravity
1.	Organic matter	➤	0.462 *1.3 = 0.60

2.	Water	➤	1 * 1 = 1
3.	Air	➤	24 * 0.000125 = 0.003
4.	Mineral matter	➤	0.45

THERMAL CONDUCTIVITY

- It is amount of heat that flow from **1 cc of substance in 1 second** when difference between two ends is **1 degree Celsius.**
- Thermal conductivity : **Sand > Loam >Clay > Peat**
- Thermal conductivity is **increase with increase in soil moisture.**
- Thermal conductivity **decreases with addition of organic matter and increase in porosity.**
- Thermal conductivity of **water** is **1.4×10^{-3} Cal cm^{-1} s^{-1} $^0C^{-1}$** .

$$\text{Thermal conductivity} = \frac{\text{Heat conductivity}}{\text{Specific heat}}$$

Thermal Diffusivity: Temperature change that takes place in a portion of a given soil as heat flows into it from adjacent layer.

MODE OF HEAT TRANSFER

1. **Conduction:** Flow of heat through matter unaccompanied by any motion.
2. **Convection:** The transfer of heat by moving matter.
3. **Radiation:** The transfer of heat through vacuum/ space.

DENSITY

1. **Liquid**: 0.998 g cm^{-3} or 1000 kg m^{-3}
2. **Solid** : 0.910 g cm^{-3}
3. **Vapour** : 1.73×10^{-5} g cm^{-3}

Unit-70: Chemical properties of soil

1. pH: SPL Sorenson (1909)

- Is the negative logarithm of H ion concentration.
- There are two type of acidity in soil , **active** acidity and **potential** acidity.
- pH measure only active acidity. Potential acidity forms the bulk of the soil acidity.

$$pH = \log 1/a^{H+} \text{ or } -\log AH^+$$

➤ The concentration of H^+ at 7 pH ($1*10^{-7}$), 0 pH ($1*10^{-0}$) and 14 pH ($1*10^{-14}$)

- **POTENTIAL ACIDITY > ACTIVE ACIDITY**
- Soil pH is also **soil reaction**.
- Soil with pH less than 6.5 are acidic, 6.5 to 7.5 are neutral and above 7.5 are alkaline.
- **One unit** change in pH changes **H ion concentration by 10 times, 2 units by 100 times** and so on.

2. Electrical conductivity (EC)

- Measure of soluble salts in **mmhos/cm** or **ds/m** in **solubridge** or **conductometer**.
- It is ion exchange method.
- Most important process occurring in soil ion exchange is a **reversible process**.

3. Base saturation

- Base saturation is the **sum of base cations** (Ca2+, Mg2+, K+, and Na+) held onto the soil exchange sites divided by the total CEC and **expressed as a percentage**.

$$\textbf{Base saturation (\%)} = \frac{Na^{+} + K^{+} + Ca^{++} + Mg^{++}}{CEC} \times 100$$

- Fertile soils are saturated with Ca^{++} and Mg^{++} ions. If soil is saturated with more than 15% exchangeable sodium, then that soil is called **alkali** soil. If soil is saturated with H^{+} ion , then the soil sad to be base unsaturated or **acidic** soil.

Unit-71: Soil Organic Matter

❖ Soil weight (i.e. of furrow slice)= **2 X 10^{6} kg/ha**

❖ Nitrogen status of soil is 0.03-0.05 % means 1000 kg of N per hectare.

Composition of organic matter

	Organic residue		Composition%
1.	Moisture	➢	75%
2.	Dry matter	➢	25%
	Dry Matter composition		
1.	Carbon	➢	10-12%
2.	Oxygen	➢	9-10%
3.	Hydrogen	➢	1.5-2.5%
4.	Nitrogen	➢	1-2%
5.	Mineral matter	➢	1-3%

Composition of plant tissue

	Plant tissue		Composition %
1.	Celluloses	➢	20-50%
2.	Hemicelluloses	➢	10-30%
3.	Starch, sugar	➢	1-5%
4.	Proteins	➢	1-15%
5.	Fats, waxes, tannins	➢	10-30%

The organic matter is classified on the basis of their rate of decomposition

	Rate of decomposition		Examples
1.	Rapidly decomposed	➢	Sugars, Starches, proteins etc.
2.	Less rapidly decomposed	➢	Hemicelluloses, Celluloses etc.
3.	Very slowly decomposed	➢	Fats, waxes, resins, lignins etc.

ELEMENTAL COMPOSITION OF HUMUS

	Elements		Percentage
1.	Carbon	➢	55 to 60%
2.	Nitrogen	➢	5 to 6%
3.	Hydrogen	➢	4-5%
4.	Oxygen	➢	35-40%

- ❖ **Soil organic matter**: Humic substances + Non humic substances.
- ❖ Humus: 40-50 % Lignin, 30-33 % Protein, rest is fat, waxes. Lignin + protein =70-80% (Ligno-protein complex).
- ❖ C : N ratio in Humus 10:1 .
- ❖ Humus absorbs PO_4^{3-} anions from soil not other ions.
- ❖ **Humus:** Colloidal in nature, negatively charged (-COOH) / (C_6H_5OH), at high pH CEC is 150-300 C mol/kg soil. Water holding capacity 4-5 times more than silicate clays, low plasticity & cohesion , favouable for aggregate formation and stability , black colour , cellulose not present so fungi first attack , wood is decompose by actinomycetes.

Acids in humus and their properties

Properties	Fulvic acid	Humic acid	Humin acid
Molecular weight	Lowest	Medium	Highest
Colour	Light	Medium	High
Solubility	Soluble in acids, alkali solution	Soluble in alkali & insoluble in acid solution	Insoluble in both acid & alkali solutions
Resistant to decomposition	Low	Medium	High

Chemical nature of humic substances

Humic substances	Elemental composition				
	C	H	N	S	O
Humic acid	54-59	3-6	1-4	1-5	33-38
Fulvic acid	41-51	4-7	1-4	3-5	40-50

Humic substances	Functional group (Cmol(p^+) kg ha^{-1})			
	Total acids	COOH	Phenolic	E4/E6
Humic acid	500-900	150-600	200-600	3-5
Fluvic acid	700-1400	500-1100	110-600	6-9

Physical properties of humus

- ❖ It posses low plasticity and cohesion
- ❖ It imparts the colour to soil

Colloidal properties of humus

- ❖ They carry the negative charges
- ❖ It composed of C, H, o with trace amount of N, S, P & other element.
- ❖ It adsorbs Ca^{2+}, H^+, Mg^{2+}, K^+ and Na^+

Nutrient availability

Organic N,P,S--------------------------- NH_4, NO_3, PO_4, SO_4

C:N <20:1, C:P <200:1, C:S <200:1

pH and base saturation

pH	% base saturation
5.0	25%
5.5	50%
6.0	75%

Comparison of humus and O.M.

Properties	Humus	OM
C:N	10-12:1	20-40:1
Decomposition	Resistant	Easily

- ❖ OM content of Indian soils is low because high rate of decomposition under tropical and sub tropical climate.
- ❖ Indian soils generally content **<0.5 % OM.**
- ❖ O.M. in most of the cultivated soils rarely exceeds 1%.
- ❖ The soil organism are most active at 24-35 ^{0}C.
- ❖ C:N ratio of arable soils is 8:1 to 15:1 .
- ❖ C:N ratio is lower in arid and sub soils.
- ❖ C:N 20-30:1 in legumess and Farm manure.
- ❖ 400:1 in saw dust.
- ❖ 4:1 to 9:1 in microbes.
- ❖ Older the plants the larger will be C:N ratio.
  - ∴ 58 g 'C' present in 100g O.M
  - ∴ 1g 'C' present in 100/58 = 1.724
  - ∴ **C: OM = 1:1.724 This is called Bemlen factor.**
- ❖ **Muck soil:** Highly decomposed soils.
- ❖ **Peat soil:** Partialy decomposed, pH<3.9 , O.M. 10-40 % and suitable for paddy.
- ❖ 95% N and 33% P of soils are obtained from O.M.
- ❖ **Mineralization:** Conversion of an element from immobilised form to an available form as a result microbial decomposition.
- ❖ **Immobilisation:** Available form of an element is fixed as immobile form.
- ❖ **Soil N :**
  - a. 20-40 % in bound Amino acid form.
  - b. 5-10 % combined hexose amines.
  - c. 1-3 % mineralised form.
- ❖ When, **C:N >30** Immobilisation occurs

< 20 Mineralisation occurs (i.e. released NH_3 & NO_3^-).

$$\begin{Bmatrix} C:N\ ratio = 15 - 30\ both\ immobilisation\ and \\ 20 - 30 = Mineralisation\ occurs \end{Bmatrix}$$

- **Natural Supply of N** (Bartholomew, 1971)
  - I. Soil organic N = 20-30 kg N/ha/yr
  - II. Rainfall = 6-8 kg N/ha/yr
  - III. N- symbiotic N fixation = 2-4 Kg N/ha/yr
  - IV. Dust and organic particles through rainfall = 12-16 kgN/ha/yr
- **Soil phosphorus:** 25-80% P present in organic form like phytin or its derivatives (40-80%) and 0-10% as nucleic acids. C:N:P ratio =100:10:1 . If C:P ratio is more than 100:1 then immobilisation of P.
- **Soil Sulphur:**
  - a. If C:S is <200:1 then SO_4^{2-} accumulation.
  - b. C:S is > 400:1 then SO_4^{2-} tie up in soil O.M.
  - c. C:S is 200-400:1 then SO_4^{2-} either released or tie up.
- **60% N loss in India is due to volatilization due to ph>8.0.**
- Gaseous loss by MO's –Nitrous oxide (N_2O), Nitric oxide (NO) and elemental nitrogen (N).
- After ratoon of sugarcane wheat yield is more due to high P residue & OM content left by ratoon crop.
- Bacteria responsible for denitrification: *Pseudomonas, denitrificans* (-ve), *Achromobacter, Bacillus, Micrococcus* etc.
- The ratio between nitrogen and organic matter is thus constant (OM:N= 20:1)
- Soil organic matter holding exchangeable cations has been estimated as 54% of the exchange by carboxyl (-COOH) group , 36% to imide nitrogen group.
- Estimated CEC C mol/kg of component:
  - Organic matter: 168-249
  - Clay: 38-51
  - Silt: 2-22

Unit-72 C:N & C:P Ratios

C:N Ratio: It is the ratio of the organic carbon to weight of the total nitrogen in soil.

S. No	Particular		C:N Ratio
1	Indian Soils	➤	8.5:1 to 12:1
2	Organic matter and humans	➤	10 :1
3	For mineralization	➤	< 20:1
4	For immobilization	➤	>30:1
5	Micro organism	➤	4:1 to 9:1 (Lowest)
6	Paddy Straw	➤	80:1
7	Saw dust	➤	400:1 (Highest)
8	FYM	➤	25-30:1
9	Legumes	➤	20 – 30:1
10	Young green leaves	➤	10 – 30:1
11	Arable land (or) cultivated land	➤	8:1 to 15:1

12	Well decomposed Compost	➤	10 : 1
13	Ideal soil	➤	10 – 12:1
14	Freshly added residues	➤	>30:1

Lower / narrow C:N ratio indicates rate of organic matter decomposition is high (high nutrient status) and high or wider C:N ratio indicates the rate of organic matter decomposition is slow (low nutrients availability).

C:N & C:P Ratio:

C:N & C:P Ratio		**Process**
C:N ratio <20:1	➤	Mineralization (release of N)
C:N ratio 20-30:1	➤	No release of N (Neither mineralization nor immobilization)
C:N ratio > 30:1	➤	Immobilization
C:P ratio 200:1 or less	➤	Mineralization
C:P ratio >200:1	➤	Neither mineralization nor immobilization
C:P ratio 300:1 and above	➤	Immobilization

Soil Carbon Sequestration: The transfer of atmospheric CO_2 into the soil as soil organic matter and as secondary carbonates through input of biomass-C

Unit- 73: Biological properties of soil

The sub- discipline of soil science which study the microorganisms present in the soil, their functions and the effect of their activities on the character of the soil and the growth and health of the plant life.

Population of micro organism in soil

Soil and pH	**Bacteria**	**Fungi**	**Actinomycetes**
Rhizosphere soil	6778×10^6	918×10^3	83×10^4
Non rhizosphere soil	25×10^6	68×10^3	1×10^4
pH- requirement	6.5 -8.0	4.5 – 6.5	Neutral

Microorganism in soil on the basis of their number/g of soil (normal soils):

- Bacteria >Actinomycetes > Fungi > Algae

☛ The smell of soils after fresh showers is due to Actinomycetes.

Soil microorganism in soil on the basis of their mass/g of soil:

- Fungi >Bacteria >Actinomycetes > Algae

Microorganism order in acid soils:

- Fungi >Bacteria > Algae> Actinomycetes

Microorganism order in arid and semi arid (alkali) soils:

- Actinomycetes > Bacteria > Fungi > Algae

Suitable pH for soil bacteria: 6-8 (nearly neutral pH)

- Sulphar oxidizing bacteria: *Thiobacillus thioxidants*
- Sulphar reducing bacteria: *Desulfovibrio*
- Most dominant (population): *Bacillus spp.*

Micro-organism habitation:

- **Psychrophiles:** Micro-organisms grow at temperature **below 10°C**
- **Mesophiles:** Micro-organisms grow temperature between **10-40 °C.**
- **Thermophiles:** Micro-organism can tolerate temperature **>45°C**

Rhizosphere: (term given by **Hiltnor**)

- Region of soil subjected to the influence of the plant roots.

Phyllosphere: (given by **Runion**)

- Region around foliage/ leaves inhabitant by the microbes.

Unit-74: Soil Of India

Soil can be defined simply as a mixture of small rock debris/particles and organ materials/humus which develop on the earth surface and support to plants growth The classification soil in the ancient time was based on two things; whether the soil is fertile or sterile. Thus the classification was: **Urvara [fertile] and Usara [sterile]**

SOIL CLASSIFICATION - Agencies involved When the **Soil survey of India** was established **in 1956,** they studied soils of India and their characteristics. The **National Bureau of Soil Survey and the Land Use Planning, Nagpur** an institute under the control of Indian Council of Agriculture Research did a lot of studies on Indian soil.

Eight (8) major groups:-

1.Alluvial soil:

- Mostly available soil in **India (about 43%)** which covers an area of **143 sq.km.**
- Indus-Ganga-Brahmaputhra plain, Narmada-Tapi plain etc., are examples.
- The old alluvium is termed as **Bhangar** and latest alluvium termed as **Khadar**.
- **Highly fertile**.
- Humus, lime and organic matters are present.
- **Colour**: Light **Grey** to **Ash Grey**.
- Texture: Sandy to silty loam or clay.
- **Rich in potash** but **Poor in phosphorous**.
- Wheat, rice, maize, sugarcane, pulses, oilseed etc., are cultivated mainly.
- **Found in state of:** Punjab to Assam, Valleys of Narmada and Tapti in MP & Gujrat, Mahanadi in the MP and Orissa, Godawari in AP and Cauvery in T.N.

2. Red soil:

- They are mainly formed due to the decomposition of ancient crystalline rocks like granites and gneisses.
- Seen mainly in **low rainfall area** and also known as **Omnibus** group.
- Porous, friable structure.
- **High phosphorus (P) fixation** capacity due to **pressure of kaolinite**.
- Absence of lime, kankar (impure calcium carbonate).
- Deficient in : lime, phosphate, manganese, nitrogen, humus and potash.
- **Colour**: Red because of **Ferric oxide**. The lower layer is **reddish yellow** or yellow.
- **Texture**: Sandy to clay and loamy.
- Wheat, cotton, pulses, tobacco, oilseeds, potato etc., are cultivated.
- **Found in state of** : Tamil Nadu, Karnataka, Andhra Pradesh, SE Maharashtra, Chhattisgarh, Parts of Orissa, Jharkhand, and Bundelkhand.

3.Black soil/Regur soil:

- Regur means cotton - best soil for **cotton** cultivation.
- Mostly black soil is occupied by **Deccan**.
- **Matured** soil.
- **High water retaining** capacity.
- **Swells** become sticky **when wet and shrink** when **dried**.
- **Self-ploughing** is a characteristic of the black soil as it develops **wide cracks** when dried.
- **Rich in**: Iron, lime, calcium, potassium, aluminum and magnesium.
- **Deficient** in Nitrogen, Phosphorous, Zinc and organic matter.
- **Texture**: Clay.
- **Colour**: Deep black to light black.
- **Found in state of:** Deccan Plateau, Maharashtra, Gujrat, MP, Karnataka, A.P. and T.N.

4.Laterite soil:

- It derived from **Latin** word **'Later'** which means **Brick**. Become so **soft when wet** and so **hard when dried**.
- Found in the **areas of high temperature and high rainfall**. So formed as a result of high leaching.
- Lime and silica will be leached away from the soil.
- **Organic matters** of the soil will be **removed** fast **by the bacteria** as it is high temperature and humus will be taken quickly by the trees and other plants. Thus, humus content is low
- **Rich in:** Iron and Aluminum
- **Phosphorus fixation is most probable in this soil.**
- **Deficient in** : Nitrogen, Potash, Potassium, Lime, Humus
- **Colour**: Red colour due to iron oxide.
- **Best for Tea ,coffee, rubber** ,Rice, Ragi, Sugarcane and Cashew nuts are cultivated mainly.
- **Found in state of:** Western ghats, Eastern ghats, Rajmahal hills, Maharashtra, Karnataka, Kerala, Orissa, W.B., Assam, T.N. *etc*

5. Desert/ arid soil:

- A large part of the arid and semi-arid regions of Rajasthan and adjoining areas of Punjab and Haryana lying between the Indus and the Aravallis receiving less tha 50 cm of annual rainfallis affected desert conditions. Deposited mainly by wind activities.

- **High salt content**, lack of moisture and humus.
- **Kankar** or **Impure Calcium carbonate** content is high which restricts the infiltration of water.
- Nitrogen is insufficient and Phosphate is normal.
- **Texture**: Sandy and **Colour:** Red to Brown.
- The changes in the cropping pattern in the Indra Gandhi Canal Command Area a **living example of the utility of the desert soils.**

6. Peaty / marshy soil: KARI IN KERALA

- Areas of **heavy rainfall and high humidity**. A large quantity of dead organic matter/humus (10-40%) which makes the **soil alkaline**.
- Growth of vegetation is very less. Heavy soil with black colour.
- **Peaty soils** are found in Kottayam and Alappuzha district of **Kerala**, where it is called **KARI.**

7. Forest soil & Mountain soil:

- Such soils are mainly found on the hill slopes covered by forest.
- The formation of these soils is mainly governed by the characteristic deposition of organic matter derived from forest growth.
- Found in: Himalayan region, higher hills in south and the peninsular region.
- They are generally brown coloured.
- Very rich in Humus but deficient in Potash, phosphorus and lime and need fertilizers.
- Plantation of tea, coffee, spices and tropical.

8. Saline and Alkaline soils

- In drier parts of Bikhar, U.P., Haryana, Punjab, Rajasthan and Maharashtra are the salt impregnated or alkaline soils. Known by different names: **Reh, kallar, USAR** , etc.
- Some of the salts are transported in solution by the rivers and canals, which percolates in the sub soil of the plains.
- The accumulation of salts makes the soil infertile and renders it unfit for agriculture.

Unit-75: Types of soils, states where found & crops grown

	Types of soils	States	Crops grown
1.	Alluvial soil	Gujrat, Punjab, Haryana, UP, Bihar, Jharkhand Etc	Wheat, Rice, Sugarcane, Cotton, Jute
2.	Black (Regur soil)	MH, MP, Guj, AP, TN, Valleys of Krishna and Godavari	Cotton, Sugarcane, Jowar, Tobacco, Wheat, Rice
3.	Red	Eastern and southern part of deccan plateau, Odisha, Chhatishgarh, southern part of middle Ganga Plain	Wheat, Rice, Cotton, Sugarcane and pulses
4.	Laterite	KT, Kerala, TN, MP, Assam and Odisha hills	Cashewnuts, tea, Coffee and rubber
5.	Arid and desert	Western Rajasthan, north Gujrat and	Only drought resistantand salt

		southern Punjab	tolerant crops such as Barley, rape, cotton, millets, Maize and pulses.
6.	saline and Alkaline	Western gujrat, Deltas of eastern coast, Sunderban areas of West Bengal, Punjab and Haryana	---------

Unit -76: Soil rich and lacks in Nutrients

	Types of soil	Rich in	Lacks in
1.	Alluvial soil	Potash and lime	Nitrogen and Phosphorus
2.	Black (Regur soil)	Lime,Fe, Mn, Al and K	P, N and Organic matter
3.	Red	Fe and K	N, P and Humus
4.	Laterite	Iron oxide and potash	O.M. ,N, P and calcium
5.	Arid and desert	Soluble salts Phosphate	Humus, Nitrogen
6.	saline and Alkaline	Na, K and Mg	N and Ca

Unit-77: Problematic soils in India:

- **Zinc deficiency** produced in **calcareous soils.**
- Total area under **acid** soils is **90 m.ha.**
- Maximum acid soils are found in Madhya Pradesh.
- The area under arable acid soils is 49 m.ha. with 25 m.ha area having pH <5.5 & 24 m.ha. area having pH 5.5 to 6.5
- Total area under **salt affected** soils **10 m.ha.**
- Saline soil covers **7.2 m.ha.** and sodic soils covers **2.8 m.ha.**
- **Solonchalk** means saline soil and **Solonetz** means sodic soils.
- Slake lime- $Ca(OH)_2$, Burnt lime or Quick lime - CAO
- SPL Soreson (1909) gave term pH (Pourvoir Hydrogen).
- pH of acidic soil =< 6.8-7 , Neutral soil= 7 and alkaline soil= >7.
- In acidic pH (<6.0) the availability of Al, Fe, Mn, Zn, Cu is high.
- In neutral pH (6-7) the availability of N, P, K, Mg, S is high.
- In alkaline pH (>7.0) the availability of Ca and Mo is high.
- **Cation Adsorption order**: $Al^{+3} > Ca^{+2} > Mg^{+2} > K^{+}$
- **Anion exchange order:** $H_2PO_4^{-2} > OH^{-} > SO_4^{-2} > NO_3^{-}$

1.ACIDIC SOILS

- The substances that donate H^+ to some other substance is called acid.
- The soils with higher concentration of exchangeable Al+3 and H+ shows acidic properties.
- Acid sulphate soils i.e. soils turned acidic due to sulphuric acid or metal sulphates.
- **Acid sulphate soils** are present in **Kuttanand** area of **Kerala** and **Sunderbans** of **West Bengal.**
- Highly organic soils are more acidic than mineral soils.

Acid soil formation factors

- Excessive rainfall, used of acid forming fertilizers, Acid rain, acidic parent material, acidic root exudates.

Types of acidity:

1. **Active acidity:** The concentration of H^+ and Al^{+3} ions in soil solution.
2. **Exchangeable acidity:** The acidity developed due to adsorbed H+ and Al+3 ions on soil colloids.
3. **Reserve acidity**: The acidity developed due to H+ and Al+3 ions in the within the clay lattice.

Management of acidic soils:

1. By addition f liming material or growing acid tolerant crops.
2. Lime stone, marketable lime, lime shells, paper mill sludge and basic slag are of the liming material.

pH level		Suitable crops in acidic soils
4.0 -6.0	➤	Rice, Tea
5.0-6.0	➤	Tobacco
5.0-6.5	➤	Soybean, cotton,oats, peas, tomato and millets
6.0-7.0	➤	Maize, sorghum, wheat
6.0-7.5	➤	Berseem, sugarcane , sugarbeet

2. SALT AFFECTED SOILS

- Occurs in arid and semi-arid regions where ET is greater than PPT. The accumulation ions causing salinity or alkalinity include sodium, potassium, mannesium, calcium, chlorides, carbonates and bicarbonates.
- Total area 10 Mha.
- Saline soils- 7.2 Mha.
- Alkali soil- 2.8 Mha.

A. SALINE SOILS:

- This soil is called **Solanchak, white alkali** because of surface crust of white salts and are said to cause boron toxicity.
- Formation process by which the saline soil formed is called **salinization**. Saline soils occur mostly in **arid or semi arid regions**.

Management:

- Flooding or Leaching of soluble salts by good quality irrigation water.
- Keep soil moist or frequent irrigated the field.
- Use of FYM for saline reclamation.

B. ALKALI/ SODIC SOILS:

- The presence of saturated complex saturated with **exchangeable sodium** and the absence of appreciable quantities of soluble salts. These soils often called ***'black alkali'*** soils because they are black, owing to the effect of the **high sodium** content which causes the dispersion of the organic matter. These soils are also called *typical usar* soils. These soils contain **sodium carbonates (Na_2CO_3) in abundance.**
- **Formation:** due to salinization and alkalization
  - Arid and semi arid climate

- Poor drainage of soil
- High water table
- Overflow of sea water over lands
- Salts blown by winds – **The salinity of Rajasthan developed to a great extent due to this reason.**
- Saline nature of parent rock material.
- Excessive use of basic fertilizers.
- Humid and sub humid regions.

Reclamation and management:

- Alkali soils cannot be reclaimed by mere flooding the land.
- In the case of saline –alkali soils, flooding is likely to do more harm.
- In alkali soils , exchangeable sodium Na-clay is so great to make the soil almost impervious to water.
- **Application of gypsum**- by cationic exchange , calcium is often used to replace sodium in alkali soil. Addition of gypsum improves physical conditions of soil . Soils become flocculated and drainage improves, pH is lowered down to a desirable level.
- **Use of sulphur**
- Addition of organic matter
- Use of sulphuric acid
- Addition of molasses

Gypsum ($CaSO_4 . 2H_2O$):

- Hydrite zypsum ($CaSO_4 . 2H_2O$) Contains 23.3 % Ca & 18.6 % sulphur
- Anhydrite zypsum ($CaSO_4$) Contains 29.2 % Ca& 18.6 % sulphur
- In general case 250 kg/ha gypsum used for sulphur & calcium especially in onion, mustard, groundnut and pulse crops.
- In alkali soil for reclamation purpose zypsum is used @ 800 kg/ha
- Plaster of Paris= $CaSO_4$ / $CaSO_4$, $1/2H_2O$
- Banking Soda = $NaHCO_3$
- Bleaching powder: $CaOCl_2$

Unit-78: Gypsum requirement

The amount of gypsum required to be added to a sodic soil to lower the ESP to a desired value is known as **gypsum requirement**. It is expressed in **miliequivalent of Ca^{++} per 100 gm** of soil.

Gypsum requirement (meq/100 g soil) = $\frac{\text{ESP (Initial)} - \text{ESP(Final)}}{100}$ x CEC

For example a sodic soil have CEC=20, Initial/ measured ESP = 60, gypsum requirement to lower the ESP to 10 will be

GR (meq/100 g soil)= $\frac{60-10}{100}$ **x 20**

$= \frac{50}{100}$ **x 20 = 10 meq of Ca^{++} per 100 g soil.**

Tonnage equivalent to 1 ton of pure gypsum for various amendments

S.No.	Amendment	Application equivalent to 1 ton of pure gypsum
1.	Gypsum	1 ton applied = 1 ton gypsum

2.	Sulfur	0.19	ton applied = 1 ton gypsum
3.	Sulfuric acid	0.61	ton applied = 1 ton gypsum
4.	Iron sulphate ($FeSO_4.7H_2O$)	1.62	ton applied = 1 ton gypsum
5.	Iron pyrite (FeS_2)	0.63	ton applied = 1 ton gypsum
6.	Calcium chloride	0.86	ton applied = 1 ton gypsum
7.	Calcium nitrate	1.06	ton applied = 1 ton gypsum
8.	Lime sulfur	0.78	ton applied = 1 ton gypsum

- Amendments are required in salt affected soil based on pH e.g. **Gypsum should be applied when the soil pH>9.0; whereas Sulphur and Iron pyrite at 8.0-9.0 and limestone at <8.0.**

Unit-79: Difference between Salt affected soils

	Character	Saline soil	Alkaline soil	Saline-Alkaline
1.	ESP	<15%	>15%	>15%
2.	EC (dSm) at 25 ^{0}C	>4%	<4%	>4%
3.	pH	<8.5%	>8.5%	>8.5
4.	SAR	<13	>13	>13
5.	Physical condition of soil	Flocculated	Deflocculated	Flocculated and deflocculated
6.	Content in soil	Excess soluble salts of sodium	Presence of excess ESP	Both saline and alkali soil characters
7.	Dominant salts	**Chlorides** and **sulphates of Ca, Mg** and Sodium	**Carbonates** and bi-**carbonates of Na.**	Both types of salts
8.	Colour of soil	**White**	**Black and dark black**	User soils
9.	Other name	Solanchak, white alkali, brown alkali	Solanetz, black alkali, typical user, alkali, sodic soil	

ESP= Exchangeable sodium percentage

EC= Electrical conductivity

pH= Power of Hydrogen

Unit-80: Soil Classification Based on pH

	Soil type		pH range
1.	Extremely acidic	➢	<4.5
2.	Moderately acidic	➢	4.5 – 5.5
3.	Slightly acidic	➢	5.5 – 6.5
4.	Neutral	➢	6.5 – 7.5
5.	Slightly alkaline	➢	7.5 – 8.5
6.	Moderately Alkaline	➢	8.5 – 9.5
7.	Extremely alkaline	➢	>9.5

Unit-81: Problematic soil & amendments

S. NO	Type of Soil		Amendment/Reclamation method
1	Alkali (or) Sodic soil	➤	Gypsum ($CaSO_4 2H_2O$)
2	Acid soil	➤	Lime
3	Calcareous soil	➤	Pyrites
4	Saline soil	➤	Leaching

Unit-82: Liming Material and Value

S. NO	Limiting Material		Value
1	Calcium oxide (CaO0	➤	179
2	Calcium Hydroxide	➤	136
3	Dolomite ($CaCCO_3$ Mg CO_3)	➤	108.7
4	Calcite ($CaCO_3$)	➤	100
5	Basic slag [$(CaO)_5P_2O_5$ SiO_2)]	➤	86

Unit-83: Tolerance of plants to Boron

	Tolerant	Semi tolerant	Sensitive
1.	Sugar beet	Sunflower	Apple
2.	Onion	Potato	Grape
3.	Turnip	Tomato	Fig
4.	Cabbage	Radish	Cherry
5.	Lettuce	Wheat	Apricot
6.	Carrot	Corn	Orange
7.	-	Beans	Lemon

Unit-84: Crops related to salinity hazards (dsm^{-1})

	Crops	Threshold salinity (dsm^{-1})	Rating
1.	Barley	8.0	Tolerant
2.	Cotton	7.7	Tolerant
3.	Guar	8.8	Tolerant
4.	Rice	3.0	Semi-tolerance
5.	Sorghum	6.8	Moderate tolerant
6.	Soybean	5.0	Moderate tolerant
7.	Sugar beet	7.0	Tolerant
8.	Sugarcane	1.7	Tolerant
9.	Wheat	6.0	Moderately tolerant
	VEGETABLE		
1.	Cabbage	1.8	Semi tolerant
2.	Carrot	1.0	Semi tolerant
3.	Onion	1.2	Semi tolerant

4.	Potato	1.7	Semi tolerant
5.	Tomato	2.5	Semi tolerant
	Other crops		
1.	Date-palm	4.0	Tolerant
2.	Grape	1.5	Semi tolerant
3.	Citrus	1.7	Sensitive

Unit-85: Alkalinity Classes based on RSC/ RSBC ratio

	Water quality		Quantity of RSC / RSBC (Me/lit.)
1.	Very high alkalinity water	➢	>10.0 **Me/lit.**
2.	High alkalinity water	➢	5.0-10.0 **Me/lit.**
3.	Medium alkalinity water	➢	2.5-5.0 **Me/lit.**
4.	Low alkalinity water	➢	2.5 **Me/lit.**
5.	Normal water	➢	0 **Me/lit.**
6.	Non- alkaline water	➢	Negative

Chlorides: In irrigation water chloride ions increases with increase in EC and sodium ions. So ions are more dominant in very high salinity water.

Unit-86: Chloride concentration in Irrigation water (Me/lit.)

	Water quality	➢	Quantity of chloride (Me/lit.)
1.	Not suitable	➢	>20
2.	Not suitable	➢	12-20
3.	Slightly usable	➢	7-12
4.	Moderately good water	➢	4-7
5.	Excellent water	➢	4

Unit-87: Sulphate concentrations in irrigation water (Me/lit.)

	Sulphate (Me/lit)	➢	Remarks
1.	>12	➢	Injurious to unsatisfactory
2.	4-12	➢	Good to injurious
3.	<4	➢	Excellent water

Unit-88: Nitrate (NO_3^-) concentration (Me/lit.)

	Nitrate Me/lit.	➢	Remarks
1.	>30	➢	Intensity of problem is severe
2.	15-30	➢	Intensity of problem is moderate
3.	<5	➢	No problem

Unit-89: Acid sulphate soils (ASS)

- Soil with sufficient sulphides (FeS_2 and others) which becomes strongly acidic when drained are termed acid sulphate soils or as the Dutch refer to thos soils **CAT CLAYS**. These are two types

1. **Potential acid sulphate soils (PASS)**- ASS which has not been oxidized by exposure to air is known as PASS. They are neutral to ph(6.5-7.5), contains un-oxidized iron sulfide. It is generally soft, sticky and saturated with water and are usually **gel-like muds** but can include wet sands and graves have the potential to produce acid if exposed to oxygen.
2. **Actual acid sulphate soils(AASS)**- When PASS is exposed to oxygen, the iron sulphate are oxidized to produce sulfuric acid (H2SO4) and the soils become strogly acidic (usually below pH 4). They contain oxidized iron sulfides , vary in texture and often contain **jarosite (a yellow mottle produced** as a byproduct of the oxidation process).

❖ **Sodium Adsorption Ratio (SAR)** is commonly used as an index for evaluating the sodium hazard associated with an irrigation water supply.

$$SAR = \frac{NA}{\sqrt{\frac{Ca^{++} + Mg^{++}}{2}}}$$

SOIL SURVEY

Kind of Survey	Scale of Base Map	Area represented by 1 cm² on map (ha)	Between field Observations	Frequency of Observation
Rapid Reconnaissance (for more intensive study)	1: 1,000,000	10,000	10 km	1 in 10,000 ha
Reconnaissance	1:250,000	625	2.5 km	1 in 625 ha
(for regional planning)	1:100,00	100	1.0 km	1 in 100
Semi detailed for (for district planning))	1:50,000	25	500 m	1 in 25
Detailed (for village, watershed, urban	Low intensity (1: 10,000)	1	100 m	1 per ha
development, pilot projects and agricultural research station	High intensity (1: 5,000)	0.25	50 m	4 per ha

Unit-90: Land capability classification:

Land Capability classification (LCC) may be defined as a system of grouping land into various classes based on inherent limitations imposed on sustained use by soil attributes, topography, drainage and climate .

The capability classes Falls in two groups:

1. Suited for cultivation

2. Not suited for cultivation

The subclasses are further divides into unit based on a specific management practice

1.Thus land is classified into **8 land capability classes** under two broad groups as: **Land suitable for agriculture** and other uses which includes **class I to class IV** lands.

2. **Land not suitable for agriculture** but very well suited for forestry grass land and wildlife which include **class V to class VIII** land.

ON MAP , THE CAPABILITY CLASSES ARE INDICATED INDICATED IN DIFFERENT COLOUR

	Land Class		Colour
1.	I	➤	Green
2.	II	➤	Yellow
3.	III	➤	Pink
4.	IV	➤	Blue
5.	V	➤	Dark green
6.	VI	➤	Orange
7.	VII	➤	Red
8.	VIII	➤	Purple

DETAILED CHARACTERISTICS OF LAND CAPABILITY CLASSES (LCC)

	LCC		Characteristics
1.	I	➤	Very good cultivable, deep nearly level productive land with almost no limitation or very slight hazard. Soils in this class are suited for a variety of crops, including wheat, Barley, cotton, Maize, tomato and Bean. Need no special practices for cultivation
2.	II	➤	Good cultivable land on almost level plain or on gentle slopes, moderate depth, subject to occasional overland flow, may require drainage, moderate risk of damage when cultivated, use of Crop rotations, water control system or special tillage practices to control erosion.
3.	III	➤	Soils are moderate fertility on moderate steep slopes subject to more severe erosion and severe risk of damage but can be used for crops provided adequate plant cover is maintained, hay or other sod crops should be grown instead of row crops.
4.	IV	➤	These are good soils on steep slopes, subject to severe erosion with severe risk of damage but may be cultivated occasionally if handled with great care, keep in hay or pasture but a grain crop may be grown once in 5 or 6 years.
	Land unsuitable for cultivation but suitable for permanent vegetation		
5.	V	➤	Land is too wet or stony which make it unsuitable for cultivation of crops, subject to only slight erosion if properly managed, should be used for pasture or forestry

			but grazing should be regulated to prevent cover from being destroyed.
6.	VI	➢	These are shallow on steep slopes, used for grazing and Forestry; grazing should be regulated to preserve plant cover; if the plant cover is destroyed, use should be restricted until cover is re-established.
7.	VII	➢	These are steep rough, eroded lands with shallow soils, also includes droughtly and swampy land, severe risk of damage even when used for pasture or forestry, strict grazing or forest management must be applied.
8.	VIII	➢	Very rough land, not suitable even for Woodland or grazing, reserve for wildlife, recreation or wasteland consideration.

Unit-91: Plant nutrients

Earlier **16 elements** were considered as essential for plant growth. They are carbon, hydrogen,oxygen, nitrogen phosphorus, potassium, calcium, magnesium, sulphur, iron, manganese, zinc, copper, molybdenum, boron and chlorine. Recently **Nickel** is added anow **become 17 essential** elements. Other than 17 sodium, cobalt, vanadium, silicon, selenium, gallium, aluminium and iodine are added to the above list. One or the other of these elements (recently added) has been found to be essential for a particular group or species of plants. Carbon dioxide, water and molecular oxygen are the forms in which C, H and O are assimilated by plants. Others are taken up by plants from the soil. Nutrient uptake by plants accounts for about 10 percent of total dry weight of crops, the remaining percentage being water.

- ❖ The process of absorption, translocation and assimilation of nutrients by the plants is known as **mineral nutrition.**
- ❖ Plant analysis using modern techniques reveals that plant body contains about **30 elements** and in some cases as many as **60 elements**.
- ❖ **Arnon and Stout (1939)** proposed **criteria of essentiality** which was **refined** by **Arnon (1954).**
- ❖ **Nicholas (1961)** proposed the term **"functional nutrient"** for any mineral element that functions in plant metabolism whether or not its action is specific.

Unit-92: Critical Information On Nutrients in Relation to Plants

S. No	Nutrient	Discoverer	Year	Plant Usable from
1	H	Since time immemorial	-	H_2O
2	O	Since time immemorial		H_2 and O_2
3	C	Priestly et.al	1800	CO_2
4	N	Theodore de Saussure	1804	NO^-_3 NH^+_4
5	K	C. Sprengel	1839	K^+
6	Ca	C. Sprengel	1839	Ca^{+2}
7	Mg	C. Sprengel	1839	Mg^{+2}
8	P	C. Sprengel	1839	$H_2PO^-_4$ HPO^{-2}_4
9	S	Sachs and Knop	1860	SO_4^{-2}
10	Cl	T.C Broyer, A.B Carlton, C.M Johnson and P.R Stout	1954	Cl^-

11	Fe	E Gris	1843	Fe^{+2}
12	B	K. Warrington	1923	H_3BO_3, $H_2BO_3^-$, HBO_3^{-2} and BO_3^{-3}
13	Mn	J.S. McHargue	1922	Mn^{+2}
14	Zn	A.L. Sommer, C.P Lipman	1926	Zn^{+2}
15	Cu	A.L. Sommer , C.P. Lipman and G. Mc Kinney	1931	Cu^{+2}
16	Mo	D.I Arnon and P.R.Stout	1939	MoO_4^{-2}
17	Ni	P.H Brown, R.M Welch and E.E. Cary	1987	Ni^{+2}

Unit- 93: The Chemical Symbol and the Ionic Forms of essential Elements

S.No.	Element	Symbol	Form(s) of absorption by plants
1.	Carbon*	C	CO_2
2.	Hydrogen	H	H from H_2O
3.	Oxygen	O	Elemental O_2 and O_2 from H_2O
4.	Nitrogen	N	NH_4^+, NO_3^- also as organic $CO(NH_2)_2$ and molecular nitrogen
5.	Phosphorus	P	HPO_4^{2-}, $H_2PO_4^-$ also as Nucleic acid, Phytin
6.	Potassium (Kalium)	K	K^+
7.	Calcium	Ca	Ca^{++}
8.	Magnesium	Mg	Mg^{++}
9.	Sulphur	S	SO_3^{2-}, SO_4^{2-}
10.	Iron	Fe	Fe^{++}, Fe^{+++}
11.	Zinc	Zn	Zn^{++}
12.	Manganese	Mn	Mn^{++}
13.	Copper	Cu	Cu_2^{++}
14.	Boron	B	BO_3^{3-}
15.	Molybdenum	Mo	MoO_4^{2-}
16.	Chlorine	Cl	Cl^-
17.	Nickle	Ni	Ni^{2+}
18.	Silicon	Si	$Si(OH)_4$
19.	Sodium	Na	Na^{2+}
20.	Cobalt	Co	Co^{2+}
21.	Vanadium	V	V+

Unit-94: Classification of Essential Elements

1. **Based on the relative Quantity that is normally present in Plants**

A. *Macro nutrients* (*Major Nutrients/primary nutrients*): C, H, O, N, P, K

B. *Secondary nutrients:* Ca, Mg, S

C. Micro Nutrients (Minor/Tertiary/Trace elements): Fe, Mn, Zn, Cu, Mo, B, Cl, Ni and Na, Se, Co,V, Ga, Al and I_2.

2. Based on their Chemical Nature

A. Metals: K, Ca, Mg, Fe, Zn, Mn, Cu, Co and V etc.

B. Non-Metals: C, H, O, N, P, S, B, Mo, C1, Si, etc.

C. Cations: NH_4^+ ,K^+, Ca^{2+} , Fe^{2+}, Mg^{2+}, Mn^{2+} , Cu^{2+} , Zn^{2+}

D. Anions: NO_3^- , HPO_4^{2-}, $H_2PO_4^-$, SO_4^{2-}, BO_3^{3-}, MoO_4^{2-}, $C1^-$ etc.

3. Based on General Function

A. As a constituent of either organic or inorganic compounds–N, S, P, Ca, B, Fe and Mg.

B. As an activator, cofactor in prosthetic group of enzyme systems–K, Mg, Ca, Fe, Zn, Mn, Cu,Mo, Na and Cl.

C. As a charge carrier in oxidation–reduction reactions–P, S, Fe, Mn, Cu, Mo.

D. As an osmosis regulator and for electron chemical equilibrium in cells–K, Na and Cl.

4. Based on the Mobility in Plants

A. Highly mobile : N, P, K

B. Moderately mobile : Zn

C. Less mobile : S, Fe, Cu, Mn, Cl, Mo

D. Immobile : Ca, B

Transport of nutrients to root surface:

Two important theories , namely soil solution theory and contact exchange theory explain nutrient availability to plants.

1. **Soil Solution Theory:** Soil nutrients are dissolved in water and are transported to root surface by both mass flow and diffusion. **Mass flow** is a movement of nutrient ions and salts along with moving water. **Diffusion** occurs when there is **concentration gradient** of nutrient between the root surface and surrounding soil solution .The **ion move from the region of high concentration to the region of low concentration.**
2. **Contact Exchange Theory:** A close contact between root surface and soil colloids allows a direct exchange of H^+ released from the plant roots with cations from soil colloids. The importance is less.

❖ Nutrient absorption by plant roots is directly dependent on the concentration of soil solution **(intensity factor)** which in turn is regulated by the labile pool **(quantity factor).**

Mechanism of nutrient absorption:two ways

1. **Active absorption:** Absorption of nutrients from soil solution containing low concentration of nutrients compared to plant sap, by expending energy, is called active absorption
2. **Passive absorption:** Nutrients enter the plants along with transpiration stream without the use of energy.
3.

Unit-95: Essential nutrients, their quantity and functions in plants

Elements Quantity (Dry → Important functions

	wt. basis)		
N	1-5%	→	Growth and protein production
P	01-0.4%	→	Root development, energy , early maturity of fruits
K	1-5%	→	High quality, optimum water absorption
S	0.1-0.4%	→	Assist in protein and oil synthesis
Ca	0.2-1.0%	→	Cell structure and division
Mg	0.1-0.4%	→	Main constituent of chlorophyll, energy transfer
Cl	0.2-2	→	Tissue dehydration, photosynthesis
B	6-60 ppm	→	pollen fertility , seed growth and development of cell wall.
Cu	5-20 ppm	→	Enzyme activation and chlorophyll production
Fe	50-250 ppm	→	Respiration and chlorophyll production
Mn	20-500 ppm	→	Enzyme activation and photosynthesis
Mo	<1 ppm	→	N- fixation in pulses
Zn	25-150 ppm	→	Protein synthesis and enzyme activation

Unit- 96: Source of plant nutrients and optimum pH for availability

S.No.	Plant nutrients	Main source	pH range
1.	C	Air (mostly), water	-
2.	H	Air and water	-
3.	O	Air and water	-
4.	N	Parts of N from air but mainly from soil	6-7
5.	P	Soil	6.5-7.5
6.	K	Soil	6.5-7.5
7.	Ca	Soil	7.0-8.5
8.	Mg	Soil	7.0-8.5
9.	S	Soil and air	6 & >6.0
10.	Fe	Soil (Oxide, sulphite, silicates)	6.0 & <6.0
11.	Mn	Soil (Oxide, sulphite, silicates)	5-6.5 (best 6.2-6.4)
12.	Zn	Sulphides, carbonates,, silicates	5-7
13.	Cu	Silicates	5-7
14.	B	Borosilicates, Borates	5-7
15.	Mo	Sulphides,Oxides, Molybdenum	7.0 & >7.0 (7-8)
16.	Cl		
17.	Ni		
18.	Na		-
19.	Co		5-6.5
20.	Si		6 & >6.0

Unit-97: Source of plant nutrients in soils:

S.No. Nutrient → Source

1.	C	→	Carbamate
2.	N	→	Organic matter
3.	P	→	Apatite (Calcium phosphate minerals), Fe or Al phosphate, O.M.
4.	K	→	Micas, Feldspars
5.	Ca	→	Dolamite, calcite, Apatite, calcium carbonate, Gypsum, Augite
6.	Mg	→	Dolamite, muscovite, Biotite, Olivine, Augite, Hornblende
7.	S	→	Pyrites, Gypsum, Organic matter
8.	Fe	→	Pyrites, Magnetite
9.	B	→	Tourmaline
10.	Cu	→	Chalcopyrite, Olivine, Hornblende, Augite, Biotite
11.	Mn	→	Manganite, pyrolusite, Olivine, Hornblende, Augite
12.	Mo	→	Olivine
13.	Zn	→	Sphalerite, Olivine, Hornblende, Augite, biotite
14.	Cl	→	Apatite

Unit-98: Different nutrient test methods in soil

	Nutrient determination	➤ **Analyzing process**
1.	Total Nitrogen in soil	➤ Kzeldahl Process
2.	Available Nitrogen	➤ Alkaline permanganate method
3.	Phosphorus in acid condition	➤ Bray No. 1
4.	Phosphorus in Neutral and alkaline condition	➤ Olsen's Method
5.	K & B	➤ Flame photometer
6.	Sulphate sulphure (SO_4)	➤ Terbimatric Method
7.	Organic carbon	➤ a. Walke & Black method b. Rapid Oxidation Process ($KMnO_4$) c.Morgan's Method
8.	Available K (Potash)	➤ Chromic acid digestion method

SOIL TEST RATING CHART FOR AVAILABLE NUTRIENTS

1.	Nutrient	Low level	Medium Level	High level
2.	N	<250 kg/ha	250-500 kg/ha	>500 kg/ha
3.	P	<20kg/ha	20-50 kg/ha	>50 kg/ha
4.	K	<125 kg/ha	125-300 kg/ha	>300 kg/ha
5.	Zn/Cu	<0.5 ppm	0.5-1.0 ppm	>1.0 ppm
6.	Mn	<1.0 ppm	1.0-3.0 ppm	>3.0 ppm
7.	B	<0.33 ppm	0.33-0.67 ppm	>0.67 ppm
8.	OC	<0.5%	0.5-.75%	>0.75%

Unit-99: Classification of Essential Plant nutrients

	Elements	Remarks
1. Frame Work Elements (available from air)	C, H, O	They account for **approximately 96%** of dry plant weight , mostly in the form of carbohydrates
2. Mineral Nutrients (plants taken from soil)	**A. Macro Nutrients:** a. Primary nutrients (N, P, K) b. Secondary nutrients (Ca, Mg, S)	They account for approximately **3.5%** of dry plant weight
	B. Micro Nutrients – Chlorine (Cl), Iron (Fe), Manganese (Mn), Zinc (Zn), Boron (B), Copper (Cu), Molybdenum (Mo) and Nickel (Ni)	It contributes about **0.04%** of dry plant weight

Unit-100: Difference between Macro and Micro Nutrients

Macronutrients	Micronutrients(Trace Elements)
It required in relatively large amount. In excess of **10 mmole kg^{-1} of dry matter).**	Required in very small amount (**less than 10 mmole kg^{-1} of dry matter)**
The macronutrients include Carbon, Hydrogen, Oxygen, Nitrogen, Phosphorous, Sulphur, Potassium, Calcium and Magnesium	These includes Iron, manganese, Copper, Molybdenum, Zinc, Boron, Chlorine, and Nickel.
They are non toxic in slightly excessive quantity.	They are show toxic effects even in slight excess
Some macronutrients contribute in the development of osmotic potential in the cells.	They do not play any role the development of osmotic potential in the cells.

Unit-101: Essential Nutrients for plant growth and their principal forms for uptake

Nutrient	Chemical Symbol	Concentration in % or ppm	Principal forms for uptake	Sources for nutrients
Carbon	C	6.0	CO_2	Carbonate and air
Hydrogen	H	45.0	H_2O	Air and water
Oxygen	O	45.0	H_2O, O_2	Air and water
Nitrogen	N	1.5	NH^{+4}, NO^{-3}	Organic Matter
Phosphorus	P	0.1-0.3	$H2PO^{-}_4$, HPO^{2-}_4	Pica
Patassium	K	1.0	K^+	Micas, Feldspar

Calcium	Ca	0.5	Ca^{2+}	Dolomite, Apatite, Calcite
Magnesium	Mg	0.2	Mg^{2+}	Mica, Hornblende, lime stone
Sulfur	S	0.1	SO^{2-}_4, SO_2	Organic sources- Protein, amino acids Inorganic sources- Gypsum, pyrites
Iron	Fe	100 ppm	Fe^{2+}, Fe^{3+}	
Manganese	Mn	50 ppm	Mn^{2+}	
Boron	B	20 ppm	$H_3BO^-_3$, $B_4O_7^{2-}$	Tourmaline
Zinc	Zn	20 ppm	Zn^{2+}	
Copper	Cu	6 ppm	Cu^{2+}	
Molybdenum	Mo	0.1 ppm	MoO_2^{4-}	Olivine
Chlorine	Cl	100 ppm	Cl^-	Apatite

THE PLANT CONTENT OF MINERAL ELEMENTS IS AFFECTED BY MANY FACTORS AND THEIR CONCENTRATIONS IN CROPS VARIES CONSIDERABLY

Nutrient		Relative concentration (Times)	Concentration (%)
Primary	N, K	400-1000	1-1.5
	P	30	0.1-0.3
Secondary	Ca, Mg	100-200	0.2-0.5
	S	30	0.1
Micro	Fe, Mn, B	1-2	0.002-0.01
	Others	<1	<0.002

Unit-102: Nutrients are classified based on mobility in soils and plants

Base of classification	Nature of elements	Examples
Mobility in Soil	Mobile	NO^-_3, SO^{2-}_4, BO^-_3, Cl^- and Mn^{2+}
	Less mobile	NH^+_4, K^+, Ca^- Mg^{2+}, Cu^{2+}
	Immobile	H_2PO_4, HPO_4^{2-}, Zn^{2+}
Mobility in Plants	Mobile	N, P, K
	Less mobile	Zn
	Immobile	Ca and B

Unit-103: Specific function of nutrients in plants

S. No.	Function	➤	Examples
1.	Energy storage and bonding nutrients	➤	N, S and P
2.	Act as regulatory and carriers	➤	Ca, Mg and K
3.	Catalyzed and activator	➤	Fe, Mn, Zn and Cu
4.	Energy and Exchange nutrients	➤	H and O

Unit- 104: Deficiency symptoms on plant leaves

S. No.	Type of leaves	➤	Nutrients
1.	Old leaves	➤	N, P, K, Mg and Mo
2.	New leaves	➤	S, Fe, Mn and Cu
3.	Old and new leaves	➤	Zn
4.	Terminal buds	➤	Ca and Boron

Unit-105: Antagonistic effect of nutrients

	Excess of nutrient	➤	Causes deficiency
1.	Ca	➤	P
2.	Ca, Mg	➤	K
3.	K, NH_4	➤	Mg
4.	Fe, SO_4	➤	Mo
5.	P	➤	Zn
6.	N, P, K	➤	Cu
7.	NO_3	➤	Fe
8.	Zn, Al	➤	Cu
9.	N, K ,Ca	➤	B

Unit-106: Plant used for nutrient deficiency indicator

	Nutrient	➤	Indicator plant
1.	Nitrogen	➤	Cauliflower, Cabbage
2.	Phosphorus	➤	Mustard, Rapeseed
3.	Potassium	➤	Potato
4.	Calcium	➤	Cauliflower, Cabbage
5.	Boron	➤	Sunflower, Sugar beet
6.	Sodium	➤	Sugar beet, Turnip
7.	Chlorine	➤	Lettuce
8.	Ferrous	➤	Sorghum, Citrus, Barley
9.	Copper	➤	Wheat
10.	Magnesium	➤	Potato, Cauliflower, Sugar beet
11.	Manganese	➤	Sugar beet, Apple, Apricot
12.	Molybdenum	➤	Cauliflower
13.	Zinc	➤	Maize

Unit-107: Soil test rating chart for available nutrients:

Nutrients	Compounds (units)	Rating		
		Low	Medium	High
Carbon	Organic carbon (%)	<0.5	0.5-0.75	>0.75

Nitrogen	Alkaline $KMnO_4$ (kg/ha)	<250	250-500	>500
Phosphorus	Olsen's method (P kg/ha)	<12.5	12.5-25	>25
Phosphorus	Olsen's method (P_2O_5kg/ha)	< 28	28-56	>56
Potassium	Ammonium acetate (kg/ha)	<140	140-280	>280
Calcium	Ammonium acetate, cmol (p^+)/kg	<1.5	-	>1.5
Sulphur	0.01M $CaCl_2$ (kg/ha)	<22.4	22.4-35	>35
Magnesium	Ammonium acetate, cmol (p^+)/kg	<1.0	-	>1.0
Zinc	DTPA extractable (mg/kg)	<0.6	0.6-1.2	>1.2
Iron (Fe)	DTPA extractable (mg/kg)	<5	5-10	>10
Manganese (Mn)	DTPA extractable (mg/kg)	<5	5-10	>10
Copper	DTPA extractable (mg/kg)	<0.2	0.2-0.4	>0.4
Boron	Hot water soluble (kg/ha)	<0.5	0.5-1.0	>1.0
Molybdenum	Ammonium oxalate extractable (pH 3.3) (mg/kg)	<0.2	0.2-0.4	>0.4

Unit-108: Conversion factors of plant nutrients:

1.	P_2O_5	x	0.44	=	P
2.	P	x	2.29	=	P_2O_5
3.	K_2O	x	0.83	=	K
4.	K	x	1.20	=	K_2O
5.	CaO	x	0.71	=	Ca
6.	Ca	x	1.40	=	CaO
7.	MgO	x	0.60	=	Mg
8.	Mg	x	1.66	=	MgO
9.	SO_2	x	0.50	=	S
10.	S	x	2.00	=	SO_2

Unit-109: Availability of nutrients with p^H values:

pH value	**pH < 6.0**	**pH 6.0-6.5**	**pH > 7.0**
Available nutrients	**Al, Fe, Mn, Zn**	**P, B**	**Ca, Mo**

Unit-110: Methods For Nutrient Analysis

S. NO	Prameter	➤	Method
1	Organic Carbon	➤	Walkely and Black wet oxidation
2	Available Nitrogen	➤	Alkaline permanganate method (Subbiah and Asija)
3	Available Phosphorous	➤	Acid soil – Bray No. 1 reagent (0.03 N NH_4F + N HCl) For all Soil except acid soil – Olsen's reagent (0.5 M $NaHCO_3$)
4	Available Potassium	➤	Natural Normal ammonium acetate

5	CEC	➤	1N Ammonium acetate (NH_4OAC)
6	Available Sulphur	➤	0.15 $CaCl_2$, 1% NaCl and Ca (H_2PO_4)2
7	Micronutrients (Fe, Cu, Mn, and Zn)	➤	DTPA extraction [0.005 M DTPA (pH 7.3)]
8	Boron	➤	Azomethine – H test and Hot water method
9	Mo	➤	Ammonium Oxalate (Tamm's (or) Griggs reagent)
10	Phosphate Potential	➤	0.01 M $CaCl_2$
11	Total Nitrogen	➤	Kjeldhal's method (Modified)
12	Total Phosphorous	➤	Bartons reagent (Vanado molydbo yellow colour phosphoric acid method)
13	Total Potassium	➤	Flame photometer method

Unit-111: Indicators used in analysis

S. No	Parameter	➤	Indicator name
1	Organic Carbon	➤	Diphenylamine
2	Available nitrogen	➤	Mixed indicator (Bromocresol & Methyl red)
3	Chlorides	➤	Potassium chromate
4	Carbonates	➤	Phenolphthalein
5	Bicarbonates (HCO^-_3)	➤	Methyl orange
6	Calcium (Ca)	➤	Murexide
7	Ca + Mg	➤	EBT indicator
8	Gypsum requirement	➤	EBT
9	Boron	➤	Azomethine – H
10	Lime requirement	➤	Methyl orange
11	Self indicator	➤	$KMnO_4$

NOTE: In determination of organic carbon when we add 85% of orthophosphoric acid then only we must add diphenylamine otherwise we have to go for ferroin indicator.

Unit-112: Critical Limitsof micronutrients (in Soil) ppm (or) mg/kg

S. NO	Element	➤	Critical Limit
1	Zn	➤	0.6
2	Mn	➤	2.0
3	Cu	➤	0.2
4	B	➤	0.5
5	Fe	➤	4.5
6	Mo	➤	0.1
7	S	➤	10

Unit- 113: Visual Nutrient Deficiency Symptoms

S. NO	Name of the Symptom	:	Means
1	Chlorosis	:	Uniform or interveinal yellowing or light green colouring of leaves.
2	Necrosis	:	Death of leaf tips, margins or interveinal regions of leaves
3	Reddening	:	Accumulation of anthocyanins causes red or purple colour on leaf margins, interveinal regions , or whole leaves
4	Stunting	:	Reduced plant height, shortened internodes, leaves may remain dark green or exhibit light green or chlorotic symptoms.

Unit-114: Fertilizers

- Fertilizers are generally synthetic inorganic compounds and they supply one/more essential plant nutrients in large proportions.
- Fertilizer control order came into force in **1957** and revised in **September 25, 1985** known as Fertilizer Order

Classification of fertilizer:

a. **Straight fertilizer:** Fertilizer which supply only primary plant nutrient e.g. Urea
b. **Complex/compound fertilizer:** these fertilizers supplies two or more of the primary nutrients and are chemically bound e.g. DAP
c. **Complete fertilizer**: Fertilizer having all three primary major nutrients e.g. NPK
d. **Mixed fertilizers:** Physical mixing of two or more fertilizer.
e. **Low analysis fertilizers**: Having **less than 25 %** of the primary nutrient e.g. SSP
f. **High analysis fertilizer**: Contains **more than 25 %** of the total primary nutrient e.g. Urea

Fertilizer grade:

- ✓ Refers to the guaranteed analysis of its plant nutrient.
- ✓ It is minimum guarantee of the plant nutrient content in the terms of available N, P and K e.g. NPK: 19:19:19.

Fertilizer ratio:

- ✓ Refers to the relative percentage of N, P_2O_5 and K_2O.
- ✓ E.g.A ratio of 2:1:1 means 80 Kg N, 40 Kg P_2O_5 and 40 Kg K_2O.

Order of hygroscopic nature of fertilizers (decreasing)

- Ammonium nitrate > Urea > ammonium sulphate > CAN

Acidic residual nature of fertilizer:

- Anhydrous ammonia > ammonium chloride > ammonium sulphate > urea > ammonium nitrate (lowest).

Order of basic residual nature of fertilizer:

- Calcium cyanamide > sodium nitrate > di calcium phosphate > calcium nitrate

Unit-115: Manufacturing Process of fertilizers

S.No.	Fertilizer	➤	Manufacturing Processes

1. Ammonia ➤ Haber – Bosch process
2. Nitrate ➤ Arc – gap process
3. Ammonium Sulphate ➤ By product process, Neutralization process, Gypsum process or leuna process
4. Urea ➤ Wholer process or carbamate strippers process
5. Single super phosphate ➤ Den process, continuous rock phosphate acidulation process
6. Triple super phosphate ➤ Cone mixer process
7. Basic slag ➤ Open – hearth process
8. MOP ➤ Crystallization process, Flotation process
9. SOP ➤ Langbeinite process, Mannheim furnace process
10. Nitro Phosphate ➤ ODDA process, PEC process

Unit - 116: Nutrient content fo different fertilizers

NITROGEN CONTENT AND OTHER CHARACTERISTICS OF NITROGENOUS FERTILIZERS

Fertilizers	Total N (%)	Other nutrients (%)	Equivalent acidity/ Basicity (kg Ca/CO3)	Other characteristics
Ammonium fertilizers				
Anhydrous ammonia	82.2	-	147	Marketed as compressed liquid gauge pressure –75 pounds/sqm at 50oF and 197 pounds/sqm at 100oF
Ammonium sulphate	20	24% S	107-110	Marketed in fine to medium fine crystals, non-hygroscopic
Ammonium chloride	26	-	128	Not widely used, manufactures in white, crystalline form, non-hygroscopie
Nitrate fertilizers				
Sodium nitrate	16	20% Na	29	Naturally occurring chemical. In early 20th century it was prime source of nitrogen. Very hygroscopic, marketed in grey granules
Calcium nitrate	15	19% Ca	21	Available in white crystalline highly hygroscopic and not marketed in India
Ammonium and nitrate fertilizer				
Ammonium sulphate nitrate	26 (19.25% NH4 & 67.5% NO3)	5-6% S	93	Slightly hygroscopic
Calcium ammonium nitrate	25(12.5% NH4 & 12.5% NO3)	8 % Ca	Neutral	Slightly hygroscopic but excellent handling qualities
Amide fertilizers				
Urea	46	-	80	Most popular, cheap. Free flowing fertilizer. It comes in white prilled form
Calcium cynamid	20	54% Ca	-	It is no longer produced

Phosphorus in the Plant: Typical phosphorus contents of plants range between 0.1 to 0.46 percent P on a dry

	weight basis, approximately ten times less than for nitrogen or potassium.
☞	**Phosphorus in the Soil:** Concentrations in soil solution range from less than 0.1 to around 5 ppm. Most crops respond to P additions when soil solution levels are less than 0.1 to 0.2 ppm.

P Fertilizer Sources:-

☞ **Composition of phosphate fertilizers**

Fertilizers	Phosphorus (P_2O_5) (%)			Nitrogen (%)				Calcium (CaO) (%)	Magnesium (MgO) (%)
	Total	Available	Water soluble	Total	Ammonical	Nitrate	Amide		
Single super phosphate	18-20	16.5-17	16	-	-	-	-	25-30	0.5
Triple super phosphate	46	43	42.5	-	-	-	-	17-20	0.5
Diammonium phosphate	46	41	41	18	18	-	-	-	-
Ammonium phosphate sulphate (16:20:0)	20	19.5	19.5	16	16	-	-	-	-
Ammonium phosphate sulphate (20+20+0)	20	20	17	20	18	2	-	-	-
Ammonium phosphate sulphate nitrate	20	20	17	20	17	3	-	-	-
Urea ammonium phosphate (28:28:0)	28	28	25,2	28	9	-	19	-	-
Urea ammonium phosphate (24:24:0)	24	24	20.4	24	7.5	-	16.5	-	-
Nitro-phosphate (20:20:0)	20	20	5.4	-	-	-		-	-
Udaipur rock phosphate	20-35	-	-	-	-	-	-	-	-
Mussoorie rock phosphate	23-34	-	-	-	-	-	-	-	-
Jhabua rock phosphate	31-38	-		-	-	-	-	-	-

☞ **Ammonium polyphosphate**: This product was developed by Tennessee Valley Authority (TVA) of USA by ammoniation of mixtures of electric furnace superphosphoric acid and up to 30% of the P as wet-process orthophoric acid. This results in a granular product with a grade of 15-62-0 (27% P). Both liquid and solid ammonium polyphosphate are available. In addition to high nutrient content, ammonium polyphosphates have the advantage of chelating micronutrients and reduced P-fixation due to time required for their conversion to orthophosphates

- **Thermal phosphates**: These fertilizers are made by the heat treatment of phosphate rock. There are two processes, namely, "calcinations" and "fusion" by which thermal phosphates are made. In calcinations the heating is done below the melting point of the mixture, while in fusion it is done above the melting point, so that the material fuses together.

POTASSIUM SOURCES

Material	Percent Composition			
	K2O	Mg	S	N
Potassium chloride	60-62	-	-	-
Potassium sulfate	50	-	16	-
Potassium, magnesium sulfate	22	11	22	-
Potassium nitrate	44	-	-	13

COMMON INORGANIC SOURCES OF CALCIUM, MAGNESIUM AND SULFUR

Material	**Chemical Formula**	**Ca**	**Mg**	**S**
			percent	
Calcium chloride	$CaCl_2$	36	0	0
Burned Lime, or Calcium oxide	CaO	70	0	0
Calcitic Limestone	$CaCO_3$	32	3	0.1
Dolomitic Limestone	$CaCO_3$,$MgCO_3$	21-30	6-12	0.3
Gypsum	$CaSO_4$	22	0.4	17-19
Hydrated Lime	$Ca(OH)_2$	50	0	0
Magnesium ammonium phosphate	$MgNH_4PO^4.6H_2O$	0	15	0
Magnesium oxide	MgO	0	45	0
Magnesium sulfate	$MgSO_4.7H_2O$	2	10	14
Potassium magnesium sulfate	$K_2SO_4.2MgSO_4$	0	11	22
Ammonium sulfate	$(NH_4)_2SO_4$	0.3	0	24
Ammonium thiosulfate	$(NH_4)2S_2O_3$	0	26	0
Elemental S	S	0		0
Flowable			52-70	
Wettable, Flowers			90-100	
Potassium sulfate	K_2SO_4	0.7	1.0	18

Sulfuric acid	H_2SO_4	0	0	20-33

MN FERTILIZER SOURCES

Source	% Mn
Manganous oxide	1 - 3
Manganese methoxyphenylpropane	41 - 68
Manganese Frits	10 - 12
Manganese Chloride	17
Manganese Oxide	62 – 70
Manganese Sulfate	24
Basic Slag	1 - 3

ZN FERTILIZER SOURCES

Source	% Zn
Zinc Carbonate	52
Zinc Frits	varies
Zinc Phosphates	51
Zinc Chelate	
Na2Zn EDTA	9 - 14
NaZn NTA	13
NaZn HEDTA	9
Zinc Ammonium Phosphate	34
Zinc Sulfate	22 - 36
Zinc Oxide	78 - 80
Zinc Lignosulfonate	5 - 12
Zinc Polyflavonoid	7 - 10
Zinc Sulfate Monohydrate	33.0 or 35.5

COPPER FERTILIZER SOURCES

Source	% Cu	Water Soluble	Application method
Copper sulfate	22.5	yes	foliar, soil
Copper Ammonium Phosphate	30.0	slight	foliar, soil
Copper Chelates	variable	yes	foliar, soil

IRON (FE) FERTILIZER SOURCES

Source	% Fe
Iron Sulfates	19 - 23
Iron Oxides	69 - 73
Iron Ammonium Sulfate	14
Iron Ammonium Phosphate	22
Iron Chelates	5 - 14

Basic Slag	10 - 14

BORON (B) FERTILIZER SOURCES

Source	%B	Water Soluble
Borax	11.3	yes
Sodium Pentaborate	18.0	yes
Sodium Tetraborate		
Fertilizer Borate46	14.0	yes
Fertilizer Borate 65	20.0	yes
Boric Acid	17.0	yes
Solubor	20.0	yes

MOLYBDENUM (MO) FERTILIZER SOURCES

Source	% Mo
Ammonium Molybdate	up to 54
Sodium Molybdate	38 - 46
Molybdenum Frit	30
Molybdenum Trioxide	60
Molybdenum Sulfide	60

Unit-117: Fertilizers facts

S.No.	Facts	➢	Fertilizer
1.	Soil structure can be improved by	➢	Phosphatic fertilizer
2.	Common nitrogen fertilizer in India	➢	Urea
3.	High nitrogen contain fertilizer	➢	Anhydrous ammonia
4.	Common phosphorus fertilizer in India	➢	DAP
5.	Oldest synthetic fertilizer in India	➢	Ammonium sulphate
6.	1st fertilizer manufactured in Inida	➢	SSP
7.	1st Industrially made fertilizer	➢	SSP
8.	High imported fertilizer in India	➢	K (Potassic)
9.	Phosphorus native	➢	Morocco
10.	Potassium native	➢	Canada
11.	Organic fertilizers	➢	Urea and $CaCN_2$
12.	Highest hygroscopic fertilizer	➢	Ammonium nitrate (2nd Urea)
13.	Explosive fertilizer	➢	Ammonium nitrate
14.	Most acid forming fertilizer	➢	Ammonium chloride
15.	Good fertilizer based on physical condition is concern	➢	Ammonium sulphate

Unit- 118: General Recommended Fertilizer doses (N:P:K ratio)

1. Cereal crops ➢ 4:2:1

2. Pulses crops ➤ 1:2:1 or 1:2:2
3. Oil seed crops ➤ 3:2:1
4. Fodder / fiber crops ➤ 2:1:4

Unit- 119: Equivalent Acidity:

The amount of $CaCO_3$ required to neutralize the acid residue causedby acidic fertilizers in the soil e.g. 100 kg $(NH_4)_2SO_4$ produces acidity which needs 110 kg of CaCO3 to neutralist it. Therefore equivalent acidity of $(NH_4)_2SO_4$ is 110. Anhydrous Ammonia (NH_3) has more equivalent acidity than other fertilizers.

	Fertilizers		**Equivalent Acidity**
1.	Anhydrous ammonia	➤	148 (Highest)
2.	Ammonium chloride (NH_4Cl)	➤	128
3.	Ammonium sulphate $(NH_4)SO_4$	➤	110
4.	Ammonium sulphate nitrate $(NH_4)SO_4NH_4NO_3$	➤	93
5.	Urea	➤	80-85
6.	DAP	➤	77
7.	Ammonium nitrate (NH_4NO_3)	➤	60
8.	Mono-ammonium Phosphate	➤	55 (Lowest)

Unit-120: Equivalent Bacisity of fertilizers

Equivalent Basicity: Residual basicity caused by application of basic fertilizers, expressed in terms of $CaCO_3$ equivalent of basic residue left by a fertilizer material (in kg/100 kg of fertilizer salt.

	Fertilizers		**Equivalent basicity**
1.	Calcium cyanamide ($CaCN_2$)	➤	63 (Highest)
2.	Sodium Nitrate ($NaNO_3$)	➤	29
3.	Potassium Nitrate (KNO_3)	➤	29
4.	Nitrate of soda potash	➤	26
5.	Calcium nitrate $Ca(NO_3)$	➤	21 (Lowest)

Unit- 121: Conversion factors of nutrients

1.	N	➤	NO_3 x 0.22
2.	NO_3	➤	N x 4.54
3.	P	➤	P_2O_5 x 0.44
4.	P_2O_5	➤	P x 2.27
5.	K	➤	K_2O x 0.83
6.	K_2O	➤	K x 1.20

7.	Ca	➢	Cao x 0.71
8.	CaO	➢	Ca x 1.40
9.	Mg	➢	MgO x 0.61
10.	MgO	➢	Mg x 1.63
11.	OM	➢	OC x 1.724 (Bemmelen Factor)
12.	OC	➢	OM x 0.58

Unit- 122: Organic Fertilizers

Average amount of moisture and nutrient content of different animals FYM

Animals	Dung : Urine moisture Ratio	Nutrients (Kg/t)		
		Nitrogen (N)	Phosphorus (P_2O_5)	Potassium (K_2O)
Dairy Cattle	80:20	4.53	1.22	1.40
Feeder cattle	80:20	5.40	2.13	3.22
Poultry	100:0	13.54	6.48	3.17
Swine	60:40	5.84	3.22	4.94
Sheep	67:33	10.42	3.17	9.83
Horse	80:20	6.75	2.03	5.98

Unit- 123: Major elements in bulky organic manures

	Bulky manure	N%	P_2O_5%	K_2O
1.	Farm Yard Manure	0.5	0.25	0.5
2.	Compost manure	0.5	0.15	0.5
3.	Town compost	1.4	1	1.4
4.	Animal Urine	1.0	0.02	1.0
5.	Poultry urine	1.46	0.17	0.62
6.	Sheep Dung	0.7	0.5	1.8
7.	Sira (Molasses)	0.3	0.5	2.1
8.	Pressmud	0.9	2.8	0.9
9.	Night soil	5.5	4.0	2.0
10.	Poultry manure	3.0	2.5	1.4
11.	Sheep manure	3	1	2
12.	Vermicompost	1.5-2.5	1.25-2.25	1-2
13.	Green manure of sunnhemp	2.3	0.5	1.8
14.	Green manure of Daincha	2.7-3.5	0.53-0.6	1.2-2.21

Unit- 124: Major elements in concentrated organic

	Concentrated	N%	P_2O_5 %	K_2O %
1.	Castor cake	4.5	2.0	0.9

2.	Groundnut Cake	7.4	1.5	1.3
3.	Neem cake	5.2	1.0	1.4
4.	Mahua cake	2.5	0.8	1.8
5.	Linseed cake	5.5	1.4	1.3
6.	Mustard cake	5.2	1.7	1.2
7.	Sesame cake	6.2	2.0	1.2
8.	Cotton seed cake	3.4	1.9	1.6
9.	Blood manure	12	1.3	0
10.	Fish manure	4.1	3.9	0.3-1.5
11.	Bone manure	3-5	20-22	0
12.	Meat meal	10.5	2.5	0
13.	Bird Guano	7.1	8.1	0.65

Unit- 125: Green manuring:

In situ green manuring:

It is a system by which green manure crops are grown and incorporated in to the soil of the same field in which it is grown

Sino.	Crop	Botanical name
1.	Sunnhemp	*Crotalaria juncea*
2.	Daincha	*Sesbania aculeata*
3.	Sesbania	*Sesbania speciosa*
4.	Indigo	*Indigofera tinctoria*
5.	Wild Indigo	*Tephrosia purpuria*
6.	Cowpea	*Vigna anguiculata / Vigna sinensis*
7.	Green gram / Mung	*Phaseolus aureus / Vigna radiate*
8.	Black gram / urd /	*Phaseolus mungo /, Vigna mungo*
9.	Horse gram	*Macrotyloma uniflorum*
10.	Cluster bean / Guar	*Cyamopsis tetragonaloba*
11.	Berseem	*Trifolium alexandrium*

Ex- Situ green manuring / Green leaf manuring

The practice of collecting green leaves from all the available sources and incorporating them in the soil is called as green leaf manuring.

	Crop	Botanical name
1.	Glyricidia	*Glyricidia maculate*
2.	Subabul	*Leucaena leucocephala*
3.	Agase	*Sesbania grandiflora*
4.	Pongamia	*Pongamia glabra*
5.	Eupatorium	*Chromolaena odorata*
6.	Neem	*Melia azadiracta*
7.	Cassia	*Cassia siamea*

8.	Ipomea	*Ipomea carnea*
9.	Yekka/ Oak	*Calotropis gigantia*

Unit- 126: Nutrient content of green manures

	Crop name	Nutrient content (%)		
		Nitrogen	Phosphorus	Potasium
1.	Sunnhemp	089	0.12	051
2.	Daincha	0.68	0.13	040
3.	Cowpea	0.71	0.15	0.58
4.	Green gram	0.82	0.18	0.52
5.	Black gram	0.82	0.18	0.52
6.	Horse gram	0.91	0.18	0.65
7.	Glyricidia	0.68	0.16	0.30
8.	Pongamia	0.16	0.174	0.49

Unit- 127: Bio-fertilizers:

Biofertilizers are defined as preparations containing living cells or latent cells of efficient strains of microorganisms that help crop plants uptake of nutrients by their interactions in the rhizosphere when applied through seed or soil. They accelerate certain microbial processes in the soil which augment the extent of availability of nutrients in a form easily assimilated by plants. Use of biofertilizers is one of the important components of integrated nutrient management, as they are cost effective and renewable source of plant nutrients to supplement the chemical fertilizers for sustainable agriculture. Several microorganisms and their association with crop plants are being exploited in the production of biofertilizers. They can be grouped in different ways based on their nature and function.

I. N_2 fixers

a. Free living : Aerobic – *Azotobacter, Beijerinckia, Anabaena* **Anaerobic** – *Clostridium* **Faultative anaerobic** – *Klebsiella*

b. Symbiotic : *Rhizobium, Frankia, Anabaena azollae*

c. Associative symbiotic : *Azospirillum*

d. Endophytic : *Gluconacetobacter Burkholdria*

II. **Phosphorus solubilizers Bacteria** : *Bacillus megaterium var. phosphaticum B. subtilis, B. circulans Pseudomonas striata Fungi : Penicillium sp. Aspergillus awamori*

III. P mobilizers

a. **AM fungi**

b. *Ectomycorrhizal fungi*

c) *Ericoid Mycorrhiza*

d) *Orchid mycorrhiza*

IV.Silicate and Zinc solubilizers: *Bacillus sp,*

V. **Plant growth promoting Rhizobacteria:** *Pseudomans spp.*, and many more Importance of Biofertilizers Biofertilizers are known to make a number of positive contributions in agriculture. • Supplement fertilizer supplies for meeting the nutrient needs of crops. Add 20 – 200 kg N/ha (by fixation) under optimum conditions and solubilise / mobilise 30-50 kg P_2O_5/ha

1. ***Rhizobium Rhizobia*** are soil bacteria, live freely in soil and in the root region of both leguminous and non-leguminous plants. However they enter into symbiosis only with leguminous plants, by infesting their roots and forming nodules on them. **Non legume nodulated by *Rhizobia* is *Trema* or *Parasponia* sp.** The nodulated legumes contribute a good deal to the amount of N_2 fixed in the biosphere, (50-200 kg N/ha).

Beijerinck first isolated and cultivate a microorganism from the roots of legumes in **1888** and he named this as ***Bacillus radicola*** and latter modified as ***Rhizobium.*** Legume plants fix and utilise this N by working symbiotically with *Rhizobium* in nodules on their roots. The host plants provide a home for bacteria and energy to fix atmospheric N_2 and in turn the plant receives fixed N_2 (as protein).

Cross inoculation group (CGI): It refers the group of leguminous plant that will develop nodules when inoculated with the *rhizobia* obtained from the nodules from any member of that legume group.

- ❖ The bacteria depends on the host plant for carbohydrates and water , while *Rhizobium* supplies nitrogen to the host. Nitrogen fixed by the *Rhizobium* is translocated through xylem vessels of the host plant mainly in the form of **aspergine** and some extent as **gluatamine**.
- ❖ *Rhizobium* inoculums **(1.5 kg/ha)** is mixed in jiggery solution and sprinked over the seed .
- ❖ If *Rhizobium* inoculums is not available , **200 kg of surface soil** (2 to 10 cm depth) can be collected from the field where that particular leguminous crop is grown luxuriantly and this can be broadcasted over the field where crop is grown for the first time.

Unit-128: *Rhizobium* species suitable for different crops

S.No.	*Rhizobium* species	➢	Crops
1.	*R. leguminosarum*	➢	Pea (*Pisum*), lathyrus, vicia, lentil (*lens*)
2.	*R. tripoli*	➢	Berseem (*Trifolium*)
3.	*R. phaseoli*	➢	Kidney bean (*Phaseolus*)
4.	*R. lupini*	➢	Lupinus, Ornithopus
5.	*R. japonicum*	➢	Soybean (*Glycine*)
6.	*R. meliloti*	➢	*Melilotus*, Lucerne (*Medicago*), Fenugreek (*Trigonella*)
7.	*Cowpea miscellaneous*	➢	Cowpea, Clusterbean, green gram, black gram, redgram, groundnut, moth bean, dhaincha, sunnhemp, *Glyricidia, Acacia, Prosopis, Dalbergia, Albizzia, Indigofera, Tephrosia, Atylosia, Stylo.*
8.	*Separate group*	➢	Bengal gram (Chickpea)

Unit-129: Blue Green Algae (BGA):

- ❖ Most important specie are *Anabaena* and *Nostoc.*
- ❖ The amount of nitrogen fixed by blue green algae ranges from 15 to 45 kg N/ha.
- ❖ Standing water of 2 to 10 cm in the field is prerequisite for the growth of BGA.

- Temperature range for growth of BGA is 25 to 45 ^{0}C.
- For good growth of BGA bright sunshine hours, pH 7 to 8 and soils with high organic matter.
- BGA inoculums is multiplied in iron trays of 2 m X 2 m X 0.25 m size. Each tray is filled with 20kg of soil and 400 g of super phosphate. BGA inoculums is sprinkled in the tray and water is let in. Standing water of 5 to 10 cm is maintained. Within a week, a thick algal scum is formed.
- The dried flakes of BGA are collected and stored for application in the main field. The inoculums is required 10 kg/ha. For higher nitrogen fixation , 3 to 4 t/ha of FYM and 200 kg/ha SSP are applied.
- In rice soil, population ranges from 10 – 10^7 cfu g^{-1} soil.
- Contribute 20 – 25 kg N ha^{-1} and Increase the rice yield by 25-30%.
- The species of BGA, known to fix atmospheric N2 are grouped as 3 groups. (i) Heterocystous – aerobic forms (ii) Aerobic unicellular forms (iii) Non-heterocystous, filamentous, micro aerophilic forms.

Unit- 130: *Azolla: Azolla* is free floating fresh water fern.

1. *Azolla pinnata* is the most common species occurring in India.
2. It fixes nitrogen due to Anabaena species of BGA present in the lobes of *Azolla* layers.
3. It supplies **30-40 kg N/ha**.
4. Good growth in cloudiness , frequent rains, pH 5.5 to7.0 and temperature range 20-30 ^{0}C.
5. Nursery area bed size 4 m x 2 m with bund of 30 to 40 cm height. *Azolla* is applied @ 01 to 0.5 kg/m^2.
6. For faster growth SSP is applied @2.5kg/m^2 and for leaf eating insect control carbofuran granules applied @ 1.2g/m^2.
7. Azolla is applied to the main field as a green crop and as a dual crop.
8. As a green manure crop Azolla is allowed to grow on the flooded field for 2 to 3 weeks before transplanting.
9. As a dual crop 1000 to 5000 kg/ha Azolla is apllied to the soil one week after transplanting. When a thick mat forms ,it is incorporate by trampling. For better growth Azolla , 25 to 50 kg/ha SSP is applied in standing water of 5 to 10 cm.

Unit-131: *Azospirillum*:

Azospirillum was first isolated **by Beijerinck (1922)** in **Brazil** from the roots of *Paspalum* and named it as *Azotobacter paspali* and later named as Spirillum *lipoferum*. **Dobereiner and Day (1976)** reported the nitrogen fixing potential of some forage grasses due to the activity of *S. lipoferum* in their roots. **Dobereiner** coined the *term* **"Associative symbiosis"** to denote the occurrence of N_2 fixing *spirillum* in plants. Taxonomy was re-examined and Tarrand et al. (1978) designated this organism as *Azospirillum*.

Unit-132: *Azotobacter chroccum:*

Is capable fo fixing 20 to 30 kg N/ha. It can be applied by seed inoculation, seedling dip or by soil application. The inoculums required is 3 to 5 kg/ha. *Azotobacter* can be used for rice, cotton, and sugarcane. *Azospirillum* inoculums is used.

Unit- 133: Fast growing *Rhizobium* culture-

Rhizobium phaseoli ;
Rhizobium trifolii (Berseem)
Rhizobium leguminoserum (pea,vetch & vicia)
Rhizobium meliloti (Melilotus,Medicago & Trigonella)

Unit- 134: Slow growing strain producing alkali YEMA-

Rhizobium japonicum (Bradyrhizobium)
Rhizobium lupini Cowpea groups

Unit-135: Free-Living Nitrogen Fixers

S. NO	Microorganisms	Heterotrophs	Phototrophs
1	Aerobic	*Azotobacter, Derxia and Beijerinckia*	*Anabaena, Calothrix and Nostoc*
2	Microaerophilic	*Thiobacillus, Methylococcus and Xanthobactor*	*Gloeothece, Lyngbya and Plectonerma*
3	Facultative anaerobic	*Klebsiella, Bacillus and Citrobactor*	*Rhodopseudomonas and Rhodospirillum*
4	Obligate anaerobic	*Clostridium, Desulfovibrio and Desulfotomaculum*	*Chrotium and Thiocysts*

Unit-136: Different Group of N_2 Fixers

S. NO	Type of Organism	Example
1	Symbiotic	*Rhizobia, Frankia and Anabaena*
2	Associative	*Azospirillum, Acetobactor and Herbaspirillum*
3	Free Living	*Azotobactor, Derxia, Cyanobacteria, Rhodospirillum and Beijerinckia*

Unit- 137: Various Heterotrophs and Autotrophs

1.Heterotrophs

S. NO	Type of Organism	Example
1	Aerobic	*Azotobactor, Derxia and Beijerinckia*
2	Micro- aerobes	*Thiobacillus, Methylococcus and Xanthobactor*
3	Facultative anaerobes	*Klebsiella, Bacillus and Citrobactor*
4	Obligate anaerobes	*Clostridium, Desulfovibrio and Desulfotomaculum*

2. Phototrophs

S. NO	Type of Organism	Example
1	Aerobic	*Anabaena, Nostoc and Calothrix*
2	Micro- aerobes	*Plectonema, Gloeothece and Lyngbya*

3	Facultative anaerobes	*Rhodospirillum and Rhodopseudomonas*
4	Obligate anaerobes	*Chrotium and Thiocystis*

CHAPTER- 138 : SOILS AT A GLANE PYQ'S

1. **The word soil has been derived from _____ word** 3 RPSC, AAO-2009

(1) Arabic (2) Greek (3) Latin (4) French

Explanation: The word "soil" in English ultimately derives from the **Latin** word "solium," which refers to a seat or a throne, but in Medieval Latin, it came to mean "a place" or "ground." This evolved in Old French to "sol," meaning ground or soil, and then made its way into Middle English. **Latin**: Partly from Anglo-Norman "soyl" which is derived from Latin "solum" meaning "ground" or "foundation." This connection reflects the concept of soil as the underlying base for life.

Old French: Partly from Old French words "soil" or "souil" related to muddy places (think wallows or mires). This influence reflects the physical characteristics of soil.

Possible Germanic influence: There's also a theory suggesting a possible connection to Old English "sol" meaning "mud" and Proto-Germanic roots for "mud" or "thick liquid."

2. **_____ Improves the structure of sandy & clay soils –** 2 TN PSC Ag-2003

(1) Fertilizer (2) Organic matter (3) Soil organism (4) Tillage

Explanation: Organic matter improves the structure of both sandy and clay soils:

In sandy soil: Organic matter helps bind sand particles together, improving water retention and preventing nutrients from leaching away too quickly.

In clay soil: Organic matter helps break up clay particles, improving drainage and aeration. It also creates spaces for water and nutrients to be held in the soil.

3. "A-value" technique is used to estimate the available phosphorous in the soil It is calculated using the formula d IAS Pre-1998

$$A = \frac{B(1-Y)}{Y}$$

Where, 'A' is the amount of available soil phosphorous in kg/ha, 'B' is the amount of added fertilizer phosphorus in kg/ha and 'Y' is the

(a) yield of the plant grown in the soil

(b) total quantity of phosphorus present in the soil

(c) total quantity of phosphorus present in the plant

(d) fraction of the phosphorus in the plant which is derived from the phosphatic fertilizer added to the soil

Explanation: **Fried and Dean (1952)**. introduced this method as a means to assess the availability of soil phosphorus for plants. The concept involves adding a known quantity of phosphorus fertilizer to the soil and then measuring the uptake of phosphorus by the plants. By comparing the phosphorus uptake from the fertilizer to the total phosphorus uptake, researchers can estimate the amount of phosphorus available in the soil.

4. "Bhat" soils of Uttar Pradesh posses soft lime (as free $CaCO_3$%) in sub soils – c BHU PET-2014

(a) 1-5 % (b) 15-20 % (c) 30-40% (d) 60-70%

Explanation: **"Bhat"** soils in Uttar Pradesh are known for having a relatively high percentage of free calcium carbonate (CaCO3) in the subsoil. These soils typically possess about 30-40% free CaCO3, which significantly influences their physical and chemical properties. The high lime content impacts the soil structure, drainage, pH level, and nutrient availability, which are crucial factors for agricultural productivity in the region.

5. ....rating in soil is considered as low available Nitrogen status B AO KTPSC-2021

(A) 280 — 450 kgha^{-1} (B) < 280 kg ha^{-1} (C) 118 kg ha^{-1} (D) 22 kg ha^{-1} (E) Answer not known

Explanation: The correct answer is (b) < 280 kg ha^{-1}

Nutrient	Low	Medium	High
Organic carbon	< 0.5 %	0.5 - 7.5%	> 0.75%
Available nitrogen (N)	< 240Kg/ha	240- 480kg/ha	> 480Kg/ha
Available Phosphorus (P)	< 11.0 Kg/ha	11 – 22 Kg/ha	> 22 Kg/ha
Available potassium (K)	< 110Kg/ha	110-280Kg/ha	> 280Kg/ha

6. A branch of science that deals with the study of origin of the soil, its classification and description is known as : RPSC, AAO-2009 b UPPSC Pre- 1995

(a)Wdaphology (b)Pedology (c) Ecology (d) Geology

Explanation: The correct answer is (b) Pedology

Pedology is the branch of science that specifically focuses on the study of soil. This includes:

- **Origin:** How soil is formed from parent material through weathering and other processes.
- **Classification:** Grouping soils based on their physical, chemical, and biological properties.
- **Description:** Characterizing soil profiles, including color, texture, structure, and horizonation.

Edaphology (not listed in the options) is sometimes used interchangeably with pedology, but it has a slightly different emphasis. Edaphology focuses on the relationship between soil and living organisms, particularly plants.

Ecology studies the interactions between living organisms and their environment, including soil. However, it has a broader scope than just soil science.

Geology deals with the study of the Earth's solid features, including rocks, minerals, and landforms. While soil formation involves geological processes, pedology delves deeper into the specific characteristics and processes related to soil.

7. A process of soil formation is also known as : 3 RPSC ACF - 2018

(1) Salinization (2) Solonization (3) Horizonation (4) Podzolization

Explanation: The correct answer is (3) Horizonation.

Horizonation is a key process in soil formation. It refers to the development of distinct layers, called horizons, within the soil profile. These layers differ in color, texture, structure, and chemical composition due to the various physical, chemical, and biological processes that occur at different depths.

Let's break down the other options:

Salinization: This is the process of increasing salt concentration in soil, often due to evaporation or irrigation with saline water. It's not a general soil formation process but can occur in specific conditions.

Solonization: This is a specific type of soil formation process that leads to the development of a layer rich in sodium ions (Na+) near the surface. It's not as common as horizonation.

Podzolization: This is another specific type of soil formation process that occurs in cool, moist climates with coniferous vegetation. It results in a distinct layering with a leached upper layer and an accumulation of iron and aluminum oxides in a lower layer.

8. A sandy soil contains: c NSC MT M-2019

(a) 100% of sand particle (b) 85% of sand particle

(c) More than 60% of sand particle (d) Less than 60% of sand particle

Explanation: The correct answer is (c) More than 60% of sand particles.

- Sandy soil is primarily composed of sand particles, but it's not purely sand.
- It also contains some amount of silt and clay particles, although in much smaller proportions compared to sand.
- By definition, a sandy soil typically has **more than 60% sand particles.**

The other options are not quite accurate:

(a) **100% sand particles:** While sand is the dominant component, a true sandy soil would have trace amounts of silt and clay.

(b) **85% sand particles:** There's no strict cutoff, but 60% is a commonly used threshold for sandy soil. 85% sand content could still be considered sandy soil.

(d) **Less than 60% sand particles**: If the sand content is less than 60%, the soil would likely be classified as a different type, such as loam or silt loam, depending on the proportions of silt and clay.

9. A soil is having bulk density of 1.4 mg/ m3 and particle density of 2.5 mg/m3, the percent porosity of the soil? D TO MPUAT-2014

(A) 54 (B) 78 (C) 64 (D) 50

Explanation: Calculate the percent porosity of the soil, we can use the following formula:

Porosity(%)=(1−Bulk DensityParticle Density)×100Porosity(%)=(1−Particle DensityBulk Density)×100

Given:

Bulk Density (ρb) = 1.4 mg/m³

Particle Density (ρp) = 2.5 mg/m³

Let's plug these values into the formula:

Porosity(%)=(1−1.42.5)×100Porosity(%)=(1−2.51.4)×100

First, calculate the fraction:

1.42.5=0.562.51.4=0.56

Now, subtract this value from 1:

1−0.56=0.441−0.56=0.44

Finally, convert this fraction to a percentage:

0.44×100=440.44×100=44

Thus, the percent porosity of the soil is:

(D) 50

However, based on the calculation, there seems to be a discrepancy in the given options. None of the provided options match the calculated value of 44%.

10. A soil with 20 meq/100g CEC and 5meq/100g exchangeable H will have a base saturation of b IAS Pre-1997

(a) 25.0% (b) 75.0% (c) 80.0% (d) 133.3%

11. **Explanation**: The correct answer is (b) 75.0% with the following explanation:

Cation Exchange Capacity (CEC) represents the soil's total capacity to hold positively charged ions (cations) on its clay particles and organic matter. It's essentially a measure of the soil's nutrient storage potential.

Exchangeable Hydrogen (H) is one of the cations occupying the exchange sites. A higher H value indicates a more acidic soil.

Base Saturation refers to the percentage of CEC occupied by base cations (e.g., calcium, magnesium, potassium, sodium) compared to acidic cations (like hydrogen). A higher base saturation suggests a more fertile soil.

Calculating Base Saturation:

We can calculate the base saturation using the following formula:

Base Saturation (%) = (CEC - Exchangeable H) / CEC * 100

In this scenario:

- CEC = 20 meq/100g
- Exchangeable H = 5 meq/100g

Plugging these values into the formula:

Base Saturation (%) = (20 meq/100g - 5 meq/100g) / 20 meq/100g * 100

= 15 meq/100g / 20 meq/100g * 100

= 0.75 * 100

= 75%

Therefore, the base saturation of the soil is **75.0%.** This indicates a moderately fertile soil with a good balance between base cations and acidic cations.

12. A soil with a Cation Exchange Capacity of 30 meq. Per 100 grams soil contains the following amount of exchangeable cations per 20 grams soils (in milli equivalents) d IAS Pre-2000

Calcium	2.00
Magnesium	1.00
Potassium	0.75
Sodium	0.25
Total	4.00

Based on this data, the percentage base saturation of the soil will work out to

(a) 13.33 (b) 34.00 (c) 47.33 (d) 66.66

13. **Explanation**: To calculate the base saturation percentage, we first need to determine the total amount of exchangeable base cations per 100 grams of soil, since the given values are per 20 grams of soil.

Given exchangeable cations per 20 grams of soil are:

Calcium (Ca^{2+}): 2.00 me/20g

Magnesium (Mg^{2+}): 1.00 me/20g

Potassium (K^{+}): 0.75 me/20g

Sodium (Na^{+}): 0.25 me/20g

Total exchangeable cations per 20 grams of soil = 2.00 + 1.00 + 0.75 + 0.25 = 4.00 me/20g

To find the total exchangeable cations per 100 grams of soil, we scale up the values:

Total exchangeable cations per 100 grams of soil=4.00 me/20g×100 g20 g=4.00×5=20.00 me/100gTotal exchangeable cations per 100 grams of soil=4.00me/20g×20g100g =4.00×5=20.00me/100g

Next, we calculate the percentage base saturation using the formula:

Base Saturation(%)=(Sum of Exchangeable Base CationsCEC)×100Base Saturation(%)=(CE CSum of Exchangeable Base Cations)×100

Given:

CEC = 30 me/100g

Sum of Exchangeable Base Cations = 20.00 me/100g

Base Saturation(%)=(20.00 me/100g30.00 me/100g)×100Base Saturation(%)=(30.00me/100g

20.00me/100g)×100 Base Saturation(%)=(20.0030.00)×100Base Saturation(%)=(30.0020.00)×100 Base Saturation(%)=0.6667×100Base Saturation(%)=0.6667×100

Base Saturation(%)=66.67%Base Saturation(%)=66.67%

So, the correct answer is (d) 66.66.

14. A soil with exchangeable sodium percentage above 15 and EC of saturation extract greater than 4 mm hos/cm is : 1 RPSC ACF AE - 2018

(a) Saline alkali soil (b) Non-saline alkali soil (c) saline soil (d)sodic soil

Explanation:

Saline soil: EC > 4 mmhos/cm; ESP < 15 ; pH < 8.5

Sodic soil (Non-saline alkali soil): EC < 4 mmhos/cm; ESP > 15 ;pH > 8.5

Saline-alkali soil (Saline-sodic soil): EC > 4 mmhos/cm ; ESP > 15 ; pH can vary

Given:

Exchangeable sodium percentage (ESP) is above 15. EC of the saturation extract is greater than 4 mmhos/cm.

This fits the definition of **saline-alkali soil** (also known as saline-sodic soil), which has both high EC and high ESP.

Thus, the correct answer is (a) **Saline alkali soil**.

15. A solution containing 1000 g of solvent and one gram molecular weight of solute is known as b UPPSC Pre- 2005

(a) Normal solution (b) Molar solution

(c) Molal solution (d) 0.001 N solution

Explanation: The correct answer is (c) Molal solution.

Normal solution (N): This is a solution where the concentration is measured in equivalents per liter of solution. It's not relevant to the given problem.

Molar solution (M): This is a solution where the concentration is measured in moles of solute per liter of solution. Again, not relevant to the given problem.

Molal solution (m): This is a solution where the concentration is measured in moles of solute per kilogram of solvent. In this case, the problem states that there is one gram molecular weight (one mole) of solute in 1000 grams (1 kilogram) of solvent, which defines a 1 molal solution.

0.001 N solution: This refers to a normal solution with a concentration of 0.001 equivalents per liter. This is not relevant to the given problem.

Therefore, a solution containing 1000 grams of solvent and one gram molecular weight of solute is known as a **molal solution**

16. A vertical section of soil with different layers is known as : 2 RPSC Pre-2008, ACF Agri - 2011, MP PAT-2013

(1) Soil horizon (2)Soil profile

(3) Regolith (4) Parent material

Explanation: The correct answer is **(2) Soil profile.**

- **Soil horizon:** A distinct layer within the soil profile with specific characteristics like texture, color, and organic matter content. There can be multiple horizons stacked vertically to form the soil profile.
- **Soil profile:** A vertical section of soil that showcases the arrangement of various soil horizons from the surface down to the underlying parent material. It reflects the soil's development history and properties.
- **Regolith:** The unconsolidated, weathered rock and mineral fragments covering the

Earth's surface, including soil and loose rock debris. While the soil profile is part of the regolith, it's a specific section with differentiated layers.

- **Parent material:** The underlying rock or unconsolidated material from which the soil has formed. It forms the base of the soil profile but isn't strictly part of the profile itself.

Therefore, a soil profile refers to the complete vertical section with its layered structure, whereas the other terms represent components or aspects related to soil formation and composition.

17. A well developed soil has – 4 TN AO-2008

(1) A horizon (2) B horizon (3) C horizon (4) All of these

Explanation: The correct answer is (4) All of these.

A well-developed soil is characterized by the presence of all three main horizons: A, B, and C.

- **A horizon (topsoil):** The uppermost layer, rich in organic matter, minerals, and living organisms. It's crucial for plant growth.
- **B horizon (subsoil):** Located beneath the A horizon, it often contains accumulated minerals leached from the topsoil and may have distinct textures or colors.
- **C horizon (weathered parent material):** The layer below the B horizon, consisting of partially weathered rock or unconsolidated material from which the soil formed.

The presence of all these well-developed horizons indicates a mature soil that has undergone significant weathering and development over time.

18. According to Chapman (1966) halophytes are classified as per their tolerance with salinity, miohalophytes is well survived in salinity range of - 1 RPSC ARO Ag Chem - 2022

(1) 0 — 0.5% NaCl (2) 0.5 —1.0% NaCl

(3) 1.0 1.5% NaCl (4) 1.5 — 2.0% NaCl

Explanation: The correct answer is (1) 0 — 0.5% NaCl

Here's a breakdown of the classification system for halophytes based on salinity tolerance as outlined by Chapman (1966):

- **Miohalophytes:** Plants that thrive in environments with low salinity, typically ranging from 0 to 0.5% NaCl (sodium chloride) concentration in the soil water.
- **Mesohalophytes:** Plants adapted to moderate salinity levels, tolerating a range of 0.5 to 10% NaCl.
- **Euhalophytes:** Plants that can survive in high salinity conditions. They are further subdivided into:

Mesohalophytes: Prefer moderate salinity (0.5 to greater than 10% NaCl).

Meso-euhalophytes: Tolerate a wide range, from 0.5 to more than 10% NaCl.

Eu-euhalophytes: Obligate halophytes that cannot survive in environments with less than 1% NaCl concentration.

19. According to Schofields ratio law, upon dilution of Na^+ concentration by Ca + Mg must decrease by how many times so that the ratio of the cations absorbed on the colloid surface of the soil remains unchanged ? D IAS Pre-2009

(a) 4 (b) 8 (c) 12 (d) 16

Explanation: If the concentration of Na^+ is diluted by a factor of *x*, the concentration of Ca^{2+} and Mg^{2+} must decrease by a factor of *x*2 to keep the ratio on the colloid surface unchanged:

*x*2=16 ; *x*=4

So, if the concentration of Na^+ is diluted by a factor of 4, the concentration of Ca^{2+} and Mg^{2+}

must decrease by a factor of 4^2=16. Therefore, the correct answer is (d) 16.

20. According to USDA taxonomy, which one of the following constitutes 'Soil orders ? A IAS Pre-2010

(a) Gelisol, Mollosol, Entisol (b) Mollisol, Entisol, Fluvisol

(c) Entisol, Fluvisol, Gelisol (d) Fluvisol, Gelisol, Mollisol

Explanation: The correct answer is (a) **Gelisol, Mollisol, Entisol.**

The USDA soil taxonomy system classifies soils into **twelve (12)** orders based on their morphology, genesis, and chemical properties. These orders represent the broadest level of classification in the system.

- **Gelisol:** Soils with permafrost, permanently frozen ground, within two meters of the surface.
- **Mollisol:** Dark-colored, fertile soils with a thick layer of organic matter accumulation.
- **Entisol:** Young soils with minimal development, showing little horizon differentiation.

Fluvisol is not one of the twelve soil orders in the USDA taxonomy. It's a soil reference group in the World Reference Base for Soil Resources (WRB) classification system, which is another widely used soil classification system.

21. Accumulation of calcium carbonate in the profile is known as C AO SDAU-2015

A. Calcification B. Salinization

C Solarization D. Solodization

Explanation: The correct answer is:(A) Calcification

- **Calcification:** This refers to the process of accumulation of calcium carbonate (CaCO3) in soil or rock. This can happen through various ways, including precipitation from calcium-rich solutions or the breakdown of calcium-containing minerals.
- **Salinization:** This is the increase in salt concentration in soil due to various factors like evaporation, irrigation with saline water, or weathering of rocks rich in soluble salts.
- **Solarization:** This is a soil disinfestation technique that uses the heat from solar radiation to kill soilborne pathogens and weeds. It doesn't involve accumulation of calcium carbonate.
- **Solodization:** This is the process of removal of mobile elements from the soil, leaving behind a less fertile layer rich in iron and aluminum oxides. It doesn't involve accumulation of calcium carbonate.

Therefore, calcification is the most fitting term for the accumulation of calcium carbonate in the soil profile.

22. Active factors of soil formation are – d BHU PET-2010, IAS Pre-1996

(a) Climate and Parent material (b) Parent material and Relief

(c) Climate and parent material (d) Climate and Biosphere

Explanation: The correct answer is (d) Climate and Biosphere.

Soil formation is a complex process influenced by several factors. These factors can be broadly categorized into two groups:

- **Active factors:** These factors directly contribute to the weathering and breakdown of parent material, the formation of soil horizons, and the addition of organic matter.
- **Passive factors:** These factors provide the underlying conditions that influence how the active factors work. They don't directly cause changes but affect the overall

process.

Active factors:

- **Climate:** Temperature and precipitation play a crucial role in weathering parent material and influencing the type of chemical reactions occurring in the soil. Higher temperatures generally accelerate weathering, while precipitation patterns affect water movement through the soil profile, leaching of elements, and decomposition of organic matter.
- **Biosphere:** Living organisms, including plants, animals, and microorganisms, contribute significantly to soil formation. Plants add organic matter to the soil, while animals like earthworms help aerate the soil and mix different layers. Microorganisms decompose organic matter, releasing nutrients and influencing soil chemistry.

Passive factors:

- **Parent material:** The rock or unconsolidated material from which the soil originates determines its initial composition and properties. Different parent materials will weather differently and impact the resulting soil type.
- **Relief (Topography):** The slope and elevation of the land influence drainage, erosion, and the accumulation of organic matter. Steeper slopes are more prone to erosion, whereas lower areas may experience waterlogging.
- **Time:** Soil formation is a slow process that takes place over long periods. The longer a soil has been developing, the more mature and distinct its horizons will become.

Therefore, climate and biosphere are the active factors that directly influence the formation and characteristics of soil.

23. Active soil particle is — A — AO SDAU-2015

A. Clay B. 'Sand C. Silt D. None of these

Explanation: The correct answer is (A) Clay.

Clay particles are considered the most active soil particles due to several factors:

- **Size:** Clay particles are the smallest soil separates, having a diameter less than 0.002 millimeters. This large surface area per unit mass makes them highly reactive compared to larger sand or silt particles.
- **Charge:** Clay particles typically have a net negative charge on their surfaces. This negative charge attracts and holds positively charged ions (cations) like calcium, magnesium, potassium, and even hydrogen, which are essential plant nutrients. This adsorption process plays a vital role in soil fertility and nutrient availability for plants.
- **Surface chemistry:** The structure of clay minerals allows them to participate in various chemical reactions within the soil. They can undergo cation exchange, where they release one cation and adsorb another, influencing soil pH and nutrient availability. Additionally, they can participate in adsorption and desorption of organic molecules and other soil contaminants.

While sand and silt particles also play a role in soil structure and water holding capacity, their larger size and lower surface area make them less reactive compared to clay particles.

24.	Alfisol is a type of: (a) Red Soil (b) Black Soil (c) Desert Soil (d)Laterite Soil **Explanation**: More correct answer is Forest and hill soils	a	NSC MT P-2018 ,TN AO-

S.No.	Genetic System		Soil Taxonomy	
				2018
8.	Alluvial soils	➢	Entisol, Inceptisol	
9.	Black (Cotton) soils	➢	Vertisols	
10.	Red Soils	➢	Alfisol, Ultisols	
11.	Laterite and Lateritic soils	➢	Ultisols	
12.	Desert soils	➢	Aridisol	
13.	Forest and Hill soils	➢	Alfisols	
14.	Salt affected soils	➢	Aridisols, Inceptisols	

25. Among different soil textural classes, which is an ideal one for most of the crops ? c ARO Agro-2016

(a) Sandy (b) Clayey (c) Loamy (d) Silty

Explanation: The correct answer is (c) Loamy

- **Sandy soil:** While well-drained and allowing for good aeration, sandy soils have low water holding capacity and nutrient retention. This can lead to frequent irrigation needs and potential nutrient leaching.
- **Clayey soil:** Clayey soils have high water holding capacity and nutrient retention. However, they can be poorly drained, prone to compaction, and difficult to till for planting.
- **Loamy soil:** Loamy soil is a textural class that combines sand, silt, and clay particles in a relatively balanced proportion. This creates a soil with good drainage, aeration, water holding capacity, and nutrient retention. It's considered the most ideal texture for most crops as it provides the necessary balance for root growth, water availability, and nutrient uptake.
- **Silty soil:** Silty soils have characteristics somewhat between sandy and clayey soils. They can have good water holding capacity but may be prone to compaction and may not drain as well as loamy soils.

Loamy soil offers the best of both worlds, providing adequate drainage, aeration, water availability, and nutrient retention for optimal plant growth for a wide range of crops.

26. Among the 1:1 clay minerals, the most widely distributed one in Indian soils is - 2 RPSC ARO Ag Chem - 2022

(1) Halloysite (2) Kaolinite (3) Dickite(4) Nackrite

Explanation: The correct answer is (2) Kaolinite

- **Kaolinite:** This is the dominant clay mineral in many Indian soils, particularly in red soils, laterites, and alluvial soils formed from the weathering of kaolinite-rich rocks. It's known for its low cation exchange capacity (CEC) and resistance to weathering.
- **Halloysite, Dickite, and Nacrite:** These are other 1:1 clay minerals, but they are less common than kaolinite in Indian soils. They may be present in specific regions or soil types, but not as extensively distributed as kaolinite.

Factors favoring Kaolinite dominance in Indian soils:

- **Climate:** The warm and humid climate in many parts of India promotes the formation of kaolinite through the intense weathering of silicate minerals.
- **Parent material:** The presence of kaolinite-rich rocks like granite and gneiss contributes to the formation of kaolinite-dominant soils upon weathering.

Therefore, kaolinite is the most prevalent 1:1 clay mineral in Indian soils due to its stability under warm and humid conditions and the abundance of kaolinite-rich parent material in many regions.

27. Among the following which one is the para-crystalline alumina silicate mineral? 2 RPSC

(1) Opaline (2) Imogolite (3) Chlorite (4) Illite ARO Ag Chem - 2022

Explanation: The correct answer is (2) Imogolite

- **Para-crystalline:** This term refers to a mineral with a partially ordered crystal structure, meaning it exhibits some degree of crystallographic organization but not a fully defined and rigid structure like true crystalline minerals.
- **Alumina silicate:** These minerals consist of aluminum oxide (Al_2O_3) and silicon dioxide (SiO_2) as their main components.

Let's analyze the other options:

- **Opaline:** This is a hydrated amorphous form of silica (SiO_2) and doesn't contain alumina (Al_2O_3).
- **Chlorite:** This is a layered phyllosilicate mineral with a well-defined crystalline structure.
- **Illite:** This is another phyllosilicate mineral with a layered structure and a more crystalline nature compared to imogolite.

Imogolite: This is a poorly crystalline or para-crystalline aluminosilicate mineral. It's a hydrous aluminum silicate hydroxide ($Al_2O_3 \cdot SiO_2 \cdot H_2O$) with a poorly organized structure compared to true crystalline minerals like chlorite or illite. It's often found in volcanic ash soils and weathered volcanic rocks.

Therefore, imogolite best fits the description of a para-crystalline alumina silicate mineral among the provided choices.

28. Among the following, the sequence of textural classes of soil with increasing order of fineness of texture is D IAS Pre-2003

(a) CL, L, LS, SL, SCL (b) L, CL, SCL, SL, LS

(c) SL, SCL, LS, L, CL (d) LS, SL, L, SCL, CL

29. **Explanation**: The correct answer is (d) LS, SL, L, SCL, CL

- **L:** Loam - This represents a balanced mixture of sand, silt, and clay particles, offering a middle ground in terms of texture.
- **S:** Sand - Sand particles are the coarsest soil separates, resulting in the least fine texture.
- **Si:** Silt - Silt particles are finer than sand but coarser than clay.
- **C:** Clay - Clay particles are the finest soil separates, providing the most fine texture.

Now, let's decode the combinations in the answer choices:

- **LS (Loamy Sand):** This has some clay and silt along with sand, making it finer than pure sand (S).
- **SL (Sandy Loam):** Similar to LS, but with more sand than LS, placing it between S and LS in fineness.
- **SCL (Sandy Clay Loam):** This has a significant sand fraction but also contains appreciable amounts of silt and clay, making it finer than SL.
- **CL (Clay Loam):** This has a good balance of clay, silt, and sand, with more clay than SCL, resulting in a finer texture.

Therefore, the order from least fine to most fine texture progresses from LS to SL to L to SCL to CL.

30. Among the three fractions of Humus, i.e.Humic acid,Fulvic acid and Humin, which fraction is maximum in vertisols? 1 RPSC ARO Ag Chem -

(1) Humin (2) Humic acid (3) Gray fulvic acid (4) Fulvic acid

2022

Explanation: Among the three humus fractions in Vertisols, Humin is generally the most abundant.

Here's a breakdown of the fractions and their typical proportions in Vertisols:

- **Humin (30-50%)**: The most resistant fraction, insoluble in most chemical solutions. It plays a crucial role in soil structure and cation exchange capacity (CEC).
- **Humic Acid (20-40%)**: Soluble in alkaline solutions but insoluble in acids. It has a high molecular weight and contributes significantly to CEC and soil fertility.
- **Fulvic Acid (5-20%)**: The most mobile and readily available fraction, soluble in both acidic and alkaline solutions. It has a low molecular weight and plays a role in nutrient cycling and metal complexation.

31. Application of mulches to soil helps in- 4 TN PSC Ag-II: 2001

(1) Soil conservation and structure improvement (2) Temperature moderation

(3) Reduction in soil salinity and weeds (4) All of these

32. Application of sulphur is advised to the problem soil containing D TNPSC Ag- 1998

(A)$CaCO_3$ (B) $CaSO_4$ (C) $Mg(HCO_3)_2$ (D) Na_2CO_3

Explanation: The correct answer is **(D) Na_2CO_3**

- **Sulfur's Role:** Sulfur application aims to lower soil pH in alkaline conditions.
- **Effect on Different Compounds:**
  - **$CaCO_3$ (Calcium carbonate):** A base that contributes to alkalinity. Adding sulfur wouldn't be very effective as it would react with the carbonate, but a large amount would be needed to overcome the buffering capacity.
  - **$CaSO_4$ (Calcium sulfate):** A salt that doesn't directly affect soil pH.
  - **$Mg(HCO_3)_2$ (Magnesium bicarbonate):** A weak base that can slightly increase alkalinity. Sulfur might have a moderate effect here.
  - **Na_2CO_3 (Sodium carbonate):** A strong base that causes significant alkalinity. Sulfur can be most beneficial in reducing the pH of soil containing Na_2CO_3.

Therefore, for the greatest impact on lowering pH in an alkaline soil, sulfur application is most suitable for soil containing sodium carbonate (Na2CO3).

33. approximate weight of 10 cm surface soil of one ha field in kg is - 2 RPSC, AAO-2018

(1)1×10^6 (2) 1.5×10^6

(3) 2.25×10^6 (4) 3×10

Explanation: The correct answer is (2) 1.5×10^6 kg

1. **Area:** 1 hectare (ha) is equal to 10,000 square meters (m^2)
2. **Depth:** Convert 10 centimeters (cm) to meters: 10 cm / 100 cm/m = 0.1 m
3. **Density:** Assume an average soil bulk density of 1.5 g/cm^3 (grams per cubic centimeter). This is a common value, but it can vary depending on soil type.
4. **Conversion:** Convert g/cm^3 to kg/m^3: 1.5 g/cm^3 * 1000 g/kg = 1500 kg/m^3
5. **Weight:** Weight = Area * Depth * Density Weight = 10,000 m^2 * 0.1 m * 1500 kg/m^3 Weight = 1,500,000 kg

Expressing in scientific notation:

- We want 1 significant digit for an approximate answer.
- The weight is 1,500,000 kg, which can be written as 1.5×10^6 kg.

Therefore, considering the typical soil density, 1.5×10^6 kg is a reasonable estimate for the weight of 10 cm of surface soil from a one-hectare field.

Important Note:

- The actual weight can vary depending on the specific soil type (which can affect density) and moisture content.

34. Approximate weight of surface 15 cm soil of one hectare field is : (c) UPPSC Pre- 2000

(a) 1.0 million kg (b) 1.5 million kg (c) 2.0 million kg (d) 2.5 million kg

Explanation: The correct answer is (c) 2.0 million kg

1. **Area:** 1 hectare (ha) is equal to 10,000 square meters (m^2).
2. **Depth:** Convert 15 centimeters (cm) to meters: 15 cm / 100 cm/m = 0.15 m
3. **Density:** We'll use an average soil bulk density of 1.5 g/cm^3 (grams per cubic centimeter) as before. This is a common assumption, but the actual density can vary.
4. **Conversion:** Convert g/cm^3 to kg/m^3: 1.5 g/cm^3 * 1000 g/kg = 1500 kg/m^3
5. **Weight:** Weight = Area * Depth * Density Weight = 10,000 m^2 * 0.15 m * 1500 kg/m^3 Weight = 2,250,000 kg

Rounding for Approximation:

Since we're aiming for an approximate value, it's common practice to round the answer to one significant digit. In this case, the leading digit is 2, so rounding 2,250,000 kg gives us 2,000,000 kg.

Therefore, based on the average density assumption, 2.0 million kg is a good approximation for the weight of 15 cm of surface soil from a one-hectare field.

Remember: The actual weight can vary depending on the specific soil type and moisture content.

35. Aridisols are mostly found in : a UPPSC Pre- 2008

(a) Rajasthan (b) Bihar (c) Bengal (d) Orissa

Explanation: The correct answer is: **(a) Rajasthan**

Aridisols are soils characteristic of arid and semi-arid regions with low precipitation. Here's why the other options are less likely:

- **Bihar:** This state experiences a humid subtropical climate with moderate to high rainfall, making Aridisols unlikely.
- **Bengal (West Bengal):** Similar to Bihar, West Bengal has a humid subtropical climate with significant rainfall, not suitable for Aridisols.
- **Orissa (Odisha):** Although Odisha has a drier climate compared to the previous two, it's still not arid enough for extensive Aridisol formation.

Rajasthan, on the other hand, has a large western portion falling under a desert climate with low rainfall. This makes it the most suitable choice for finding Aridisols in India.

36. Arrangement of soil particles is known as – 2 TN AO- 2012

(1) Soil texture (2) Soil structure (3) Soil contour (4) Soil order

Explanation: The correct answer is: (2) Soil structure

- **Soil texture** refers to the proportions of sand, silt, and clay particles in the soil. It describes the "feel" of the soil, not its arrangement.
- **Soil structure** describes how these individual particles are grouped together. This grouping can influence factors like drainage, aeration, and root growth.
- **Soil contour** refers to the shape of the land surface, not the internal structure of the soil.
- **Soil order** is the broadest classification of soil types based on their formation and properties. It doesn't directly address the arrangement of particles.

37. As per ISSS soil classification, the diameter of silt particles should be…… mm. 1 Ag sup

(1) 0.02 – 0.002 (2) 0.2-0.02 (3) 2.0 – 0.2 (4) < 0.002 2021

Explanation: The correct answer is: (1) 0.02 – 0.002 mm

Here's a breakdown of the ISSS classification for soil particle sizes:

- Sand: 2.0 mm - 0.02 mm
- Silt: 0.02 mm - 0.002 mm
- Clay: < 0.002 mm

38. As per the soil classification of Agriculture Department, Rajasthan 'Raverina' soil is found in 1 RPSC FSO-2019

(1) Ganganagar (2) Bikaner (3) Udaipur (4) Jalore

Explanation: The correct answer is: (1) Ganganagar

Raverina soil is found in the Ganganagar district of Rajasthan. This soil type is typically sandy loam to loamy sand, suitable for various agricultural practices. Ganganagar is located in the northwestern part of Rajasthan and benefits from the irrigation provided by the Indira Gandhi Canal, making the Raverina soil productive for growing crops like wheat, mustard, and cotton.

39. Assessment of soil texture by feel method is done by – a BHU PET-2015

(a) Ball formation (b) Ribbon formation

(c) Staining (d) Dryingup

Explanation: The correct answer is: (a) Ball formation

The assessment of soil texture by the feel method involves manipulating a moistened soil sample to determine its physical properties. One key technique in this method is ball formation. Here's how it works:

Ball Formation: You take a moist sample of soil and try to form a ball by rolling it between your hands. The ability to form a ball and the behavior of the ball provide information about the soil texture:

Clay Soil: Forms a firm ball that holds its shape.

Sandy Soil: Does not form a ball and falls apart easily.

Silty Soil: Forms a ball but is less firm than clay and may crack.

While **ribbon formation** is also part of the feel method, ball formation is a primary initial step in assessing soil texture. **Both techniques are commonly used together to provide a more accurate assessment**.

40. Assuming bulk density and particle density of a soil as 1.5 and 2.5 g/cc, respectively, value of porosity will be: B PPSC ADO-2017

a) 20% b) 40% c) 60% d) 80%

Explanation: The correct answer is: (b) 40%

Porosity = (1 - (bulk_density / particle_density)) * 100

Given:

Bulk Density (ρb) = 1.5 g/cc

Particle Density (ρp) = 2.5 g/cc

Plugging the values into the formula:

Porosity(%)=(1−1.5/2.5)×

First, calculate the fraction:

1.5/2.5=0.6

Then, calculate the porosity:

Porosity(%)=(1−0.6)×100=0.4×100=40%

Therefore, the value of porosity is:(b) 40%

41. At field capacity of soil – 3 TN AAO-2019

(1) Macropores and Micropores are filled with water

(2) Macropores and Micropores are filled with air

(3) Macropores are filled with air and Micropores are filled with water

(4) Macropores are filled with water and Micropores are filled with air

Explanation: The correct answer is: (3) Macropores are filled with air and Micropores are filled with water.

- **Field capacity (FC):** The amount of water a soil can hold after excess water has drained away due to gravity.
- **Macropores (large pores):** These pores allow for rapid drainage of water due to their larger size.
- **Micropores (small pores):** These pores hold water tightly against the forces of gravity due to their small size and surface tension.

42. Available water in plant roots is greatly influenced by the hydro physical properties of soil which of the following soils have maximum available water capacity (cm/cm of soil)? **Ans.: Silt Loam** RRB SO-2018

43. A-value technique is used to calculate the original soil supply of: B PPSC ADO-2017

a) N b) P c) K d) S

Explanation: The correct answer is: (b) P

- The A-value technique is valuable for estimating the **plant-available** P in soil, particularly for making fertilizer recommendations.
- It's not a direct measure of the original total supply of P or other nutrients.

44. Average content of silica in soil is : b UPPSC Pre- 2002

(a) 23% (b) 27% (c) 31% (d) 35%

S.no.	Element	Earth crust (By Weight %)
1	Oxygen	46.60%
2	Si (Silicon)	27.70%
3	Al (Aluminium)	8.13%
4	Fe (Iron)	5.00%
5	Ca (Calcium)	3.63%
6	Na (Sodium)	2.83%
7	K (Potassium)	2.59%
8	Mg (Magnesium)	2.09%
9	Other	1.41%

45. Average diameter of the clay fraction of the soil is : d UPPSC Pre- 1999

(a) Less than 2.0 mm (b) Less than 0.2 mm

(c) Less than 0.02 mm (d) Less than 0.002 mm

Explanation: The correct answer is: (d) Less than 0.002 mm

- Soil particles are classified into three main fractions based on size: sand, silt, and clay.
- The International Society of Soil Science (ISSS) classification system defines the size range for clay particles as:

Clay: Less than 0.002 mm; **Sand**: 2.0 mm to 0.02 mm ; **Silt**: 0.02 mm to 0.002 mm

46. Average particle density of soil is : b UPPSC Pre- 2007

(a) 1 .6 mg/m^3 (b) 2.6 mg/m^3 (c) 3.6 mg/m^3 (d) 4.6 mg/m^3

Explanation: The correct answer is: (b) 2.6 g/cm³ (grams per cubic centimeter), which is equivalent to $2.6 * 10^6$ mg/m³ (milligrams per cubic meter).

- Soil particle density refers to the mass per unit volume of the solid particles themselves, excluding pore spaces.
- Common soil minerals like quartz, feldspar, and clay minerals have densities in the range of 2.6 to 2.7 g/cm³.
- While the specific density can vary depending on the mineral composition of the soil, 2.6 g/cm³ is a widely accepted average value.

Conversion to mg/m³:

The answer choices are in mg/m³. If you encounter this conversion in future calculations, you can use the following:

1 g/cm³ = 1000 mg/cm³ (since there are 1000 milligrams in a gram) Then convert cm³ to m³:

1 cm³ = $(1/100)^3$ m³ (since there are 100 centimeters in a meter)

Multiply these conversion factors to get:

1 g/cm³ = 1000 mg/cm³ * $(1/100)^3$ m³ = 1000 mg/m³

Therefore, 2.6 g/cm³ is equivalent to 2.6 * 1000 mg/m³.

Important Note:

The actual particle density of soil can vary depending on the specific minerals present. However, 2.6 g/cm³ is a good starting point for many calculations involving soil properties.

47. Biological amelioration of Salt affected soils can be done by — 3 RPSC Sch Lect.2022

(1) Flooding or leaching (2) Frequent irrigation

(3) Application of farm yard manure (4) Application of gypsum

Explanation: The correct answer is: (3) Application of farm yard manure

Biological amelioration of salt-affected soils involves using biological agents or organic materials to improve soil structure, reduce salinity, and enhance fertility. Among the options provided:

Flooding or leaching (Option 1): While flooding or leaching can help to remove salts from the soil profile, it's not a biological method. It involves using water to dissolve and wash away excess salts, but it doesn't involve biological agents.

Frequent irrigation (Option 2): Similar to flooding or leaching, frequent irrigation can help to leach salts from the soil, but it's not a biological method on its own.

Application of farmyard manure (Option 3): This is a biological method that involves adding organic matter to the soil, which can improve soil structure, increase microbial activity, and enhance soil fertility. Organic matter helps to bind with salts, reducing their concentration in the soil solution and improving the soil's ability to support plant growth.

Application of gypsum (Option 4): Gypsum is a chemical amendment that can help to improve the structure of sodic soils by displacing sodium ions and replacing them with calcium ions. While gypsum application can be effective, it's not a biological method.

Therefore, among the options provided, the most appropriate biological amelioration method for salt-affected soils is the application of farmyard manure.

48. Black colour of soil is due to _____ a IFFCO T-2019

(a)Titaniferous magnetite (b) Geothite (c) Glauconite (d) Organic matter

Explanation: The correct answer is: (a) Titaniferous magnetite

The black color of soil can also be attributed to the presence of titaniferous magnetite. Titaniferous magnetite is a mineral that contains iron and titanium oxides. When present in soil in significant amounts, it imparts a black color to the soil. This mineral is commonly found in soils derived from volcanic materials or those with a high content of mafic minerals.

While **organic matter also contributes to soil coloration, especially in soils rich in humus**, the specific black color associated with titaniferous magnetite is notable in certain soil types where this mineral is abundant. Therefore, in the context of black-colored soil, the presence of titaniferous magnetite is the most relevant factor.

49. Black colour soil rich in ? D IBS,AFO-2014

(A) Zinc (B) Nitrogen (C) Phosphorus (D) Calcium carbonate, Mg, K

(E)All of these

Explanation: The correct answer is:(E) All of these

- **Primary Contributor:** Organic matter, particularly humic substances formed during decomposition, is the main reason for the black color.
- **Secondary Contributors:** While not as dominant as organic matter, some minerals can also influence the color:
  - **Iron oxides:** Specifically, magnetite (black) can contribute to the black color, but its influence is less significant compared to humic substances.
  - **Calcium carbonate ($CaCO_3$), Magnesium (Mg), and Potassium (K):** These elements themselves wouldn't cause a black color, but black soils can also be rich in these essential plant nutrients due to their high organic matter content, which helps retain these elements. Note that the color and nutrient content are separate characteristics, although they might be linked in black soils.

Therefore, while organic matter is the primary reason for the black color, black soils are often rich in a combination of nutrients like calcium, magnesium, and potassium, alongside the dark-colored organic matter.

50. Black cotton soil come under order a TNPSC Agri-1997

(A) Vertisol (B) Inceprisol (C) Aridisol (D) Oxisol

Explanation: The correct answer is : (A) Vertisol

- **Vertisols:** This soil order is characterized by clays that shrink and swell significantly with changes in moisture content.
- **Black cotton soil:** Also known as regur soil, black cotton soil is a type of Vertisol found in India's Deccan Plateau region. It's known for its black color due to high organic matter content and its clayey texture with high shrink-swell properties.
- **Inceptisols:** These are young soils with limited development, not typically associated with black cotton soil properties.
- **Aridisols:** These soils are formed in arid and semi-arid climates, lacking the moisture conditions that contribute to the development of black cotton soil.
- **Oxisols:** These highly weathered soils are found in humid tropics, not typically associated with black cotton soil characteristics.

51. Black cotton soil is rich in : a UPPSC Pre- 2002, UPPSC Pre- 2009

(a) Montmorillonite (b) Kaolinite (c) Illite (d) Chloride

Explanation: The correct answer is : (a) Montmorillonite

- **Black cotton soil:** This type of soil, also known as regur soil, is known for its:
  - Black color due to high organic matter content.
  - Clayey texture with high shrink-swell properties.
- **Clay Minerals:** The specific type of clay mineral significantly impacts the properties of black cotton soil. The dominant clay mineral in black cotton soil is:

Montmorillonite: This clay has a plate-like structure with a high cation exchange capacity (CEC), meaning it can hold onto positively charged ions (cations) like calcium, magnesium, and potassium. This contributes to the fertility of black cotton soil.

The other options are less common clay minerals in black cotton soil:

Kaolinite: This clay mineral is less expansive than montmorillonite and is not as dominant in black cotton soil.

Illite: This clay mineral can be present in some black cotton soils, but it's not the primary type.

Chloride: Chloride is a salt anion and wouldn't be a major component of black cotton soil. High chloride content can be detrimental to plant growth.

52. Black cotton soils are different in – Delhi PGT-2014, TN PSC Ag-2003 — 1 — TN PSC Ag-2003

(1) Iron (2) Nitrogen (3) Lime (4) Potash

53. Black soils (Vertisols) are formed mainly from the weathering of — d — BHU PET-2012

(a) Feldspars (b) Amphiboles (c) Granite (d) Basalts

Explanation: The correct answer is : (d) Basalts

- **Vertisols:** These soils are known for their high clay content, dark color, and characteristic shrink-swell properties.
- **Parent Material:** The type of rock from which the soil originates (parent material) plays a crucial role in its formation. Black cotton soil, a type of Vertisol, is often associated with weathering of:
  - **Basalts:** These volcanic rocks are rich in weatherable minerals like calcium-rich plagioclase feldspar and pyroxene. Weathering of these minerals releases calcium, iron, and other elements that contribute to the formation of clay minerals like montmorillonite, which is dominant in black cotton soil.

The other options are less likely parent materials for black soils:

- **Feldspars:** While feldspars are common minerals and weather to form clay, they can be present in various rock types. Basalts specifically offer a good combination of weatherable minerals suitable for black soil formation.
- **Amphiboles:** These minerals can be present in some rocks that weather to form Vertisols, but they are not the primary contributor in black cotton soil formation.
- **Granite:** Granite is a type of igneous rock that can weather to form various soil types, but it's not typically associated with the specific mineral composition needed for black cotton soil development.

54. Black soils of India belongs to - NABAR-2019 — 3 — TNPSC – Ag: 1999

(1) Entisol (2) Aridisol (3) Vertisol (4) Oxisol

55. Branch of soil science that deals with the study of origin of the soil , its classification and description is known as : — 2 — RPSC, AAO-2009

(1) Edaphology (2) Pedology (3) Ecology (4) Geology

56. Brown colour of soil is due to? — D — IBS,AFO-2014

(A)Humus (B) Iron oxide (C) $ZnSO_4$ (D) Organic matter and manganese dioxide (E)All of these

57. Brown soil is due to — C — AO KTPSC-2021

(A)Clay Humus complex (B) Titaniferous and Magnetite compound (C) Organic matter and Fe oxides (D) Humus and Quartz (E) Answer not known

58. Calcium and magnesium belong to: — b — NSC SR

(a) Primary plant nutrient group (b) Secondary plant nutrient group T-2019

(c) Micro-nutrient group (d) Beneficial but not essential group

59. Carrier material used in biofertilizers should possess following qualities D AO KTPSC-2021

(a) Non-polluting (b) Non-toxic (c) Bio degradable (d) High water holding capacity

(A) a,b and c are correct (B) a, b and d are correct (

C) a,c and d are correct (D) a,b,c,d are correct (E) Answer not known

60. cation exchange capacity is highest in : b UPPSC Pre- 2008

(a) Alluvial soil (b) Black cotton soil (c) Laterite soil (d) Red soil

Explanation: The correct answer is : (b) Black cotton soil

Soil Type	**Cation Exchange Capacity (CEC)**
Alluvial soil	10 meq/100g
Black cotton soil	40 meq/100g
Laterite soil	5 meq/100g
Red soil	15 meq/100g

61. Cation exchange capacity of most soils a UPPSC Pre- 2005

(a) increases with pH (b) is maximum at pH 7.00

(c) is constant at pH lower then 6.00 (d) is independent of pH.

Explanation: The correct answer is : (a) increases with pH.

- CEC refers to a soil's ability to hold onto positively charged ions (cations).
- The surface of clay particles and organic matter in soil holds negative charges. These negative charges attract and hold positively charged cations.
- Soil pH affects the charge characteristics of these surfaces.

Explanation of the relationship with pH:

- **Lower pH (acidic soils):** At lower pH, more hydrogen (H+) ions occupy the exchange sites on the soil particles. This reduces the availability of sites for other cations, leading to a **decrease** in CEC.
- **Higher pH (alkaline soils):** As pH increases, the concentration of H+ ions decreases. This allows other cations to occupy the exchange sites more readily, leading to an **increase** in CEC.

Important Note:

- The relationship between CEC and pH isn't always perfectly linear. Other factors like the specific clay mineral composition and organic matter content can also influence CEC.
- However, the general trend is that CEC increases with increasing pH for most soils.

Other options are not as accurate:

- (b) Maximum at pH 7.00: While CEC often increases with pH, it might not reach a specific maximum value exactly at pH 7.00. It's a gradual trend.
- (c) Constant at pH below 6.00: CEC doesn't remain constant at lower pH. It generally decreases as pH goes down.
- (d) Independent of pH: CEC is demonstrably influenced by pH. It's not an independent factor.

62. Chemical amendment for reclamation of alkali soil is : d UPPSC Pre- 2009

(a) Calcium oxide (b) Calcium hydroxide

(c) Calcium phosphate (d) Calcium sulphate

63. Chemical formula of pyrite reclaimant is : d UPPSC Pre- 2000

(a) FeS (b) CuS (c) MnS (d) FeS_2

64. Chemically anhydrous aluminosilicates of potassium, sodium and calcium found in 1 RPSC ARO Ag Chem - 2022

(1) Feldspar (2) Silicates (3) Zeolites (4) Pyroxenes

65. Choose the correct Electrical Conductivity (EC) level for very high salinity water – 4 TN AAO-2019

(1) > 2250 dSm^{-1} (2) >225 dSm^{-1}. (3) >22:5 dSm^{-1} (4) >2.25 dSm^{-1}

66. Choose the correct sequence in soil taxonomical classification A TNPSC Ag- 1998

(A) Order - Suborder - Great group - Subgroup - Family - Series -Type-Phase

(B) Order - Great group - Suborder - Family - Series - Subgroup-Type-Phase

(C) Order - Subgroup - Great group - Family - Type - Phase -Series - Sub order

(D) Order - Great group - Family - Suborder - Type - Phase -Series - Subgroup - Phase

67. Clay soil contains which type of pores to a large extent? A HPSC ADO-2022

(A) Capillary pore (B) Coarse pore (C) Medium pore (D) Macro pore

68. Clay particles of soil has diameter (mm) : 3 RPSC ACF Agri -2018

(1) >0.02 mm (2) >0.002 mm (3) < 0.902 min (4) None of these

69. Coarse sand particle size? A IBS,AFO-2015

(A) 0.2 mm (B) 0.002 mm (C) 1 mm (D) 0.02 mm (E) All of above

70. Coherant mass of soil broken into any shape by artificial means like tillage C AO KTPSC-2021

(A) Fragment (B) Concretion (C) Clod (D) Ped (E) Answer not known

71. Colour of Laterite soil is – a BHU UET-2014

(a) Red (b) Yellow (c) Green (d) Black

72. Colour of which of the following soils is red due to diffusion of iron rather than pressure of environment? **Ans.: Red Soil.** NABARD -2021

73. Commercial grade montmorillonite is also available in the market as - 1 RPSC ARO Ag Chem - 2022

(1) Bentonite (2) Beidellite (3) Saponite(4) Nontronite

74. Commonly used chemical as an amendment of alkali soil is a TNPSC Agri-1997

(A) Gypsum (B) Sulphur (C) Sulphuric acid (D) FYM

75. Composed magnesium –aluminium –iron silicate soil is – 3 TN AAO-2019

(1) Perlite (2) Peat (3) Vemiculite (4) Sphagnum moss

76. Concentration of which element is higher than others in soil : UPPSC Pre- 2000 a UPPSC Pre- 2002

(a) O_2 (b) Si (c) Al (d) Fe

77. Consider the following C IAS Pre-2004

1. Iron 2. Oxygen 3. Manganese 4. Nitrate

The sequential reduction of elements occurring in soil under submergence follows which one of the orders?

(a) 1,4,3,2 (b) 3,4,1,2 (c) 2,4,3,1 (d) 4,2,1,3

Explanation: The correct answer is : (c) 2,4,3,1

Explanation:

The sequential reduction of elements occurring in soil under submergence typically follows a specific order, known as the "reduction sequence." This sequence reflects the order in which different elements are reduced under anaerobic (low oxygen) conditions commonly found in submerged or waterlogged soils. Here's the order:

Oxygen (Oxygen Reduction): Under submerged conditions, oxygen is rapidly depleted from the soil due to limited diffusion. Oxygen reduction occurs first, leading to the establishment of anaerobic conditions.

Nitrate (Nitrate Reduction): After oxygen is depleted, nitrate (NO_3^-) serves as an alternative electron acceptor for microbial respiration. Nitrate reduction occurs next, where nitrate is reduced to nitrogen gas (N2), nitrous oxide (N2O), or other nitrogenous compounds.

Manganese (Manganese Reduction): Following the reduction of nitrate, manganese reduction occurs. Manganese serves as an electron acceptor for microbial respiration in anaerobic environments.

Iron (Iron Reduction): Finally, iron reduction occurs after manganese reduction. Iron compounds, particularly ferric iron (Fe^3+), are reduced to ferrous iron (Fe^2+) under anaerobic conditions.

Therefore, the correct sequence of reduction for the elements listed is 2 (Oxygen), 4 (Nitrate), 3 (Manganese), and 1 (Iron), which corresponds to option (c) 2,4,3,1.

78. Consider the following : **B** **IAS Pre-2007**

1. Brucite 2. Gibbsite 3. Albite 4. Boehmite

Which of the above are Al-containing minerals?

(a) 1,2 and 4only (b) 2,3 and 4 only

(c) 1,3 and 4only (d) 1,2 and 3 only

Explanation: The correct answer is : (b) 2,3 and 4 only

Brucite (Option 1) - Brucite is a mineral composed of magnesium hydroxide (Mg(OH)2) and does not contain aluminum (Al). Therefore, Brucite is not an Al-containing mineral.

Gibbsite (Option 2) - Gibbsite is an aluminum hydroxide mineral with the chemical formula Al(OH)3. It is one of the most common minerals in the Earth's crust and is a major component of bauxite, which is the primary ore of aluminum. Therefore, Gibbsite is an Al-containing mineral.

Albite (Option 3) - Albite is a plagioclase feldspar mineral with the chemical formula NaAlSi3O8. It contains aluminum (Al) as part of its chemical composition and is commonly found in igneous and metamorphic rocks. Therefore, Albite is an Al-containing mineral.

Boehmite (Option 4) - Boehmite is an aluminum oxide hydroxide mineral with the chemical formula γ-AlO(OH). It is a polymorph of diaspore and is a component of the bauxite ore. Therefore, Boehmite is an Al-containing mineral.

79. Consider the following compounds **a** **IAS Pre-1999**

1. Calcium carbonate 2. Magnesium carbonate 3. Calcium hydroxide 4. Magnesium hydroxide

Limestone consists of

(a) 2and 3 (b) 1and 2 (c) 3and 4 (d) 1 and 4

Explanation: The correct answer is : (a) 2 and 3

Explanation:

Limestone is primarily composed of calcium carbonate ($CaCO3$), which is the mineral calcite or aragonite. Therefore, among the compounds listed:

Calcium carbonate (Option 1) - This compound is indeed present in limestone.

Magnesium carbonate (Option 2) - While magnesium carbonate can be found in some carbonate minerals, it is not a primary component of limestone. Limestone typically consists mainly of calcium carbonate, with only minor amounts of magnesium carbonate, if any.

Calcium hydroxide (Option 3) - Calcium hydroxide is not a primary component of limestone. Limestone is primarily composed of calcium carbonate ($CaCO3$), not calcium hydroxide.

Magnesium hydroxide (Option 4) - Similar to calcium hydroxide, magnesium hydroxide is not a primary component of limestone.

80. Consider the following elements : S IAS Pre-2009

1. Aluminium 2. Iron 3. Oxygen 4. Silicon

In terms of their contents present in the Earth's crust in descending order, what is the sequence of the above elements ?

(a) 2 – 4 – 3 – 1 (b) 2 – 3 – 4 – 1

(c) 3 – 4 – 1 – 2 (d) 3 – 1 – 4 – 2

Oxygen (O): Oxygen is the most abundant element in the Earth's crust, making up about 46.6% by weight.

Silicon (Si): Silicon is the second most abundant element, constituting about 27.7% by weight.

Aluminium (Al): Aluminium is the third most abundant element, comprising about 8.1% by weight.

Iron (Fe): Iron is the fourth most abundant element, making up about 5.0% by weight.

81. Consider the following materials: C IAS Pre-1997

1. Montmorillonite 2. Humus 3. Kaolinite 4. Illite

The correct sequence of these materials in decreasing order of their CEC is

(a) 1,2,3,4 (b) 2,1,3,4 (c) 2,1,4,3 (d) 1,2,4,3

82.

83. Consider the following minerals B IAS Pre-2003

1. Siderite 2. pyrolusite 3. Smithsonite 4. Dolomite

Which of these contain carbonate in their composition?

(a)1,2 and 3 (b) 2,3 and 4 (c) 1,2 and 4 (d) 1,3 and 4

84. Consider the following minerals A IAS Pre-2003

1. Magnestie 2. Muscovite 3. Anorthite 4. Apatite

The sequence of these minerals in the increasing order of resistance to weathering is

(a) 1,2,3,4 (b) 2,3,4,1 (c) 3,4,1,2 (d) 4,1,2,3

85. Consider the following mining materials having different neutralizing values (ability to neutralize the soil acidity) C IAS Pre-2004

1. Calcium carbonate 2. Calcium hydroxide

3. Calcium oxide 4. Magnesium carbonate

The correct sequence in the increasing order of neutralizing values of these liming materials would be

(a) 1,2,3,4 (b) 2,4,3,1 (c) 1,4,2,3 (d) 4,1,2,3

86. consider the following notation : The colour of soil, as per Munsell notation is denoted as 5 YR 5/6 C IAS Pre-2001

Study critically, the following explanations of this notation:

1. 5 YR denotes 'hue' of the colour where YR means yellow red the figure 5 incicates that the contribution of Yellow colour to the soil iis 5 times more than that of Red colour.

2. The figure 5 in 5/6 is the value' of the colour, whhc indicates that the colour is visually midway between absolute white and absolute black.

3. The figure 6 in 5/6 denotes the 'Chroma' of the colour. It shows the chroma is in the 7th place from 0 (including 0) in the scale of 0 to 20

Which of the above explanations are correct?

(a) 1and 2 (b) 2and 3 (c) 1and 3 (d) 1,2 and 3

Munsell colour chart

- Munsell colour chart contains 175 different colour papers/ chips.
- Musell colour chart consists of with 7 cards, each has constant hue.
- In each card value is constant with in horizontal row and increase towards top.
- In each card chroma is constant with in vertical colomn and increase to th right.
- Value of 0 indicates Black colour .
- Value of 10 indicates white colour.
- Chroma increases with decreasing greyness.
- Chroma 0 for neutral grey and 20 for high purity.
- Normally hroma above 8 is rarely found in soil.
- Achromatic colour have neutral hue and zero chroma and differ only in value.

87. Consider the following phenomena/events: c IAS Pre-1997

1. Weathering 2. Biogrowth 3. Soil development 4. profile differentiation

The correct chronological sequence of these phenomena/events is

(a) 2,1,3,4 (b) 1,2,4,3 (c) 1,2,3,4, (d) 2,1,4,3

88. Consider the following situations: B IAS Pre-2000

1. Presence of hydrogen ions (H^+) in the soil

2. Presence of active aluminium ions (AI^{+3}) in the soil

3. Conversion of soil phosphorus to insoluble, complex phosphates of iron and aluminium

4. Adverse effect on the growth and activities of the beneficial micro organisms like nutrifiers and symbiotic bacteria

Which of the above produce harmful effects of soil activity on many crops?

(a) 1,2 and 2 (b) 2,3 and 4 (c) 1,3 and 4 (d) 1,2 and 4

89. Consider the following statement : a UPPSC Pre- 2001

Assertion (A) : Alkali soils are poor in nitrogen.

Reason (R) : Nitrogen is leached from alkali soil.

Select the correct answer from the code given below :

(a) A is true but R is wrong.

(b) R is true but A is false.

(c) Both A and R are correct.

(d) Both A and R are false.

90. Consider the following statements b IAS Pre-1998

Cation exchange of soil colloidal clay is due to

1.silicon tetrahedral layer 2. isomorphous substitution

3. hydration of clays 4. broken edges of clay lattices

Of these statements

(a) 1and 2 are correct (b) 2and 4 are correct

(c) 3and 4 are correct (d) 1and 3 are correct

91. Consider the following statements D IAS Pre-2000

1. Flocculation and aggregation are synonymous

2. Cation like sodium deflocculates the clay

3. Soil devoid of organic matter does not get readily aggregated

Which of the above statements are correct?

(a) 1and 2 (b) 1and 3 (c) 2and 3 (d) 1,2 and 3

92. Consider the following statements C IAS Pre-2005

Modern soil classification (taxonomy) is based on

1. Soil morphology 2. Soil genesis

3. Climate of soil formation 4. Age of soil

Which of the statements given above are correct?

(a) 1,2 and 3 (b) 2 and 3 (c) 1,2 and 4 (d) 1 and 4

93. Consider the following statements C IAS Pre-2007

1. Diffusion is the dominant mechanism for transporting soil Zn^{2+} to plant roots

2. Zinc solubility in soil solution decreases 100fold for each unit increase in pH

Which of the statements given above is/are correct?

(a) 1only (b) 2only (c) Bothe 1and 2 (d) Neither 1 nor2

94. Consider the following statements 4 TN PSC Ag-I:1999

I. Smaller the size of the particle, greater is the surface area

II. Smaller the size of the particle, lower is the caution exchange capacity

(1) Both I and II are true (2) Both I and II are false

(3) Statement I is true, but II is false (4) Statement I is false, but II is true

95. Consider the following statements 1 TN PSC Ag-II: 2001

I. pH is an index of soil reaction

II. pF is an index of soil moisture

(1) Both statements are true

(2) Both statements are false

(3) Statement I is true and statement II is false

(4) Statement II is true and statement I is false

96. Consider the following statements – 3 TN ACF-2012

I. Lime is used for correcting soil acidity

II. Gypsum is used for reclamation of alkali soils of these

(1) Only (I) is correct (2) Only (II) is correct
(3) Both are correct (4) None of these

97. Consider the following statements : **4** **RPSC Pre-1994**
soil is a medium of plant growth, because :
A. It provides mechanical support and plant nutrient
B. It contain beneficial micro-organisms
C. It contains water and oxygen
D. Plant can not grow without soil
Of these statements :
(1) A alone is correct (2) B and C are correct
(3) A, C and D are correct (4) A, B and C are correct

98. Consider the following statements : **B** **IAS Pre-2006**
1. The bulk Density of clay loam is higher than that of sandy loam
2. The field capacity of clay loam is higher than that of sandy loam
Which of the statements given above is/are correct?
(a) 1only (b) 2only (c) both 1and 2 (d) Neither 1nor 2

99. Consider the following statements : **a** **IAS Pre-2009**
1. A fine-textured acid soil requires much larger quantity of lime than does a sandy soil or a loamy soil with the same pH value.
2. One molecule of calcium oxide, magnesium oxide or calcium hydroxide neutralizes the same amount of acidity as does one molecule of calcium carbonate.
Which of the statements given above is/are correct ?
(a) 1 only (b) 2 only (c) Both 1 and 2 (d) Neither 1 nor 2

100. Consider the following statements : **(a)** **UPPSC Pre-1999**
Assertion (A) : Nitrification inhibitors are the chemicals used to control nitrogen transformation in the soils.
Reason (R) : They promote the activities of nitrifying bacteria.
Select the correct answer using the code given below :
Code :
(a) A is true but R is false (b) A is false but R is true (c) Both A and R are true and R is the correct explanation of A
(d) Both A and R are true but R is not the correct explanation of A.

101. Consider the following statements : **c** **UPPSC Pre-2002**
Assertion (A) : Liming improves better plant growth.
Reason (R) : Soil pH is improved and this provides better environment for plant growth. Select the correct answer from the code given below :
(a) A is true but R is false. (b) **R is true but A is false.**(c)Both A and R are correct and R is the correct explanation of A. (d) Both A and R are correct but R is not the correct explanation of A.

102. Consider the following statements : **a** **UPPSC Pre-2007**
Assertion (A) : Alkali soils are poor in nitrogen.
Reason (R) : Nitrogen is leached from alkali soils.

Select the correct answer from the code given below :

Codes :

(a) (A) is ture, but (R) is wrong (b) (R) is true. but (A) is false

(c) Both (A) and (R) are correct (d) Both (A) and (R) are false

103. Consider the following statements: B IAS Pre-2000

A soil series has similar

1. profile character 2. horizon thickness 3. soil structure

Which of the above statements are correct?

(a) 1,2 and 3 (b) 1 and 3 (c) 2and 3 (d) 1 and 2

104. Consider the statement A TNPSC Ag-1998

Assertion (A) : White encrustation on saline soils is referred toas white alkali

Reason (R) : On evaporation of moisture, the dissolved salts are left on the surface.

Now select your answer according to the coding schemegiven below

(A) Both (A) and (R) are true, and (R) is the correct explanation of (A)

(B) Both (A) and (R) are true, but (R) is not the correct explanation of (A)

(C)(A) is true, but (R) is false

(D) (A) is false, but (R) is true

105. Consider the statement a TNPSC Ag-1996

I) Phosphorus fixed by clay minerals and organic matter in soil

II) Phosphorus as superphosphate ion is available for plant uptake

III) Phosphorus as primary or secondary orthophosphate ion is available for plant uptake.

IV) Phosphorus availability is high in soil having a pH of 8.2

Of statements

(A) I alone is correct (B) I and II are correct

(C) II and III are correct (D) All are correct

106. Conversion of organic form of nutrient into inorganic form – 1 TN AO-2012

(1) Mineralization (2) Immobilization (3) Fixation (4) Stabilization

107. Cracking during summer is predominant in C TNPSC Ag-1998

(A) Red Soil (B) Laterite soil (C) Black soil (D) Alluvial soil

108. Cracking is a common feature of which type of soil ? 3 Raj JET-2020

(1) Red (2) Alluvial (3) Black (4) Laterite

109. Cray suggested certain modification in the Mitscherlich equation. The modified equation is written as d IAS Pre-1994

(a) $dy/dx = (A-y) C$ (b) $A=B (1-y)/y$

(c) $\log (A-y) = \log A-Cx$ (d) $\log (A-y) = \log A-C_1 b-Cx$

110. Critical oxygen diffusion requirement of most aerable crops is : a UPPSC Pre-2005

(a) 20×10^{-8} g cm^{-2} min^{-1} (b) 20×10^{-8} mg cm^{-2} min^{-1}

(c) 40×10^{-8} mg cm^{-2} min^{-1} (d) 10×10^{-8} mg cm^{-2} min^{-1}

111. Deposition of soil by gravity is termed as? RRB SO-2020

Ans.: Colluvial Soil

112. Depth of cultivated soils is upto- B ADA Guj-

(A) 5 cm (B) 15 cm (C) 30 cm (D) 45 cm 2013

113. Detachment, transportation and deposition of soil particles from one place to another place is termed as: b Agri Pre PG-2021
(a) Soil degradation (b) Soil erosion (c) Soil flow (d) Soil movement

114. Devarda alloy is composed of - 4 RPSC ARO Ag Chem - 2022
(1) 50% Al, 45%Zn, 5%Cu (2) 50% Al, 45%Cu, 5% Zn
(3) 50% Zn, 45%Al, 5% Cu (4) 50% Cu, 45%A1, 5% Zn

115. Diagnostic subsurface horizon is- 2 RPSC AAO-2022
(1) Epipedon (2) Endopedon (3) Plaggen (4) Histic horiozn

116. Diagnostic subsurface horizon is- 2 RPSC AAO Ag - 2022
(1) Epipedon (2) Endopedon (3) Plaggen (4) Histic horiozn

117. Diameter of clay particle is A TO MPUAT- 2014
(A) <0.002 mm (B) 0.02 to 0.002 mm
(C) 0.20 to 0.02 mm (D) 2.0 to 0.2 mm

118. Diameter of soil clay particles is in the range of RPSC Pre-2008 3 RPSC, AAO-2009
(1) 0.25 – 0.50 mm (2) 0.02 – 0.05 mm (3) <0.002 mm (4) 0.05 – 0.1 mm

119. Dolomite is D IAS Pre- 2002
(a) $CaCO_3$ (b) $MgSO_4$ (c) Ca $(OH)_2$ (d) Mg CO_3 $CaCO_3$

120. Electrial conductivity of saline water should be less than – 1 TN AO- 2012
(1) 4.0 dSm^{-1} (2) 5.0 dSm^{-1} (3) 6.0 dSm^{-1} (4) 7.0 dSm^{-1}

121. Electric conductivity of saturation extract of saline - sodic soil in m mhos per cm is D AO GPSC- 2013
(A) 2.0 (B) 2,0 - 3.0 (C) 3.0 - 4.0 (D) More than 4.0

122. Electrical conductivity of saturation extract of saline-sodic soils in mmhos per cm is : d UPPSC Pre- 1997
(a) 2.0 (b) 3.5 (c) between 2.0 and 3.0 (d) more than 4.0

123. Emission wavelength for potassium is - 4 RPSC ARO Ag Chem - 2022
(1) 554 nm (2) 589 nm (3) 670 nm (4) 766 nm

124. Emitted colour for sodium is - 3 RPSC ARO Ag Chem - 2022
(1) Violet (2) Red (3) Yellow (4) Orange

125. E-value is a IAS Pre- 1996
(a) Defined as the isotopically exchangeable P in the soil and soil solution as determined by crop uptake
(b) defined as the isotopically exchangeable P in the soil as determined ^{32}P
(c) the same as the L-value
(d) the difference between A and L values

126. Exchange of O_2 and CO_2 between soil pores and atomospheric air refers to : (UPPSC

(a) soil-air capacity (b) soil-oxygen diffusion b Pre- 2005
(c) soil-air permeability (d) soil aeration)

127. Exchangeable sodium percentage of Alkali soil is c TNPSC
(A) Less then 15% (B) 15% (C) Greater than 15% (D) Zero Ag-1996

128. Ferrous sulphate-heptahydrate contains: A PPSC
a) 19% iron and 11% sulphur b) 11% iron and 19% sulphur ADO-
c) 9% iron and 21% sulphur d) 21% iron and 9% Sulphur 2017

129. Fine textured soil is C AO
A. Silt B. Sand C. Clay D. None of these SDAU- 2013

130. For determination of half life of radiactive materials, the instrument used is - 3 RPSC
(1) Mass spectrometry (2) Neutron scattering meter ARO Ag
(3) Geiger Muller counter (4) TOC analyser Chem - 2022

131. For making sandy soil compact? A IBS,AFO- 2014
(A) Conserve water (B) Mixed lime (C) Mixed fertilizer
(D) Making ditch (E) None of these

132. For most tenaciously bound by soil colloids, the sequence of cations are as - 1 RPSC
(1) $Al^{3+} > Ca^{2+} > Mg^{2+} > K^{+} > Na^{+}$ (2) $K^{+} > Al^{3+} > Ca^{2+} > Na^{+} > Mg^{2+}$ ARO Ag
(3) $Ca^{2+} > Mg^{2+} > K^{+} > Na^{+} > Al^{3+}$ (4) $N^{a+} > K^{+} > Mg^{2+} > Ca^{2+} > Al^{3+}$ Chem - 2022

133. Form of potassium held against the negative charge of the soil colloid is : c BHU
(a)Non- Exch. K (b)Water soluble K (c) Exch. K (d) Insert K PET-2016

134. Formation of soil is known as - 2 MP PG
(1) Humification (2) Pedogenesis (3) Sedimentation (4) None of these PAT-2016

135. Fraction of humus not solubilized by acids or alkali is known as : c UPPSC
(a) Humic acid (b) Fulvic acid (c) Humin (d) None of the above Pre- 2005

136. Given that a IAS Pre- 1996
$\left(\frac{dy}{dx}\right)$ = increase of yield per unit of growth factor
A = maximum yield, Y = yield without growth factor, C = a constant
Mitscherlich equation for evaluation of soil fertility is given
(a) $\frac{dy}{dx}$ = (A-y) C (b) $\frac{dy}{dx}$ = (Y-A) C (c) $\frac{dy}{dx} = \frac{A-y}{dx}$ (d) $\frac{dy}{dx}$ = (A + Y) C

137. Granular structure is found in soils rich in : b UPPSC
(a) Organic matter and sodium (b) Organic matter and calcium Pre- 1999
(c) Clay and sodium (d) Clay and potassium

138. Group of salts found in sodic soils are : c UPPSC
(a)Na_2CO_3+Na_2SO_4 (b)NaCl+Na_2CO_3 (c) Na_2CO_3+$NaHCO_3$ (d)NaCl+Na_2SO_4 Pre- 2007

139. Gypsum blocks are not suitable for – 3 TN PSC
(1) Sandy soil (2) Clay soil (3) Saline soil (4) Neutral soil Ag-2003

140. H^{+} and Al^{3+} ions present in non- exchangeable form with organic matter and silicate B HPSC
clays and aluminium hydroxyl ions account for ADO- 2022
(A) active acidity (B) reserve acidity

(C) exchangeable acidity (D) non-exchangeable acidity

141. Half-life of ^{14}C is — D — IAS Pre-2003
(a) 30.2 years (b) 281 years (c) 80 days (d) 5730 days

142. Higher saturation with which of the following ions by soil colloids causes deflocculation? — C — IAS Pre-2010
(a) Ca^{2+} (b) Fe^{2+} (c) Na^{+} (d) Al^{3+}

143. How many soil orders found in soil taxonomy ? — C — ADA MP-2015
(A) 8 (B) 10 (C) 12 (D) 5

144. How many soil textural classes are there ? — 2 — TN AAO-2019
(1) 10 (2) 12 (3) 9 (4) 14

145. How much is the porosity percentage if the particle density of soil is 2.6 and bulk density is 1.3 : — c — UPPSC Pre- 2001
(a) 35% (b) 40% (c) 50% (d) 55%

146. Hue denotes ______? — a — IFFCO T - 2019
(a) Dominant spectrum (b) Lightness or brightness (c) Purity (d) Intensity

147. Hydraulic conductivity in different soil is found to decrease in following order : — 2 — RPSC ACF AE - 2018
(a) Sand > Silt Loam >Silty Clay Loam > Loamy Sand
(b) Sand > Loamy Sand > Silt Loam >Silty Clay Loam
(c) Sand > Silt Loam > Loamy Sand >Silty Clay Loam
(d) Loamy Sand> Sand> Silt Loam >Silty Clay Loam

148. Hydraulic conductivity of a soil under saturated flow of water is a function of : — c — UPPSC Pre- 2010
(a) soil pore size (b) soil moisture content
(c) soil pore size and soil moisture content (d) None of the above

149. Hydrogen bond found in which clay mineral? — a — IFFCO T - 2019
(a) Kaolinite (b) Montmorillonite (c) Vermiculite (d) Beidelite

150. Hymatomelanic acid is soluble in - — 1 — RPSC ARO Ag Chem - 2022
(1) Alkali and Alcohol (2) Acid and Alkali
(3) Alkali and Hot water (4) Hot and Cold water

151. Identify the correct match – — 2 — TNPSC – TNPSC – Ag: 1999
(1) Acid soils – Gypsum (2) Alkali soil – Gypsum
(3) Saline soils – Gypsum (4) Clay soils – Gypsum

152. If a soil has bulk density of 1.50 mg/m3 and a particle density of 2.65 mg/m3 then the percentage pore space of that soil will be — c — IAS Pre-1996
(a) 35.0 (b) 38.5 (c) 43.5 (d) 48.5

153. If electrical conductivity (dS/m) of soil is more than 4, exchangeable sodium percentage is more than 15 and pH is more than 8.5, the soil is — B — TO MPUAT-2014
(A) Sodic (B) Saline - Sodic (C) Acidic (D) Saline

154. If $Nay^{+}/(Cl^{-} + SO_4^{2-})$ ratio is <1 and pH of the saturated soil paste (pHs) is < 8.2, the soil is designated as - — 1 — RPSC ARO Ag Chem - 2022
(1) Saline (2) Sodic (3) Acidic (4) Saline-sodic

155. If soil A is having higher buffering capacity than soil B, then- — 1 — RPSC

(1) Soil A will require more lime than soil B for pH increment — ARO Ag

(2) Soil A will require less lime than soil B for pH increment — Chem -

(3) Both the soil will require same amount of lime — 2022

(4) None of the above

156. If the concentration of water soluble Ca^{2+} + Mg^{2+} is 18 me/L and that of Na^{+} is also 18 me/L and the SAR of the solution is – — 3 — TN PSC Ag-I:1999

(1) 2 (2) 4 (3) 6 (4) 8

157. if the contents of exchgeable ions (c mol kg^{-1}) determined in soil are Na^{+} = 5; k^{+} = 5; Ca^{2+} = 10; Mg^{2+} = 2; H^{+} = 1; Al_3+ = 1; Cl^{-} 1.6 and HCO_3^{-} = o.4, the cation exchange capacity of soil is — D — IAS Pre-2003

(a) 12 c mol (p^{+}) kg^{-1} (b) 22 c mol (p^{+}) kg^{-1}

(c) 24 c mol (p^{+}) kg^{-1} (d) 26 c mol (p^{+}) kg^{-1}

158. If the soil pH is below 4.5, the soil is designated as – — 1 — TN ACF-2012

(1) Extermely Acidic (2) Neutral (3) Slightly Acidic (4) Fermentation

159. In aqua regia, ratio of HCl : HNO_3 is — 2 — RPSC ARO Ag Chem - 2022

(1) 1 : 3 (2) 3 : 1 (3) 9 : 4 (4) 9 : 5

160. In black soils, the black colour is due to – — c — BHU UET-2013

(a) iron oxide (b) magnesium oxide (c) humus (d) copper oxide

161. In $CaCl_2$-extractable Sulphur determination (Williams &Steinbergs, 1969 method), the chemical used for turbidity development is — — 1 — RPSC ARO Ag Chem - 2022

(1) Barium chloride (2) Gum acacia

(3) Potassium sulphate (4) Calcium chloride

162. In clay minerals identification X-ray Differaction analysis (XRD) is a - — 3 — RPSC ARO Ag Chem - 2022

(1) destructive method (2) semi destructive method

(3) non-destructive method (4) None of the above

163. In comparison to particle density of soil, bulk density is : — a — UPPSC Pre- 2009

(a) Smaller (b) Greater (c) Equal (d) No relationship

164. In deep soil, the soil profile is generally studied up to a depth of :- — 2 — RPSC, AO-2016

(1) 60 cm (2) 150 cm (3) 500 cm (4) 250 cm

165. In determination of Phosphorus, phosphate -ammonium molybdate does undergo which of the following process to produce blue colour? — 2 — RPSC ARO Ag Chem - 2022

(1) Oxidation (2) Reduction (3) Solubilization(4) Precipitation

166. In ideal surface soil, solid, liquid and gaseous phase exist in the following proportion — a — Agri Pre PG-2020

(a) Solid (50%) : liquid (25%) : gaseous (25%)

(b) Solid (25%) : liquid (50%) : gaseous (25%)

(c) Solid (25%) : liquid (25%) : gaseous (50%)

(d) Solid (70%) : liquid (15%) : gaseous (15%)

167. In Mansell soil colour chart the Chroma number ranges from - — 3 — RPSC ARO Ag

(1) 0 – 8 (2) 1 – 8 (3) 0 -10 (4) 1 - 10

Chem - 2022

168. In neutralization reaction, the reactivity of phenolphthalein indicator works at pH range of - **4** RPSC ARO Ag Chem - 2022
(1) 5.0 — 8.6 (2) 6.0 — 7.6 (3) 6.4 — 8.0 (4) 8.0 --10.0

169. In neutron scattering method, fast moving neutrons emission radioactive source is – **1** RPSC ARO Ag Chem - 2022
(1) Americium – Beryllium (2) Lithium - Radium
(3) Aluminium – Lithium (4) Titanium - Beryllium

170. In Tamil Nadu, the alluvial soils are mostly located in – **1** TN AO-2008
(1) Coastal areas (2) Plains (3) Deltaic areas (4) All of these

171. In terms of the order from the most easily weathered to the most resistant to weathering of the soil in semi arid grasslands? **A** IAS Pre-2006
(a) Olivine- calcite – montmorillonite – gibbsite
(b) olivine – gibbsite – montmorillonite
(d) olivine – montmorillonite – calcite – gibbsite

172. In terms of the order from youngest to the oldest soil, which one of the following is the correct chronological order? **B** IAS Pre-2006
(a) Oxisol _ inceptisol _ alfisol _ entisol (b) Entisol _ inceptisol _ alfisol _ oxisol
(c) Entisol _ alfisol _ inceptisol _ oxisol (d) Inceptisol _ entisol _ oxisol _ alfisol

173. In the black cotton soils of India, dominant group of layer silicate clay minerals found is - **3** RPSC ARO Ag Chem - 2022
(1) Kaolinite (2) Illite (3) Smectite (4) Chlorite

174. In U.S. Soil Taxonomy, the number of soil orders is – **c** BHU PET-2010
(a) 10 (b) 11 (c) 12 (d) 13

175. In which district of U.P. red soil is found ? **b** UPPSC Pre- 2009
(a) Kanpur (b) Lalitpur (c) Etawah (d) Varanasi

176. In which of the following fertility classes, the soils having 200 kg available potassium oxide per ha can be put to : **2** RPSC Pre-1999
(1)Low (2) Medium (3)High (4)Very high

177. In which of the following order humic acid contains the different elements : **4** UPPSC Pre- 2003
(1) C>H>O>N (2) N>O>C>H (3) C>H>N>O (4) C>O>H>N

178. In which of the following state Vertisols is found highest ? **a** IBS,AFO-2020
(a) Madhya Pradesh (b) Uttar Pradesh (c) Karnataka (d)Maharshtra (e) Kerala

179. In which year soil health card scheme was launched? **2** RPSC ARO Ag Chem - 2022
(1) Febnirary, 2017 (2) Februrary, 2015
(3) Februrary, 2016 (4) Februrary, 2014

180. In which zone soil mineral are deposit after leaching known as illuviation? **c** IBS,AFO-2020
(a) A-Horizon (b) O-Horizon (c) B-Horizon (d) C-Horizon (e) R-Horizon

181. Inceptisol are otherwise called as – **1** TN AO-

(1) Alluvial soils (2) Black soils (3) Red soils (4) Laterite soils 2018

182. Incineration is - 4 RPSC ARO Ag Chem - 2022
(1) heating of contaminated soil to make or reduce toxic compounds
(2) acidification of crop residues
(3) injecting air into contaminated soil
(4) burning of waste at very high temperatures

183. Increase in concentration of a pollutant in food chain is known as - 1 RPSC ARO Ag Chem - 2022
(1) Biomagnification (2) Bioaccumulation (3) Biomethylation(4) Eutrophication

184. Intensity of problem is said to be `nil'/no problem' if the chloride content in the irrigation water is C AO KTPSC- 2021
(A) > 10 meq.l-1 (B) 4-10 meq.l-1 (C) <4 meq.l-1 (D) None of these (E) Answer not known

185. Ions are held on clay by a process called C IAS Pre- 2002
(a) adhesion (b) cohesion (c) adsorption (d) coagulation

186. Isomorphous substitution in tetrahedral and octahedral sheets of layer lattice aluminosilicate clay minerals leads to permanent negative charge of the clay. Such substitution for the mineral nontronite occurs in B IAS Pre- 2010
(a) the 'tetrahedral' layer
(b) the 'octahedral' layer
(c) both 'tetrahedral' and 'octahedral' layers
(d) the 'octahedral' layer and in the interlayer space

187. It is a phosphate containing mineral : b UPPSC Pre- 2002
(a) Dolomite (b) Apatite (c) Marble (d) Pyrites

188. Laterite soil in Tamil Nadu are also called as - 2 TN PSC Ag-I:1999
(1) Entisols (2) Ultisols (3) Vertisols (4) Inceptisols

189. Laterite soils are dominated by b UPPSC Pre- 2008
(a) Montmorillonite (b) Kaolinite (c) Illite (d) Chlorite

190. Laterization is a process of accumulation on soil surface : a UPPSC Pre- 2007
(a) Fe and Al oxides (b) Silica (c) $CaCO_3$ (d) $CaSO_4$

191. Laterization is a process of accumulation on soil surface of : a UPPSC Pre- 2002
(a) Iron and aluminium oxides (b) Silica (c) CaCO3 (d) CaSO4

192. LEISA is related to : d UPPSC Pre- 2002
(a) Inorganic farming (b) Organic farming (c) Both of the above (d) None of the above

193. Lime requirement is calculated for D ADA MP- 2015
(A) Saline soil (B) Alkaline soil (C) Sodic soil (D) Acidic soil

194. Limestone belongs to d IAS Pre- 2000
(a) igneous rocks (b) sedimentary rocks
(c) metamorphic rocks (d) glacial deposits

195. Magnesium in octahedral sheet of clay mineral indicates : 2 UPPSC Pre- 2003
(1) Dioctahedral (2) Trioctahedral (3) Tetrahedral (4) Monohedral

196. Major types of soils in India are - 4 TN PSC

(1) 4 (2) 6 (3) 5 (4) 8 Ag-2003

197. Match List — I with List — II and select the correct answer by using cod. given below : 3 RPSC AAO - 2018

List — I (Soil Orders)	List — II (Formative Elements in the name of orders)
1. Entisols	A. ept
2. Vertisols	B. ent
3. Inceptisols	C. ert
4. Spodosols	D. od

Code :

ABCD ABCD ABCD ABCD

(a) 4 1 2 3 (b) 2 3 1 4 (c) 3 1 2 4 (d) 1 3 4 2

198. Match List (Principal soils of India) with List second (Taxonomic soil order) and select the correct answer: d IAS Pre-1995

List first	List second
A. Black soils of Maharashtra	1. Alfisol
B. Laterite soils of Kerala	2. Entisol
C. Red soils of Chotanagpur	3. Ultisol
D. Gangetic alluvial soils	4. Vertisol

	A	B	C	D		A	B	C	D
a)	3	4	1	2	b)	3	4	2	1
c)	4	3	2	1	d)	4	3	1	2

199. Match List I (Charges on Clay) with List II (Properties) and select the correct answer B IAS Pre-2004

List IList II

A. Permanent charge	1. Zeta potential
B. Variable charge	2. Isoelectric point
C. Zero point charge	3. Isomorphous
D. Manitude of charge	4. Ionisation of OH groups

	A	B	C	D		A	B	C	D
(a)	2	4	3	1	(b)	3	1	2	4
(c)	2	1	3	4	(d)	3	4	2	1

200. Match List I (Soil order) with ListII (Diagnostic properties) and select the correct answer: B IAS Pre-2000

ListI	ListII
A. Vertisols	1. Aridic or dry or saline
B. Entisols	2. Cracking or swell shrink clays
C. Aridisols	3. No distinctive horizons
D. Alfisols	4. Presence of argillic horizon

	A	B	C	D		A	B	C	D
(a)	2	3	1	4	(b)	3	2	1	4
(c)	4	1	2	3	(d)	2	3	4	1

201. Match List I correctly with List II and select your answer using the codes given below. 3 TN PSC Ag-II:

List I	List II	2001
(A) Red soils	1. Poor in the all plant nutruients	
(B) Alluvial soils	2. Rice	
(C) Black soils	3. Sodic soils	
(D) Laterite soils	4. Clayey soils	
	5. Hungry and Thirsty soils	

of these

(1) A-V, B-II, C-I, D-IV (2) A-II, B-V, C-III, D-I

(3) A-V, B-II, C-IV, D-I (4) A-III, B-II, C-I, D-V

202. Match list I correctly with list II and select your answer using the codes given below- c TNPSC Ag-1996

List-I	List-II
(A) Organic matter	(1) micronutrients
(B) 17:17:17	(2) Serpentine
(C) Sulphur	(3) calcium fertilizer
(D) Magnesium	(4) Nitrogen source
(E) EDTA	(5) Superphosphate
(F) Basic slag	(6) Compound fertilizer

Codes

	a	b	c	d	e	f
(A)	1	2	4	3	5	6
(B)	1	3	2	4	6	5
(C)	4	6	5	2	1	3
(D)	3	4	2	1	6	5

203. Match List I with List II an select the select the correct answer using the code given below the lists A IAS Pre-2008

List I (*Occurrence of soil order*)	List II (*Dominant clay mineral*)
A. Vertisol	1. Montmorillonite
B. Entisol	2. Hydrous oxides, Illite, Intergrades
C. Spodosol	3. Hydrous oxides. Kaolinite
D. Oxisol	4. Montmorillonite, Illite

	A	B	C	D		A	B	C	D
(a)	1	4	2	3	(b)	1	2	4	3
(c)	3	2	4	1	(d)	3	4	2	1

204. Match List I with List II and select the correct answer using the code given below the lists C IAS Pre-2006

List I (Ore)	List II (Mineral)
A. Dolomite	1. Al_2O_3 $3H_2O$
B. Gibbsite	2. $CaSo_4$ $2H_2O$
C. Gypsum	3. $CaCo_3$ $MgCO_3$
D. Geothite	4. FeOOH

205. Match the following and select your answer using the codes given below a TNPSC

SAR Retting Ag-1996

(A) 0-10 (1) Marginal

(B) 10-18 (2) Medium

(C) 18-26 (3) Unsafe

(D) Greater than 26 (4) Safe

Codes

	a	b	c	d
(A)	4	1	2	3
(B)	2	4	3	1
(C)	3	2	1	4
(D)	1	3	4	2

206. Match the following correctly using the codes given below c TNPSC Ag-1996

Chemical	Eq. wt.
(A) $CaSO_4 . 2H_2O$	(1) 49
(B) $MgSO_4 .7H_2O$	(2) 40
(C) NaOH	(3) 86
(D) H_2SO_4	(4) 123

Codes

	a	b	c	d
(A)	1	2	4	3
(B)	2	3	1	4
(C)	3	4	2	1
(D)	4	1	3	2

207. Maximum residual acidity is associated with the continuous soil application of C IAS Pre-2003

(a) urea (b) ammonium nitrate

(c) ammonium sulphate (d) calcium ammonium nitrate

208. Mehlich's cunninghamella plaque method of soil fertility valuation is for – 4 Agri Pre PG-2018

(1) Zinc (2) Nitrogen (3) Boron (4) Phosphorus

209. Metabolic transformation of inorganic plant nutrients into organic plant constituents is known as :- 2 RPSC, AO-2016

(1) Fixation (2) Assimilation (3) Fusion (4) Mobilization

210. Methanogenesis is a process taking place under b TNPSC Agri-1997

(A) Aerobic (B) Anaerobic (C) Microaerophilic (P) Saline

211. Mica is a type of clay mineral : b IFFCO T-2019

(a) 1:1 (b) 2:1 (c) 2:1:1 (d) None of the above

212. Minute particles in the earth curst are : 3 RPSC Pre-1993

(1) silt (2) sand (3) clay (4) gravel

213. Moist soils which are relatively darker have lower...........than drier ones. b Agri Pre PG-2022

(a) Impedance (b) Albedo (c) Aggregate (d) Tilth

214. Mollisols are characterized by high : a UPPSC Pre-2008

(a) Organic matter (b) $CaCO_3$ (c) Salinity (d) Acidity

215. Most common soil type is- b MP PAT-2016

(a) Sand Soil (b) Alluvial Soil (c) Laterite Soil (d) Red Soil

216. Most fertile soils developed due to transportation and deposition of parent material, is called as – **1** RPSC ARO Ag Chem - 2022
(1) Alluvium (2) Colluvium (3) Lacustrine (4) Aeolian

217. Most Porous soil structure is : **b** UPPSC Pre- 2005
(a) Granular (b) Crumb (c) Prismatic (d) Platy

218. Most productive soil of Inidia is – **a** BHU UET-2011
(a) alluvial soil (b) saline soil (c) red soil (d) black soil

219. Most resistance mineral among the following is : **2** RPSC Pre-2008
(1) Muscovites (2)Quartz (3) Calcite (4) Dolomite

220. Mostly gypsum is used in the reclamation of – **2** TN AO-2008
(1) Acidic soil (2) Alkali soil (3) Saline soil (4) None of these

221. Number of broad groups into which soil of India have been divided according to morphogenetic approach proposed by USDA **D** AO GPSC-2013
(A) 18 (B) 24 (C) 28 (D) 25

222. Nutrient index is used to prepare the – **2** TN PSC Ag-2003
(1) Soil productivity map (2) Soil fertility map
(3) Both 1 & 2 (4) None of these

223. On the basis of International Society of Soil Science (ISSS), which of the following is the size of fine sand ? **1** RPSC AAO 2018
(a) 0.2-0.02 mm (b) 0.025 - 0.05 mm (c) 0.002 - 0.0002 mm (d) 0.05 -0.005 mm

224. On the basis of International Society of Soil Science (ISSS), which of the following is the size of fine sand ? **1** RPSC, AAO-2019
(1) 0.2 – 0.02 mm (2) 0.025- 0.05 mm
(3) 0.002 – 0.0002 mm (4) 0.05 – 0.005 mm

225. On the basis of total mass, the relative abundance of the given elements in the earth's crust is such that **a** IAS Pre-1997
(a) Si> O_2> Fe> Al (b) O_2> Al > Si > Fe
(c) O_2> Si > Fe> Al (d) O_2> Si > Fe > Al

226. One milliequivalent of Ca is equal to : **b** UPPSC Pre- 2010
(a) 40 mg Ca (b) 20 mg Ca (c) 4 mg Ca (d) 12 mg Ca

227. Order of alluvial soil is: **c** IFFCO T - 2019
(a) Vertisol (b) Alfisol (c) Entisol (d) Histosols

228. Order of the organic soils is : **c** UPPSC Pre- 2004
(a) Alfisol (b) Oxisole (c) Histosol (d) Antesol

229. Organic matter makes up about ....% of soil volume. **A** AO KTPSC-2021
(A) 5 (B) 12 (C) 25 (D) 38 (E) Answer not known

230. Organic matter of soil decreases the fixation of – **3** RPSC AAO Ag - 2022
(1) Nitrogen (2) Potassium (3) Phosphorus (4) None of the Above

231. Particle size of colloids is (in microns) **b** ICAR Gen

(A) < 2 (B) 1-100 (C) >100 (D) None Agri-2004

232. Particle size of silt is – 2 Ag Sup
(1) 0.2- 2.0 mm (2) 0.02-0.002 mm (3) 0.002-0.0002 mm (4) 2.0-20.0 mm JAU 2017

233. 'Peat' soil are generally characterised as : a UPPSC
(a) Black, heavy and acidic soil (b) Red, light and acidic soil. Pre- 2001
(c) Black, light and alkaline soil (d) Black, heavy and neutral soil

234. 'Peat' soils are generally : a UPPSC
(a) Black, heavy and acidic (b) Red, Light and basic Pre- 1995
(c) Black, light and basic (d) Black, heavy and neutral

235. Pedogenesis is the study of : a UPPSC
(a) Soil formation (b) Rock formation Pre- 2007
(c) Soil structure formation (d) None of the above

236. Pedology is the study of 3 RPSC Pre-
(1) rocks (2) crop cultivation (3) soils (4) plant nutrients 1993

237. Percentage of clay in sandy loam? E IBS,AFO-
(A)20-30% (B) 40-60% (C) 25% (D) 35% (E)0-20% 2015

238. Percentage of sand in clay soil is: d NSC S T-
(a) 80% (b) 70% (c) 50% (d) 30% 2019

239. Permanent soil property is : c UPPSC
(a) Fertility status (b) pH (c) Texture (d) Structure Pre- 2000

240. Persistence of pesticides is found to be more in- 1 TN PSC
(1) Clayey soil (2) sandy soil (3) Loamy soil (4) Red soil Ag-I:2001

241. Phosphorus fixation is more severe in soil dominant with TNPSC
(A) Vermiculite (B) Montmorillionite (C) Kaolinite (D) Illite b Ag-1995

242. Physical condition of the soil is known as : (a) UPPSC
(a) Soil tilth (b) Soil texture (c) Soil structure (d) Soil Fertility Pre- 2007

243. Physical properties of soil are – d MP PAT-
(A) Soil separates (B) Soil air (C) Soil colloids (D) All of these 2013

244. Possible ingredience of salts accumulated in a saline soil include – 1 TN AO-
(1) NaCl (2) $CaCo_3$ (3) $KClO_3$ (4) $NaNO_3$ 2008

245. Potassium constitutes how much percent of the earth's crust? 2 RPSC
(1) 1.5% (2) 2.5% (3) 3.5% (4) 4.5% ARO Ag Chem - 2022

246. Potential-determining ions on the exchange complex of soil are C IAS Pre-
(a) Na^+ and K^+ (b) Ca^{2+} and Mg^{2+} (c) H^+ and OH^- (d) Cl^- and NO^{-3} 2010

247. Proportion of soil separates is called – c Agri Pre
(a) Soil minerals (b) Soil structure (c) Soil texture (d) Soil structure PG-2017

248. Pyrites contains sulphur in the form of : a UPPSC
(a) Sulphite (h) Sulphate (c) Sulphide (d) Thiosulphate Pre- 2009

249. Quartz mineral is composed of 2 RPSC,
(A) Aluminium silicate (B) Silicon dioxide AAO-2018

(C) Ferro - magnesium silicate (D) Hydrated aluminium silicate

250. Read the following statements and mark your answer according to code given below c UPPSC Pre- 2004

I. Hilly region soils arc acidic.

II. Hilly region soils contain more organic matter.

III. Hilly soils with acidic pH are rich in Ca.

IV. Hilly soils with acidic pH are rich in salts.

Code :

(a) I and III are correct (b) I and IV are correct

(c) I and II are correct (d) II and Ill are correct

251. Read the following statements and mark your answer according to the code given below : b UPPSC Pre- 2001

I. Soil acidity increases with exchangeable Alt^{+++}

II. Soil acidity increases with exchangeable H.

III. Soil alkalinity increases with exchangeable calcium.

IV. Soil alkalinity increases with exchangeable aluminium.

Answer code :

(a) I and III are correct (b) I and II are correct

(c) II and III are correct. (d) III and IV are correct.

252. Read the following statements and mark your answer according to the code given below : a UPPSC Pre- 2001

I. Altisols are lighter in texture.

II. Vertisols are heavier in texture.

III. Entisols have low potassium content.

IV. Ultisols have lowphosphate fixation.

Answer code :

(a) I and II are correct. (b) I and III are correct.

(c) I and IV are correct. (d) III and IV are correct.

253. Reclamation of sodic soil can be achieved by – 1 TN AO- 2012

I. Applying gypsum

II. Green manure

III. Leaching

IV. Ponding

(1) I, II, and III of the above (2) I, III and IV of the above

(3) II, III and IV of the above (4) I, II, III and IV of the above

254. Red colour of soil is due to the presence of : d BHU PET-2016

(a)Gibsite (b) Geothite (c) Magnetite (d) Hematite

255. Red colour of soil is due to? A IBS,AFO- 2014

(A) FeO (B) $CuSO_4$ (C) H_2SO_4 (D) $ZnSO_4$ (E)None of these

256. Relative proportion of sand, silt and clay in soil is called – d BHU PET-2017

(a) soil structure (b) soil horizon (c) soil profile (d) soil texture

257. Removal of silica from soil and accumulation of sesquioxide is known as : b IFFCO T - 2019

(a) Podzolization (b) Laterization (c) Gleization (d) Both A and B

258. Saline-alkali soils are characterised by : b UPPSC

(a) High sodium and high pH Pre- 2006
(b) High carbonates and high exchangeable sodium percent
(c) High potasium and high magnesium (d) High chlorides and high sulphates

259. Salted soil formation is due to d TNPSC
(A) Excessive percolation + Free drainage Ag-1996
(B) Lack of percolation + Free drainage
(C) Excessive percolation + Impeded drainage
(D) Lack of percolation + Impeded drainage

260. Sandy soils are considered as – b BHU
(a) Plastic (b) Partially plastic (c) Highly plastic (d) Non-plastic PET-2012

261. SAR of alkali soil is : c UPPSC
(a) less than 15 (b) less than 13 (c) more than 15 (d) more than 13 Pre- 1997

262. Shelf life of EC formulations are usually TNPSC
(A) 3 years (B) 5 years (C) 10 years (D) 7 years a Agri-1997

263. Silica-sesquioxide ratio is useful in the evaluation of soil in respect of d IAS Pre-
(a) nutrient availability (b) silicon content 1998
(c) iron and aluminium content (d) its age

264. Silt is intermediate between a ICAR Gen
(A) Sand and clay (B) Clay loam and clay Agri-2009
(C) Loam and clay (D) None of these

265. Silt size is – c Gujrat
(a) Bigger than sand (b) Smaller than clay AO-2017
(c) Bigger than clay but smaller than sand
(d) Bigger than sand and clay

266. Silts have particle size range between : 3 RPSC Pre-
(1) 2.00 to 0.20 m. m. (2) 0.20 to 0.02 m. m. 1993
(3) 0.02 to 0.002 m. m. (4) 0.002 m. m. and less

267. Sodium adsorption ratio is TNPSC
(A) Na=_[Na]/ (([Ca]+[Mg])/2)1/2 (B) Mg (C) Na/Mg (D) Na/ Ca+Mg a Ag-1995

268. Soil acidity in crop production system Is influenced by several factors identify the most appropriate c TNPSC Ag-1995
(1) Use of commercial fertilizers, especially ammoniacal sources which produce H^+ ions during nitrification
(2) Weathering of primary and secondary mineral like granite and shale
(3) Crop removal of basis cations, including calcium, magnesium, potassium and sodium in exchange for H+
(4) Leaching of these cation being replaced by H+ and subsequently by Aluminium
Of these statements
(A) 1 and 2 are correct (B) 1,2 are correct
(C) 1,2 and 4 are correct (D) All correct

269. Soil body is generally occupied by soil pores to the extent of – c BHU
(a) 20-30% (b) 30-40% (c) 40-50% (d) 60-70% PET-2012

270. Soil colour determination chrome refers to which of the following : 3 UPPSC

(1) Dominant sprectal colour (2) Lightness or darkness of colour Pre- 2003
(3) Purity of strength of colour (4) None of the above

271. Soil containing more than 70% sand is known as : a UPPSC
(a) Light soil (b) Medium soil (c) Heavy soil (d) Most heavy soil Pre- 2008

272. Soil fertility is reduced due to : a UPPSC
(a)Continous cropping (b) Over irrigation Pre- 1995
(c) Imbalanced use of fertilizers (d) Poor drainage

273. Soil forming factors refer to among the following b TNPSC
(A) Climate - Organism matter - Clay - Sand - Relief Ag-1996
(B) Climate - Organism - Relief - Parent rock - Time
(C) Climate - Organism - Relief - Parent rock - Wind
(D) Climate - Organism - Relief - Time - Depth

274. Soil having highest sand % and low water holding capacity? **Ans.: Sandy** PSB AO-2019

275. Soil horizon A, E and B together is called 1 Agri Pre
(1) Soil solum (2) Epipedons (3) Soil profile (4) None of these PG-2016

276. Soil particle size of silt soil ranges between - c RPSC,
(a) 2.0 mm to 0.2 mm (b) 0.2 mm to 0.02 mm AAO-2012
(c) 0.02 mm to 0.002 mm (d) 0.002 mm to 0.0002 mm

277. Soil properties unaffected by tillage is – b BHU
(a) Structure (b) Texture (c) Bulk density (d) Porosity PET-2010

278. Soil samples are collected and stored in – 2 TN PSC
(1) Metal containers (2) Plastic bags (3) Gunny bags (4) Woolen bags Ag-2003

279. Soil structural units having horizontal axis much longer than vertical axis. 4 Agri Pre
(1) Blocky (2) Prismatic (3) Columnar (4) None of these PG-2016

280. Soil structure appropriate for crop production is: c NSC ST-
(a) Columnar (b) Oblique (c) Granular (d) Compact 2019

281. Soil structure concerns with : b UPPSC
(a)Particle size distribution (b)Arrangement of soil particle Pre- 2000
(c)Aggregation of soil particle (d)Water holding capacity

282. Soil structure in improved by : b UPPSC
(a) Application of Urea (b)Application of superphosphate Pre- 2000
(c)Application of muriate of potash (d)Application of zinc sulphate

283. Soil structure is influenced by : 2 RPSC Pre-1993
(1) soil water, soil density, cation exchange capacity and soil pH
(2) soil management, absorbed cation, micro-organisms and soil moisture
(3) SAR, soil pH, CEC and micro-organisms
(4) soil management, soil pH, CEC and soil moisture

284. Soil structure refers to: d NSC MT
(a) Geometry of soil particle (b) Size of soil particle M-2019
(c) Photograph of soil particle (d) Arrangement of soil particle

285. 'Soil Taxonomy' published by US soil survey staff in the year of – 4 RPSC
(1) 1960 (2) 1964 (3) 1967 (4) 1975 ARO Ag

Chem - 2022

286. Soil temperature is influenced by — d — BHU PET-2016
(a)Nitrogen (b)Phosphorus (c)Potassium (d)Humus contents

287. Soil textural class having equal proportion of sand, silt and clay – — 4 — TN AAO-2019
(1) Clay (2) Silt loam (3) Sandy clay loam (4) Loam

288. Soil textural class having highly desirable properties for most uses is – — c — Agri Pre PG-2020
(a) Sand (b) Silty clay (c) Loam (d) Sandy loam

289. Soil textural class which is the most suitable for crop growth – — 3 — TN AAO-2019
(1) Clay loam (2) Silt loam (3) Loam (4) Silty clay

290. Soil type occupying largest area in India is : — d — UPPSC Pre- 1996
(a) Black Soil (b) Laterite soil (c) Red soil (d) Alluvial soil

291. Soils brought by Ganga-Yamuna and Indus rivers and their tributaries are deep and are known as : — d — UPPSC Pre- 1995
(a)Bhabar soils (b) Desert soils (c)Vindhyan soils (d) Alluvial soils

292. Soils having a hard subsoil will affect the – — 4 — TN ACF-2012
(1) Drainage (2) Cropping pattern (3) Erosion (4) All of these

293. Soils in foot hills are :- — b — ARO Agro-2016
(a) Matured (b) Immatured (c) Fully mature (d) None of these

294. Soils of dry region are said to be – — 4 — TN PSC Ag-I:1999
(1) Hungry (2) Thirsty (3) Weed free (4) Both 1 and 2

295. Soils of Tamil Nadu containing 40kg available P2O5 per hectare are rated as – — 2 — TN PSC Ag-I:1999
(1) Very low in available P (2) Low in available P
(3) Medium in available P (4) High in available P

296. Soils of which soil order have no diagnostic horizon : — b — UPPSC Pre- 2002
(a) Mollisols (b) Entisols (c) Andisols (d) Aridisols

297. Soils of which soil order have no diagnostic horizons ? — b — UPPSC Pre- 2007
(a) Mollisols (b) Entisols (c) Andisols (d) Aridisols

298. Soils with most stable structure are dominated by which clay mineral ? — a — UPPSC Pre- 2007
(a) Kaolinite (b) Montmorillonite (c) Vermiculite (d) Chlorite

299. Specific heat is higher in : — d — UPPSC Pre- 2002
(a) Sand (b) Silt (c) Clay (d) Humus

300. Specific heat is higher in : — d — UPPSC Pre- 2007
(a) Sand (b) Silt (c) Clay (d) Humus

301. Specific heat is higher in: — b — MP PAT-2016
1. Clay 2. Humus 3. Sand 4. None of the above

302. Specific heat of dry soil is : — c — UPPSC Pre- 2004
(a) 1.0 cal/g. (b) 0.1 cal/g. (c) 0.2 cal/g. (d) 0.5 cal/g.

303. Specific heat of dry soil is about : — d — UPPSC Pre- 2008
(a) 1.0 cal/g (b) 0.1 cal/g (c) 0.5 cal/g (d) 0.2 cal/g

304. Specific heat of mineral fraction and organic fraction of soil are ………& ……..Cal/gm/^{0}C — b — BHU PET-2016
(a) 0.18 & 0.24 (b) 0.18 & 0.46 (c) 0.46 & 0.18 (d) 0.24 & 0.18

305. Structure in which all the four oxygens of the silica tetrahedron are shared by the neighbouring silicon tetrahedral, i.e. there are two ions of oxygen for every ion of silicon thus forming a 3- dimensional frame work and represented by SiO_2 and is called – a Agri Pre PG-2017
(a) Tectosilicates (b) Inosilicates (c) Inosilicates (double chain) (d) Clay minerals

306. Structure of coarese textured soil is improved by the addition of : c UPPSC Pre- 2008
(a)Lime (b)Gypsum (c)Organic (d)Fertilizers

307. Study of soil in relation to growth, nutrition and yield of crops is known as – 3 Agri Pre PG-2019
(1) Soil Pedology (2) Soil Petrology (3) Soil Edaphology (4) Petrogenesis

308. Study of soil in relation to plant is called : 2 RPSC Pre- 2008
(1) Pedology (2)Edaphology (3)Climatology (4) Agroclimatology

309. Sub soiling – 3 TN PSC Ag-II: 2001
(1) It is a secondary tillage operation carried to prepared fine seed bed
(2) It is a primary tillage operation carried to prepared fine seed bed
(3) It is a primary tillage operation carried to break the hard pan in sub surface
(4) It is an interculturing tillage operation carried control weeds

310. Suitable soil for plant growth is: b NSC ST-2019
(a) Sandy (b) Loamy (c) Clay loam (d) Clayey

311. 'Tarai' soils are deficient in : d UPPSC Pre- 2000
(a) Nitrogen (b) Phosphorus (c) Sulphur (d) Zinc

312. Texture of the soil can be changed by : c UPPSC Pre- 2002
(a) Use of fertilizer (b) Use of manure (c) Use of tillage practices (d)None of the above

313. The "**goradu**" soil is predominant in – b Gujrat AO-2017
(a) South Gujarat (b) Middle Gujarat (c) North Gujarat (d) Saurashtra

314. Diagnosis and Recommendation Integrated system is used to evaluate 1 Agri Pre PG-2016
(1) Soil fertility (2) Soil productivity
(3) Water quality (4) Soil salinity

315. Carbon Sequestration is facilitated by – 2 TN AO-2012
(1) Alley cropping (2) Agro Forestry (3) Monocropping (4) Strip cropping

316. The acid-neutralizing value of the liming materials in ascending order is B IAS Pre-2010
(a) $CaCO_3 > CaSiO_3 > CaO > Ca(OH)_2$ (b) $CaSiO_3 < CaCO_3 < Ca(OH)_2 < CaO$
(c) $CaO \leq Ca(OH)_2 < CaSiO_3 < CaCO_3$ (d) $Cao < Ca(OH)_2 < CaSiO_3 < CaCO_3$

317. The active factor of soil formation is – c BHU PET-2012
(a) Parent (b) Relief (c) Climate (d) Time

318. The active factor of soil formation is – 1 RPSC AAO-2022
(1) Climate & Biosphere (2) relief
(3) Parent Material (4) Time

319. The active factors of soil formation are : UPPSC Pre- 2010 a UPPSC Pre- 2004
(a) Climate and biosphere (b) Parent material and Climate
(c) Parent material and relief (d) Parent material and biosphere

320. The amount of different sizes of mineral particles in a soil define the soil ...... 4 Agri Pre

(1) structure (2) bulk density (3) profile (4) texture PG-2015

321. The amount of organic matter by wt. in organic soil is : 4 RPSC Pre-2008
(1) >20% (2)>15% (3) >10% (4) >5%

322. The approximate persistence of Benzene Hexachloride (BHC) in soil is - 3 RPSC ARO Ag Chem - 2022
(1) 9 years (2) 10 years (3) 11 years (4) 12 years

323. The approximate relationship between Total Dissolved Solids (TDS) and Electrical Conductivity (EC) of waters having EC less than 5 ds/m is expressed : 3 RPSC AAO - 2018
(a) TDS (mg/L) = 425 × EC(ds/m) (b) TDS (mg/L) = 515 × EC(ds/m)
(c) TDS (mg/L) = 640 × EC(ds/m) (d) TDS (mg/L) = 720 x EC (ds/m)

324. The arrangement of primary soil particles and their aggregates into a certain definite pattern is called as – 1 TN AO-2018
(1) Soil structure (2) Soil monolith (3) Soil texture (4) Soil reaction

325. The arrangement of sand, silt and clay particles in definite set of pattern in soil is called as : 2 UPPSC Pre- 2003
(1) Texture (2) Structure (3) Plasticity (4) Series

326. The arrangements of soil particles and their aggregate into certain defined patterns is called as- 2 TN PSC Ag-2003
(1) Texture (2) structure (3) Density (4) Porosity

327. The aspect of origin of the soils classification and description are studied in : 3 RPSC Pre-1993
(1) Ecology (2) Agronomy (3) Pedology (4) Edaphology

328. The average diameter of fine soil pores is 1 Agri Pre PG-2015
(1) 2-20 microns (2) less than 2 microns
(3) 20-200 microns (4) more than 200 microns

329. The best soil for agricultural use is D AO SDAU-2013
A. Clay B. Clay loam C. Sandy D. Sandy loam

330. The best soil suited for the cultivation of groundnut is TNPSC
(A) Alluvial soil (B) Red soil (C) Black soil (D)Taraisoil b Agri-1997

331. The black colour of vertisols is due to the presence in these soils of C IAS Pre-2006
(a) Iron and magnesium (b) copper and organic matter
(c) Manganese, titanium and organic matter complex
(d) Organic matter and calcium

332. The black cotton soils of Central India have been derived from c IAS Pre-1996
(a) granites (b) granodiorites (c) basalt (d) rhyolite

333. The branch of Soil Science which deals with origin of soil, its classification and description is called as – d BHU PET-2017
(a) Petrology (b) Edaphology (c) Geology (d) Pedology

334. The capacity of soil to be moulded, that is to change shape in response to stress and to keep that shape when the stress is removed is termed : 2 RPSC Pre-1993
(1) stickiness (2) plasticity (3) consistence (4) cementation

335. The category 'great group' is based on : 4 RPSC Pre-

(1) Land use plan (2) Morphology of soil — 2007
(3) Moisture and temperature (4) Diagnostic sub surface horizon

336. The cation exchange capacity is maximum in : — d — UPPSC Pre- 2004
(a) Podeol soils (b) Laterite soils (c) Gley soils (d) Chernozercsoils

337. The chemical and physical properties of soils are controlled by : — 1 — RPSC Pre- 1993
(1) soil texture (2) soil structure
(3) soil moisture status (4) clay and humus

338. The Chromusterts occurring in Bharuch district is commonly known as – — c — Gujrat AO-2017
(a) Goradu soils (b) Sandy soils
(c) Deep black cotton soils (d) Red and brown soil

339. The clay percentage in sandy loam soil is: — c — NSC SR T-2019
(a) More than 55% (b) 40–55% (c) 20–30% (d) Less than 10%

340. The composition of soil particles viz, sand, silt and clay is known as – — 3 — TN AAO- 2019
(1) Soil consistency (2) Soil structure
(3) Soil texture (4) Soil bulk density

341. The concentration of carbon dioxide found in the soil is — B — ADA Guj- 2013
(A) 0.90% (B) 0.25% (C) 0.75% (D) 0.95%

342. The degraded land in India occupy approx an area (mha) of – — c — BHU PET-2010
(a) 118 (b) 149 (c) 175 (d) 225

343. The diagnostic surface horizons are called : — 3 — UPPSC Pre- 2003
(1) Genetic horizons (2) Pendons (3) Epipedons (4) Endopendons

344. The diameter of clay particle is : — d — UPPSC Pre- 1996
(a) 0.2 m (b) 0.002 cm (c) 0.02 cm (d) 0.002 mm

345. The diameter of clay particle is : — a — UPPSC Pre- 2007
(a) less than 0.002 mm (b) more than 0.002 mm
(c) between 2.0-0.2 mm (d) between 0.2-0.02 mm

346. The diameter of clay particles is : — a — UPPSC Pre- 1998
(a) Below 0.002 mm (b) Above 0.002 mm
(c) Between 0.05 to 0.002 mm (d) between 0.01 to 0.05 mm

347. The diameter of particle used for estimating soil texture is : — c — UPPSC Pre- 2010
(a) Larger than 2 mm (b) 2 mm to 0.2 mm
(c) Less than 2 mm (d) More than 2.5 mm

348. The diameter of very fine sand particles is : — RPSC Pre- 1998
(1)<0.002mm (2)0.05-0.002 mm
(3) 0.10-0.05 mm (4) 0.25-0.10 mm

349. The dominant clay mineral in black soil is – — 2 — TNPSC – TNPSC – Ag: 1999
(1) Kaolinite (2) Montmorillonite (3) Allophane (4) Chlorite

350. The effectiveness of Rock phospate increases in …… — C — AO KTPSC- 2021
(A)Alkaline (B) Neutral (C)Acid (D) Dry (E0 Answer not Known

351. The electrical conductivity of 0.01N potassium chloride solution at 25°C is – — 2 — RPSC ARO Ag
(1) 0.14 dSm^{-1} (2) 1.41 dSm^{-1} (3) 2.76 dSm^{-1} (4) 4.10 dSm^{-1}

Chem - 2022

352. The elements that gets depleted progressively in the plough layer of submerged rice soil is – **a** BHU PET-2012
(a) Oxygen (b) Hydrogen (c) Carbon (d) Iron

353. The equation pH $-\frac{1}{2}$ p^{ca} = constant is called as – **1** RPSC ARO Ag Chem - 2022
(1) Lime potential (2) Phosphate potential
(3) Potassium potential (4) None of the above

354. The examples of amphiboles mineral are as - **4** RPSC ARO Ag Chem - 2022
(1) Augite, actinolite, tremolite (2) Augite, diopside, enstatite
(3) Hornblende, actinolite, enstatite (4) Hornblende, tremolite, actinolite

355. The examples of isotopes are - **1** RPSC ARO Ag Chem - 2022
(1) $_{19}K^{39}$ $_{19}K^{40}$ $_{19}K^{41}$ (2) $_{18}Ar^{48}$ $_{19}K^{40}$ $_{82}pb^{210}$
(3) $_1H^2$ $_2He^3$ $_2He^4$ (4) $_8O^{16}$ $_{18}Ar^{38}$ $_2He^3$

356. The expanded form of FACE is - **3** RPSC ARO Agro-2022
(1) Free Air Carbon Enrichment Technology
(2) Free Air Carbon monoxide Enrichment Technology
(3) Free Air Carbon dioxide Enrichment Technology
(4) Free Air Carbon dioxide Enhancement Technology

357. The favourable climate for the operation of podzolization process is – **b** BHU PET-2017
(a) warm humid climate (b) cold humid climate
(c) arid climate (d) semi-arid climate

358. The fertile soil has: **c** MP PAT-2016
1. More organic matter 2. More water holding capacity
3. Both of the above 4. None of these

359. The force of attraction binds the molecules of the same kind is : **3** RPSC Pre-2003
(1) Adhesion (2) Matric force (3) Cohesion (4) None of these

360. The given diagram is that of a soil textural triangle A soil having 15% clays, 65% sand and 20% silt will be classified on the basis of the given diagram, as Made diagram trangle ? **d** IAS Pre-1996
(a) sandy clay loam (b) loam (c) loamy sand (d) sandy loam

361. The growth of plants is best in– **a** MP PAT-2016
(a) Loam soil (b) Sandy soil (c) Clay (d) Marshy land

362. The half lives of two radio isotopes, i.e. ^{32}P and ^{33}P is - **1** RPSC ARO Ag Chem - 2022
(1) 14.3 and 25.3 days (2) 14.3 and 25.3 weeks
(3) 14.3 and 25.3 months (4) 14.3 and 25.3 years

363. The half-life of U – 238 is 4.5 x 10^9 years . if the geological age of the earth is 2.5 x 10^9 years approximately then the amount of original supply of U-238 that has disappeared due to radioactive decay is **b** IAS Pre-1999

(a) 10% (b) 25% (c) 50% (d) 75%

364. The hilly soils of Uttar Pradesh are formed by : b UPPSC Pre- 1996
(a) Granite and quartzite rock (b) Schist and biotite rock
(c) sand stone (d) Lime stone

365. The horizon of eluviation is currently designated as – a BHU PET-2013
(a) E (b) A_2 (c) AB (d) AC

366. The horizons which make up the profile of a forest soil would include d IAS Pre- 1994
(a) A, Band C (b) A,C and O (c) Band O (d) A,B,C and O

367. The increasingly dominant active in soil formation is – 1 TN AO- 2018
(1) Climate (2) Nature of parent rock
(3) Man and animal (4) Micro organisms

368. The IUPAC name of the compound "CH2 = CH2" is: d NSC S T- 2019
(a) Butane–1 (b) Hexane–1 (c) Decene–1 (d) Ethene–1

369. The K_2O content in Illite varied between ? a IFFCO T - 2019
(a) 6 to 10% (b) 2 to 4% (c) 10 to 15% (d) 33%

370. The layer in the soil profile where material removed from the two overlying horizons is deposited is called : 2 RPSC Pre- 1998
(1)A horizon (2)B horizon (3) C horizon (4) D horizon

371. The layer of soil are referred to as ….. 1 RPSC Pre- 1995
(1) horizons (2) profiles (3) hard pans (4) pedocals

372. The liming material used for reclaiming acid soils? **Ans.: Lime stone** RRB SO- 2021

373. The main causes of soil degradation is/ are – 4 TN AO- 2008
(1) Deforestation (2) Over grazing (3) Industrialization (4) All of these

374. The main reservoir of available Sulphur in soil is – a BHU PET-2012
(a) Organic sulphur (b) Sulphate S (c) Sulphite S (d) Sulphide S

375. The major factor affecting land degradation in india is – c Delhi PGT-2014
(a) Water erosion (b) Wind erosion
(c) Chemical deterioration (d) Physical

376. The mass (weight) per unit volume of a dry soil including pore space is called – 4 TN AO- 2018
(1) Particle density (2) Soil density (3) Soil porosity (4) Bulk density

377. The maximum area affected under land degradation in Rajasthan is - 2 RPSC AARO – Ent -2022
(1) by water erosion (2) by wind erosion(3) by salinity(4) by water logging

378. The maximum area of soils of Rajasthan comes in the soil orders of - 3 RPSC ARO Ag Chem - 2022
(1) AlfisolsVertisols (2) Alfisols – Inceptisols
(3) AridisolsEntisols (4) Aridisols - Inceptisols

379. The mean particle diameter of sand particle is – 1 TN AO- 2018
(1) 2.0-0.05 mm (2) < 0.02 mm (3) <0.002 mm (4) 0.05-0.002 mm

380. The micronutrient available in soil at high pH values is – 4 TN PSC Ag-2003
(1) Zinc (2) Iron (3) Manganese (4) Molybdenum

381. The mineral 'Hausmannite' is a source of – 1 Ag Sup

(1) Manganese (2) Iron (3) Zinc (4) Copper JAU 2017

382. The mineral elements present in the soil are also classified as per their role in plant system. Which of the following element is classified as regulator and carrier? **Ans.: Calcium** RRB SO-2018

383. The minimum sand content was observed inwhich textural class? * RPSC ARO Ag Chem - 2022
(1) Sandy loam (2) Loamy. sand (3) Silt clay loam (4) Silt loam

384. The most abundant primary minerals are quartz and .... c Agri Pre PG-2022
(a) Alumina (b) Feldspar (c) Silica (d) Calcium Carbonate

385. The most active portion of soil is 4 RPSC Pre-2007
(1) Clay (2) Sand (3) Gravel (4) Silt

386. The most effective method of returning minerals to the soils is : 1 RPSC Pre-1993
(1) decomposition of organic matter (2) crop rotation
(3) mixed cropping (4) relay cropping

387. The most fertile soil is available in – 4 TN PSC Ag-2003
(1) Maharashtra (2) Tamil Nadu (3) Arunachal Pradesh (4) Punjab

388. The most important cementing agent in laterite soil is – 4 RPSC ARO Ag Chem - 2022
(1) Silt particles (2) Calcium carbonate
(3) Organic matter (4) Hydrous oxides of Fe & Al

389. The most important factor fo laterite soil formation is – c BHU PET-2011
(a) Parent material (b) Topography (c) Climate (d) Vegetation

390. The most important feature of soil taxonomy is that it is based upon – c BHU PET-2017
(a) soil forming factors (b) soil forming processes
(c) measurable soil properties (d) climate

391. The most severe land degradation process in India is - b BHU PET-2011
(a) Waterlogging and salinity (b) Water erosion
(c) Soil structural degradation (d) Wind erosion

392. The neutralising values of the following liming materials are such that b IAS Pre-1995
(a) $CaO > Ca(OH)_2 > CaCO_3 > CaMg(CO_3)_2$
(b) $(CaO > Ca(OH)_2 > CaMg(Co_3) > CacO_3$
(c) $Ca(OH)_2 > CaO > CaMg(CO_3)_2 > CaCO_3$
(d) $CaCO_3 > CaO > Ca(OH) > CaMg(CO_3)_2$

393. The neutralizing values of various liming materials in decreasing order are as - 3 RPSC ARO Ag Chem - 2022
(1) $CaSiO_3 > CaMg(CO_3)_2 > Ca(OH)_2 > CaO$
(2) $Ca(OH)_2 > CaO > CaMg(CO_3)_2 > CaSiO_3$
(3) $CaO > Ca(OH)_2 > CaMg(CO_3)_2 > CaSiO_3$
(4) $CaMg(CO_3)_2 > CaSiO_3 > CaO > Ca(OH)_2$

394. The new Integrated Watershed Development Programme (IWDP) was launched in the year – 3 RPSC ARO Ag Chem - 2022
(1) 2006 (2) 2007 (3) 2008 (4) 2010

395. The nitric diagnostic horizon is found in soils belonging to — c — IAS Pre-1998

(a) alfisol and inceptisol orders (b) aridisol and inceptisol orders
(c) alfisol and aridisol orders (d) inceptisol and oxisol orders

396. The normality of conc. HCl is — D — TNPSC Ag- 1998

(A) 12N (B) 16N (C) 26N (D) 36N

397. The observation recorded from open area of 2 meter of soil surface is called — A — AO GPSC-2013

(A) Macro climate (B) Micro climate (C) Topo climate (D) Local climate

398. The oven dry weight of 50 gm soil collected from field was 40 gm, if the bulk density of the soil is 1.5 gm/cm^3, the volumetric water content would be - — 3 — RPSC ARO Ag Chem - 2022

(1) 30.5% (2) 34.5% (3) 37.5% (4) 40.5%

399. The particle size of "clay" is – — 1 — Ag sup 2018

(1) < 0.002 mm (2) > 0.002 mm (3) 1.00- 2.00 mm (4) 0.25 – 0.50 mm

400. The physical condition of soil in relation to plant growth is called as – IFFCO T -2019 — b — School Lect. 2019

(a) Tillage (b) Soil tilth (c) Adherence (d) Coherence

401. The plant component broken first on addition in soil is – — c — BHU PET-2014

(a) Cellulose (b) Hemicellulose (c) Proteins (d) Lignin

402. The plough layer represents______ depth of soil – — 2 — TN AO-2008

(1) 45 cm (2) 15 cm (3) 30 cm (4) 20 cm

403. The porosity of clay soil usually ranges from : — 3 — RPSC ACF AE 2018

(a) 30 to 35% (b) 35 to 50% (c) 40 to 60% (d) 50 to 60%

404. The presence of excess salt in the soil requires — A — HPSC ADO-2022

(A) high water storage efficiency (B) low water storage efficiency
(C) high water application efficiency (D) low water use efficiency

405. The prevalence of phosphate ion changes with pH. The correct sequence of the prevalence of the given phosphate ions (with increasing pH) is — D — IAS Pre 2000

(a) H_2PO_4, HPO_4^{2-}, PO_4^{3-} (b) HPO_4^{2-}, H_2PO_4, PO_4^{3-}
(c) $H_2PO_4^-$ PO_4^{3-}, HPO_4^{2-} (d) PO_4^{3-}, HPO_4^{2-}, H_2PO_4

406. The process of formation of nitrogen and nitrous oxide gases from ammoniacal fertilizers in soils is known as — C — IAS Pre-2002

(a) ammonification (b) nitrification (c) denitrification (d) mineralization

407. The process of mechanical migration of small mineral particles from the A to the B horizons of a soil, producing in B horizons relative in clay is known as….. — b — Agri Pre PG-2022

(a) Resilication (b) Lessivage (c) Melanization (d) Braunification

408. The quality of limestone required to raise the pH value of sandy loam soils from pH 4.5 to neutral is – — 2 — TN PSC Ag-I:1999

(1) 5.0 t/ha (2) 2.5 t/ha (3) 1.25t/ha (4) 8.75 t/ha

409. The radio isotopes are traced in the plant body with the help of – — 2 — RPSC ARO Ag Chem -

(1) radio biography (2) radio autographs (3) radio nucleus (4) radio radiators

410. The ratio between organic N and S in crop residue generally ranges between: B PPSC ADO-2017
a) 5-10 : 1 b) 10-15 : 1 c) 15-20 : 1 d) 20-25 : 1

411. The ratio of weight of unit volume of dry soil including pore spaces to weight of an equal volume of water is: D PPSC ADO-2017
a) Real specific gravity b) Particle density
c) Wet bulk density d) Apparent specific gravity

412. The ratio or fraction between the size of an object on a map and its size in the real world is - 4 RPSC ARO Ag Chem - 2022
(1) Map (2) Resolution (3) Slope (4) Scale

413. The reactions show below: B IAS Pre-2000
$CaSiO_3$ + 2HOH ____ H_2SiO_3 + Ca (OH)2
$KAlSi_3O_8$ + HOH _____ $HAlSi_3O_8$ + KOH
Are examples of
(a) hydration (b) hydrolysis (c) oxidation (d) solution

414. The relationship between Anion Exchange Capacity (AEC) and soil pH is as — 2 RPSC ARO Ag Chem - 2022
(1) AEC decreases when pH decreases (2) AEC increases when pH decreases
(3) AEC increases when pH increases (4) No affect of pH on AEC

415. The relative percentage of sand, silt and clay are called – b School Lect. 2019
(a) soil profile (b) soil texture (c) soil structure (d) bulk density

416. The relative proportion of sand, slit and clay in the soil is known as – 2 TN ACF-2012
(1) Soil structure (2) Soil texture (3) Soil consistency (4) None of these

417. The Residual Sodium Carbonate (RSC) of irrigation water containing carbonate, bicarbonate, calcium and magnesium ions as 15, 20, 18 and 12 meq/lit., respectively will be - 2 RPSC ARO Ag Chem - 2022
(1) 0 meq/Lit (2) 5 meq/Lit (3) 10 meq/Lit. (4) 20 meq/Lit.

418. The rhizosphere effect can be quantitatively represented by B HPSC ADO-2022
(A) C:Nratio (B) R: S ratio (C) C:P ratio (D) O : C ratio

419. The role of parent material in soil formation is 4 RPSC, AAO-2018
(A) Initially passive and later on active (B) Initially active and later on passive
(C) Active (D) Passive

420. The safest method to dispose of the waste materials is – c BHU PET-2015
(a) Pouring in the river (b) Pouring in the drain
(c) Burying in the soil (d) Pouring in the pond

421. The science that deals with the influence of soils on living things, particularly plants including human being use of land for plant growth is known as – c Agri Pre PG-2020
(a) Agronomy (b) Crop science (c) Edaphology (d) Crop geometry

422. The secondary mineral is : c UPPSC Pre- 2004
(a) Quartz (b) Nacrite (c) Gibbsite (d) Augite

423. The size of the clay particle in soil falls one of the ranges : d UPPSC
(a) 0.25-0.10 mm (b) 0.05-0.002 mm (c) 0.10-0.05 mm (d)< 0.002 mm Pre- 1997

424. The smallest 3D volume of a soil needed to give full representation of horizontal variability of soil is termed as - 2 MP PG PAT-2016
(1) Solum (2) Pedon (3) Gleys (4) Podsol

425. the smallest volume that can be classified as a soil is called as 2 RPSC, AAO-2018
(1) ped (2) pedon (3) soil catena (4) soil profile

426. The soak pit should be filled with C AO KTPSC-2021
I. Course aggregates
II. Fine aggregates
(A) I only (B) II only (C) Both I and II (D)Soil Only (E) Answer not known

427. The sodium absorption ratio (SAR) of the soil containing Na, Mg and Ca ions as 100, 30, and 20 meq/L, respectively, will be: 4 RPSC Pre-1998
(1) 5 (2) 10 (3) 15 (4)20

428. The soil acidification of sulphur is correctly given in a TNPSC Ag-1996
(A) $2 S + 3O_2 + 2H_2O$ Thiobacillus $2 H_2SO_4$
(B) $2 S + 3O_2 + 2H_2O$ Thiocococus $2 H_2SO_4$
(C) $2 S + 3O_2 + 2H_2O$ Phosphobacter $2 H_2SO_4$
(D) $2 S + 3O_2 + 2H_2O$ Sulphodevibria $2 H_2SO_4$

429. The soil amendment mainly usede fpor reclaimation of sodic (alkali) soil is c ICAR Gen Agri-2005
(A) Lime (B) Pressmud (C) Gypsum (D) Pyrites

430. The soil having more than 30 per cent organic matter is placed in C AO GPSC-2013
(A) Oxisols (B) Aridisols (C) Histosols (D) Alfisols

431. The soil is well flocculated if it has more of : d UPPSC Pre- 1997
(a) Sodium (b) Potassium (c) Zinc (d) Calcium

432. The soil layer of maximum leaching is indicated by the symbol b IAS Pre-1994
(a) A_1 (b) A_2 (c) B_1 (d) B_2

433. The soil of Tamil Nadu have been classified as – 4 TNPSC – Ag: 1999
(1) Entisol (2) Entisol, Albisol
(3) Entisol, Albisol, Inceptisol (4) Entisol, Albisol, Inceptisol, Ultisol

434. The soil order vertisol is related to b ICAR Gen Agri-2005
(A) Red soil (B) Black soil (C) Alluvial soil (D) Laterite soil

435. The soil order which have high content of clays that swell when wetted – 3 TN AO-2018
(1) Alfisols (2) Ultisols (3) Vertisols (4) Mollisols

436. The soil sampling depth for rice crop is – 2 TN PSC Ag-II: 2001
(1) 0-10 cm (2) 0-15 cm (3) 0-30 cm (4) 0-45 cm

437. The soil type of lands in India is dominated by – 3 TN AO-2018
(1) Sandy soil (2) Clayey soil (3) Alluvial soils (4) Black soils

438. The soils difficult to cultivate because of high expansion and contraction dut to high clay content are classified as – a RPSC, AO-2012
(a) Vertisols (b) Alfisols (c) Histosols (d) Inceptisols

439. The source of K in soils is : c UPPSC Pre- 1999

(a) Apetite (b) Augite (c) Biotite (d) Quartz

440. The source of slowly available **K** in soils for crop is : a UPPSC Pre- 2010

(a) Mineral K (b) Exchangeable K

(c) Non-Exchangeable K (d) K in soil solution

441. The specific gravity (g/mL) of sulphuric acid is - 1 RPSC ARO Ag Chem - 2022

(1) 1.84 (2) 1.70 (3) 1.19 (4) 1.06

442. The specific surface area (m^2/gm) of montmorillonite clay is in the range of - 3 RPSC ARO Ag Chem - 2022

(1) 100 — 300 (2) 300 — 500 (3) 700 — 800 (4) 800 —1000

443. The study of soil in relation to higher plants is known as d Agri Pre PG-2013

(a)Petrology (b) Pedology (c) Ecology (d)Adaphology

444. The taxon 'Subclass' ends with the suffix- d Agri Pre PG-2022

(a) Mycota (b) Mycotina (c) Mycetes (d) Mycetide

445. The term 'soil fertility 'pertains to – b MP PAT- 2013

(A) the ability of the soil to produce crops

(B) the soil capacity supplying plant nutrients in an available form

(D) the balanced use of fertilizers

446. The term '**soil fertility**' pertains to : **2** RPSC Pre- 1994

(1) the ability of the soil produce crops

(2) the soil capacity supply plant nutrients in an available form

(3) the growing of crops by judicious of fertilizers

(4) the balance use of fertilizers

447. The term "hue" refers to - 2 TN ACF- 2012

(1) Homogeneity of the soil (2) Variabiltiy of soil colour

(3) Heterogeneity of the soil (4) Soil odour just after rain

448. The three important steps involved in mineralization of organic N are – 1 TN PSC Ag-II: 2001

(1) Aminization, Ammonification and Nitrification

(2) Aminization , Nitrification and Denitrification

(3) Aminization, Ammonification and Immobilization

449. The time that nature devotes to the formation of soil is termed as D AO SDAU- 2015

A. Soil Stages B.Periodical table C. Temporal D.Pedagogical table

450. The total pore space of the soil occupied by air and water is on – 1 TN AO- 2018

(1) 50:50 basis (2) 25:75 basis (3) 5:95 basis (4) 45:55 basis

451. The total porosity of the soil is higher in – 3 TN AO- 2018

(1) Sandy soils (2) Silty soils (3) Clay soils (4) Loamy soils

452. The type of soil represented by the shaded portion : **3** RPSC Pre- 1993

(1) alluvial (2) laterite (3) red (4) black

453. The type of structural unit in soils when vertical plane is better displayed than **3** RPSC Pre-

horizontal plane is known as : 1999

(1) Platy (2) Blocky (3) Prismatic (4) Granular

454. The unconsolidated material abuse the bedrock is known as : (UPPSC

(a) Soil (b) Regolith (c) Solurn (d) Pedon b Pre- 2010

)

455. The volatilization of Ammonia will be more in soils high in – 3 TN PSC

(1) Clay content (2) CaCO3 content Ag-I:1999

(3) Moisture content (4) None of these

456. The volume composition of soil which gives optimum condition for crop growth is A AO

(A) 45% Mineral matter, 5% OM, 25% water and 25% air (B) 50 % Mineral matter KTPSC-

and 50% Organic matter 2021

(C) 25% mineral matter , 25% organic matter , 25% water and 25% air. (D)40%

mineral matter, 10% organic matter , 25% water and 25% Air (E) Answer not known

457. The zeta potential of soil particles is lowest, whose exchange sites are saturated by - 3 RPSC

(1) Potassium (2) Sodium (3) Calcium (4) Ammonium ARO Ag

Chem -

2022

458. Thermal conductivity is highest in c Agri Pre

(a) Clayey soils (b) Silty loam soils (c)Sandy soils (d)Clay loam soils PG-2013

459. To improve soil physical condition and sustain soil health we should add – a Gujrat

(a) More organic matter (b) More chemical fertilizers AO-2017

(c) More herbicides (d) More pesticides

460. To which one of the soil orders do black soils of India belong? C IAS Pre-

(a) Alfisol (b) Inceptisol (c) Vertisol (d) Oxisol 2008

461. Total degraded land area (mha) in India is – d BHU

(a) 110.8 (b) 127.3 (c) 152.4 (d) 187.8 PET-2014

462. Total degraded land area in India is about c UPPSC

(a) 329.0 m/ ha (b) 240.0 rn /ha (c) 175.0 m/ ha (d) 85.0 m/ ha Pre- 2010

463. Total number of orders recognized is soil taxonomy are : b UPPSC

(a) 10 (b) 11 (c) 12 (d) 13 Pre- 2004

Now: 12

464. Total soluble solid (TSS) is measured as electric conductivity (EC) and expressed as RRB SO-

ds/m at temperature of 25 degree Celsius. What is the EC value at very high TSS? 2018

Ans.: 0

465. True soil developed by the action of soil forming factors is called – a Agri Pre

(a) Regolith (b) Solum (c) Pedon (d) Profile PG-2017

466. Truncated profile c IAS Pre-

(a) represents a typical under developed profile 1999

(b) is one where solum is buried underneath

(c) is one that has a part of th solum removed by erosion

(d) is one where horizons cannot be distinguished

467. Type of soil in which exchangeable sodium percentage is less than 15 mm hos.cm 3 TN ACF-

and exchangeable pH is less than 8.5 is known as – 2012

(1) Sodic soil (2) Saline Alkali soil (3) Saline soil (4) None of these

468. Under continued and prolonged submergence soil pH tends to become - 2 RPSC ARO Ag Chem - 2022

(1) Acidic (2) Neutral (3) Alkaline (4) No change

- When soil is submerged for a long time, the oxygen supply gets limited. This leads to a shift towards reducing conditions within the soil.
- These reducing conditions favor chemical reactions that consume protons (H+), making the soil less acidic and pushing the pH towards neutral.
- This applies to both acidic and alkaline soils. In acidic soils, the decrease in H+ ions leads to a rise in pH. Conversely, in alkaline soils, the consumption of H+ ions reduces the availability of OH- ions (which contribute to alkalinity), resulting in a decrease in pH and a move towards neutral.

Therefore, under continued submergence, the soil pH tends to neutralize, regardless of its initial state.

469. Vertical section of soil which represents sequence of horizons from surface to bed rock is B AO KTPSC-2021

(A) Solium (B) Soil profile (C) Regolith
(D) Parent material (E) Answer not known

470. Vertical section of the soil is called as : a UPPSC Pre- 2004

(a) Soil profile (b) Soil horizon (c) Soil column (d) Regolith

471. Vertical section of the soil through all horizons and extending up to parental material is – 2 TN PSC Ag-I:1999

(1) Soil layer (2) Soil profile (3) Soil texture (4) Soil structure

472. Vertisols are found in : b UPPSC Pre- 2008

(a)Uttarakhand (b)Madhya Pradesh (c)Punjab (d)Haryana

473. Vertisols are rich in …….. type of clay. 3 TN PSC Ag-I:1999

(1) Kaolinite (2) Illite (3) Montmorillonite (4) Kaolinite and illite

474. Volatilisation loss of ammonia in soil increases with the increase in A IAS Pre-2005

(a) Calcium carbonate content of soil (b) Moisture content of soil
(c) Clay content of soil (d) Cation exchange capacity of soil

475. Well drained volcanic soils are :- a ARO Agro-2016

(a) More fertile (b) Less fertile (c) Non fertile (d) Useless

476. What is the formula for Residual Sodium Carbonate (RSC)… A AO KTPSC-2021

(A) $(CO_3^{--} + HCO_3^-) - (Ca^{2+} + Mg^{2+})$
(B) $(CO_3^{--} + HCO_3^-) + (Ca^{2+} + Mg^{2+})$
(C) $(Ca^{2+} + Mg^{2+}) - (CO_3^{--} + HCO_3^-)$
(D) $(Ca^{2+} + Mg^{2+}) + (CO_3^{--} + HCO_3^-)$ (E) Answer not known

477. What is the name of the proportion of soil occupied by air and water? **Ans.: Porosity** NABARD -2021

478. What is the order of black cotton soil ? **Ans.: Vertisol** RRB SO-2019

479. What is the range of silica in neutral rocks? a IFFCO T - 2019

(a) 41-50% (b) 51-60 % (c) 45-55 % (d) 55-60 %

480. What is the sequence of textural classes of soil arranged in increasing order of C IAS Pre-

coarseness ? 2009

(a) Loam, silt loam, sandy loam, loamy sand

(b) Silt loam, sandy loam, loamy sand, loam

(c) Silt loam, loam, sandy loam, loamy sand

(d) Loamy sand, loam, sandy loam, silt loam

481. What is the size of clay particle — 1 — RPSC Pre-2010

(1) < .002 mm (2) > .002 mm (3) < .02 mm (4) > 0.2 mm

482. What is the specific conductivity of 0.01N-KCl at 25^{0}C — Agri Pre PG-2013

(a) 0.14118 dS/m (b)1.4118 dS/m (c) 1.1418 dS/m (d)14.118 dS/m

483. What is the term used when the constituent of soil in solution form percolate from the upper layer to the lower layer? **Ans.: Elluviation** — RRB SO-2019

484. What is the theme of the World Health Day 2022? — 2 — RPSC ARO Ag Chem - 2022

(1) Support Nurses and Midwives (2) Our planet our Health

(3) Health equity and its determinants (4) Invest in our planet

485. What is/are the effect(s) of heavy metals on soil? — D — HPSC ADO-2022

(A) Heavy metals like Cd, Pb, Hg, As and Ni affect the microbial processes in soil

(B) It creates phytotoxicity on plants

(C) High concentration of heavy metals affect the nutrient balance

(D) All of the above

486. What will be the percentage of porosity of a soil which has 1.5g/cm3 bulk density and 2.65 g/cm3 particle density ? — 1 — Ag sup 2021

(1) 43 (2) 40 (3) 38 (4) 41

487. When a soil with 0.5% organic matter has 15 per cent silt 20 per cent sand and rest as clay, texturally it will fall under – — c — Gujrat AO-2017

(a) Sandy (b) Loamy (c) Clayey (d) Organic soil

488. When mSm^{-1} is converted to dSm^{-1}, it may be multiplied by- — 2 — RPSC ARO Ag Chem - 2022

(1) 0.1 (2) 0.01 (3) 0.001 (4) 1.0

489. When Organic matter is added to the Soil — 2 — Agri Pre PG-2016

(1) Bulk density is increased (2) Bulk density is decreased

(3) Bulk density does not change (4) None of these

490. When the composition of upper 5 km of the earth's crust is studied, the maximum part isformed from which rocks? — 4 — RPSC ARO Ag Chem - 2022

(1) Sandstone (2) Limestone (3) Granite (4) Shale

491. When weathering of Mica into secondary minerals takes place, the CEC will be? — 1 — RPSC ARO Ag Chem - 2022

(1) Increased (2) Decreased (3) No change (4) Uneven change

492. Where in the chemical weathering of rocks is most intense ? — d — BHU PET-2013

(a) Cold regions (b) Semi-arids & Arids

(c) Mediterranean regions (d) Humid tropics

493. Which among the following is best soil structure – c Gujrat AO-2017
(a) Platy (b) Prismatic (c) Granular (d) Columnar

494. Which among the following is/are organic P containing compound(s) of soil? D HPSC ADO-2022
(A) Inositol phosphate (B) Phospholipids (C) Nucleic acids (D) All of the above

495. Which category of land covers all grazing lands whether they are permanent pastures or meadows village commons and grazing lands ? 3 TN ACF-2012
(1) Land under non-agriculture use (2) Barren and unculturalble land
(3) Permanent pastures and other grazing lands (4) Culturable wastelands

496. Which cation has higher aggregation capacity in soil : b UPPSC Pre- 2002
(a) Al^{3+} (b) Ca^{2+} (c) Mg^{2+} (d) K^{+}

497. Which cation has low adsorption capacity on clay : c UPPSC Pre- 2002
(a) H (b) Fe (c) Ca (d) Na

498. Which clay mineral is a good source of potassium to crops : c UPPSC Pre- 2002
(a) Montmorillonite (b) Kaolinite (c) Illite (d) Vermiculite

499. Which element causes dispersion of soil particles : a UPPSC Pre- 2001
(a) Na (b) K (c) Ca (d) Mg

500. Which is correct order of fertilizers on the basis of their acidifying capacity expressed in terms of kg $CaCO_3$/kgN in fertilizer? 2 RPSC ARO Ag Chem - 2022
(1) Urea > Ammonium nitrate > Ammonium sulphate> Ammonium sulphate, ammonium nitrate
(2) Ammonium sulphate> Ammonium sulphate, ammonium nitrate > Urea >Ammonium nitrate
(3) Ammonium nitrate > Urea >Ammonium sulphate, ammonium nitrate > Ammonium sulphate
(4) Ammonium sulphate, ammonium nitrate > Urea > Ammonium sulphate> Ammonium nitrate

501. Which is most harmfull salt in salt affected soils: 1 RPSC Pre-1998
(1) Sodium chloride (2)Sodium sulphate
(3) Sodium bicarbonate (4) Sodium Carbonate

502. Which is not a correct match in the following : d UPPSC Pre- 2000
(a)Flocculation - Setting of the soil particles
(b)Dispersion - Repellence of the soil particles
(c)Cohesion Attraction of the soil particles
(d)Structure - Relative distribution of thesoil particles

503. Which is principle buffer mechanism in soil c Agri Pre PG-2013
(a)Organic Carbon (b)Calcium carbonate
(c) Cation exchange capity (d)Soil structure

504. Which of following is appropriate for a clay soil: A PPSC ADO-2017
a) Sand < 45% Silt < 40% Clay >40% b) Sand > 45% Silt < 40% Clay < 40%
c) Sand < 45% Silt > 40% Clay > 45% d) None of these

505. Which of the cations occur as dominant solutes in 'mM' concentration in soil A IAS Pre-

solution? 2007

(a) Na^+, K^+, Ca^{++}, Al^{+++}, Mn^{++} (b) Na^+, K^+, Fe^{++}, Mn^{++}

(c) Na^+, K^+, Mg^{++}, Ca^{++}, NH_4^+ (d) K^+, Mg^{++}, Ca^{++}, Mn^{++}, Fe^{+++}

506. Which of the clay minerals are found most in agricultural soils? B IAS Pre-2007

(a) Cyclosilicates (b) Phyllosilicates (c) Sorosilicates (d) Nesosilicates

507. Which of the following amendment is not used during reclamation of sodic soil ? 4 Agri Pre PG-2015

(1) iron pyrite (2) Gypsum (3) phosphogypsum (4) lime

508. Which of the following carbonate salt is least soluble : 1 RPSC Pre-1999

(1) $CaCO_3$ (2) Na2CO_3 (3) $NaHCO_3$ (4) $MgCO_3$

509. Which of the following characteristics helps in the identification of alkali soils ? c BHU PET-2015

(a) White/ash color layer of salts on soil surface

(b) Reddish color spot on soil surface

(c) Black spot on soil surface (d) None of these

510. Which of the following clay mineral is dominant in red soil ? 4 RPSC AO Ag -2021

(1) Illite(2) Smectite (3) Mica(4) Kaolinite

511. Which of the following compounds can make the colour of the soil white? A IBS,AFO-2013

(A) Calcite (B) Iron oxide (C) Nitrogen (D) Glauconite (E) None of these

512. Which of the following does not influence the soil structure: d NSC MT M-2019

(a) Adsorbed cation (b) Organic matter(c) Soil micro-organism(d) Base exchange

513. Which of the following is a rock phosphate mineral of boron? **Ans.: Tourmaline** RRB SO-2019

514. Which of the following is gray-white silicaceous material of volcanic origin mined from lava flows? 3 RPSC AARO – Horticulture-2022

(1) Vermiculite (2) Peat moss (3) Pelite (4) Rockwool

515. Which of the following is not a bio mass ? 3 TN AO-2012

(1) Bagasse (2) Grass (3) Sand (4) Wood

516. Which of the following is not a mineral horizon ? 4 RPSC, AAO-2019

(1) A (2) E (3) B (4) O

517. Which of the following is not a mineral horizon ? 4 RPSC AAO - 2018

(a) A (b) E (c) B (d) O

518. Which of the following is not a part of Solid Waste Management - 2 TN AAO-2019

(1) Reduce (2) Return (3) Reuse (4) Recycle

519. Which of the following is not a soil texture class ? 4 RPSC, AAO-2019

(1) Sandy (2) Loamy sand (3) Sandy loam (4) Sand

520. Which of the following is not correctly matched : (d) UPPSC Pre- 1999

(a) Magnesium – Macronutrient (b) Sandy loam – Soil texture

(c) Rhizobium – Symbiotic N_2 fixation (d) tensiometer – Soil porosity

521. Which of the following is the characteristic of clay particles in the soil? D IAS Pre-2005

(a) Less than 0.002 mm in diameter and consist of primary minerals

(b) Less than 0.002 mm in diameter and consist of primary and secondary minerals

(c) 0.002 to 0.05 mm in diameter and consist of secondary minerals

(d) Less than 0.002 mm in diameter and consist of secondary minerals

522. Which of the following is the correct combination of the soil? **1** RPSC Pre-1993
(1) sandy: about 80% sand and 20% silt or clay
(2) loam : about 20-25% silt and clay and the rest sand
(3) sandy loam : about 20% or less clay and 30-35% of sand
(4) clay : 70% or more clay and 30% other soil particles

523. Which of the following pairs are correctly matched? **b** IAS Pre-1999
1.Oxic : A horizon enriched with Fe and AI oxides
2. Mollic : A thick dark coloured mineral horizon
3. Ochric : A silicate caly enriched horizon
4. Argillic : A light coloured low organic matter content horizon
Select the correct answer using the codes given below
(a) 1 and 3 (b) 1 and 2 (c) 2and 4 (d) 2 and 3

524. Which of the following pairs is correctly matched ? **2** TN AO-2012
(1) Red soil – Calcareous (2) Alkali soil – pH 9
(3) Black soil – Rich in kaolinite (4) Laterite soil – pH 9

525. which of the following pairs is not correctly matched? **2** RPSC, AAO-2018
(1) entisols - recently developed mineral soils
(2) vertisols - developed on high salt content
(3) mollisols - dark coloured soils rich in organic matter
(4) alfisols - strongly weathered soils with high basw saturation

526. Which of the following salt is dominant in alkali soils? **b** Agri Pre PG-2021
(a) Cl (b)HCO_3 (c) CO_3 (d) SO_4

527. Which of the following sequence of minerals is correct as per their degree of decreasing weathering resistance? **b** ICAR Gen Agri-2006
(A) Muscovite<Gypsum<Olivine<Quartz
(B) Olivine<Muscovite<Gypsum<Quartz
(C) Gypsum<Olivine<Muscovite<Quartz
(D) Quartz<Muscovite<Gypsum<Olivine

528. Which of the following soda felsepars occurs in soil : **1** RPSC Pre-1999
(1) Orthoclase (2) Microcline (3)Albite (4) Anorthite

529. Which of the following soil has highest total porosity? **3** RPSC AAO-2022
(1) Sandy soil (2) Sandy loam soil
(3) Clay-loam soil (4) Loam soil

530. Which of the following soil textural classes (as per Triangular diagram) is having higher sand content? **a** Agri Pre PG-2022
(a) Loamy sand (b) Sandy loam (c) Sandy clay (d) Loam

531. Which of the following soil texture is highly susceptible to crusting BHU PET-2015
(a) Loam (b) Clay loam (c) Silty clay (d) Silty clay loam

532. Which of the following soil types has largest pore space ? **b** Raj JET-2014
(a) Clayey (b) Sandy (c) Loamy (d) Sandy loam

533. Which of the following soils are found in hills and foothill areas? **a** IBS,AFO-2017
A. Laterites and Laeteritic soils B. Black soil C. Desert soil

D. Alluvial soil E. Red soil

534. Which of the following soils are found most extensively in India? B IBS,AFO-2017

A. Laterite soil B. Alluvial soil C. Red soil D. Black soil E. Desert soil

535. Which of the following soils has higher cation exchange capacity ? (d) UPPSC Pre- 2009

(a) Entisol (b) Alfisol (c) Ardisol (d) Vertisol

536. Which of the following soils has the property of self ploughing? **Ans.: Black Soils** NABARD -2020

537. Which of the following source improve soil structure ? c School Lect. 2019

(a) Nitrogenous fertilizer (b) Phosphatic fertilizer

(c) Green manure (d) Potassic fertilizer

538. Which of the following statement is not true for moss peat ? * RPSC ACF Horti - 2018

(1) it absorbs 15 times more water than its dry weight

(2) It is low in nitrogen content

(3) it is high in acidity (pH 3.2-4.5) (4) It it partially decomposed

539. which of the following statement is not true? 3 RPSC, AAO-2018

(1) Soils containing less than 1 milli equivalent exchangeable Mg/100g soil are considered magnesium deficient

(2) Soils containing less than 15 milli equivalent exchangeable Ca/100g soil are called Ca deficient

(3) Potassium sulphate contains 24% S.

(4) Agriculture limestone contains 80-95% $CaCO_3$.

540. Which of the followings is not a soil texture class ? 4 RPSC AAO - 2018

(a) Sandy (b) Loamy sand (c) Sandy loam (d) Sand

541. Which one among the following is used as soil amendment – a BHU PET-2011

(a) Lime (b) Sodium hexametaphosphate

(c) Sodium hydroxide (d) Sodium alginate

542. Which one great soil group of the following belongs to order zonal soils ? 1 RPSC, AAO-2019

(1) Laterite soils (2) Alluvial soils

(3) Saline soils (4) Regosols

543. Which one great soil group of the following belongs to order zonal soils 1 RPSC AAO - 2018

(a) Laterite soils (b) Alluvial soils (c) Saline soils (d) Regosols

544. Which one is an active soil forming factor? 2 Agri Pre PG-2016

(1) Parent material (2) Biosphere (3) Relief (4) All are correct

545. Which one is dominating salt in alkali soil : d UPPSC Pre- 2002

(a) CaCl2 (b) MgSO4 (c) NaHCO3 (d) Na2CO3

546. Which one of the following constitutes the largest are in India ? 1 TN AO-2012

(1) Alluvial soils (2) Black soils (3) Desert soils (4) Lateritic soils

547. Which one of the following content is more in sandy loam soil ? a Raj JET-2014

(a) Sand (b) Silt (c) Clay (d) None of the above

548. Which one of the following is a rich source of Potash ? d Raj JET-

(a) Rock phosphate (b) Basic slag (c) Bone meal (d) Fly ash 2014

549. Which one of the following is an active factor for soil formation 4 RPSC Pre-
(1) Parent material (2) Soil erosion (3) Time (4) Climate 2010

550. Which one of the following is correctly matched? d TNPSC
(A) Dolomite -- $CaCO_3$ $MgCO_3$ (B)Gypsum - $Ca(H_2PO_4)_2$ Ag-1995
(C)Basic slag - $CaSO_4.2H_2O$ (D) Super phosphate - $Ca_3(PO_4)_2$

551. Which one of the following is different in its action ? 3 AARO
(1) Hydrated Lime (2) Chalk (3) Cycocel (4) Kaoline Agro-2016

552. Which one of the following is example of primary minerals ? (UPPSC
(a) Mica and Montomorrillonite (b) Feldspars and Illite d Pre- 2009
(c) Vermiculite and Quartz (d) Mica and Feldspars)

553. Which one of the following is not 2:1 type of clay mineral ? b Raj JET-
(a) Montmorilonite (b) Kaolinite (c) Smectite (d) Illite 2014

554. Which one of the following is not a constituent of soil separate ? 3 RPSC Pre-
(1) sand (2) clay (3) humus (4) silt 1994

555. Which one of the following is not a primary soil mineral ? (UPPSC
(a) Feldspar (b) Pyroxines (c) Dolomite (d) Olivines c Pre- 2006
)

556. Which one of the following is reffered to as the unconsolidated debris covering the earth's surface? C IAS Pre- 2004
(a) Lithosphere (b) Epipedon (c) Regolith (d) Solum

557. Which one of the following is the correct order regarding thermal conductivity of sois? D IAS Pre- 2005
(a) Peat > Clay > Loam > Sand (b) Clay > Loam > Sand > Peat
(c) Loam > Sand > Peat > Clay (d) Sand > Loam > Clay > peat

558. Which one of the following is the correct sequence Of stability of iron chelates suggested by Norvell (1972) A IAS Pre- 2004
(a) EDDHA > DTPA > EDTA > NTA (b) DTPA > EDDHA > EDTA > NTA
(c) NTA > EDTA > DTPA > EDDHA (d) EDDHA > EDTA> DTPA > NTA

559. Which one of the following is used as amendment in acidic soils : (UPPSC
(a) Lime (b) Urea (c) Gypsum (d) Ammonium Sulphate a Pre- 1996
)

560. Which one of the following pairs is correctly matched : (UPPSC
(a) Red soil calcareous (b) Alkali soil-pH-9 c Pre- 1995
(c) Black soil-Rich in kaolinite (d) Laterite soil-pH-8)

561. Which one of the following pairs is correctly matched ? 2 RPSC,
(1) Red soil – calcareous (2) Alkali soil – pH > 8.5 AAO-2009
(3) Black soil - Rich in Kaolinite (4) Laterite soil – pH 8.0

562. Which one of the following pairs is *not* correctly matched ? * IAS Pre- 2010
(a) Sphalerite ZnS
(b) Hausmannite : MnO_2
(c) Magnetic : Fe_3O_4
(d) Variscite : $AlPO_4 . 2H_2O$

(a) Sphalerite (ZnS): This is a correct match. Sphalerite is indeed zinc sulfide (ZnS).

(b) Hausmannite (MnO2): This is also a correct match. Hausmannite is manganese dioxide (MnO2).

(c) Magnetic (Fe3O4): This is a correct match. Magnetic refers to magnetite, which is iron(II,III) oxide (Fe3O4).

(d) Variscite (AlPO4 . 2H2O): This is also a correct match. Variscite is indeed aluminum phosphate with water of crystallization (AlPO4 · 2H2O).

All are correct

563. Which one of the following pairs is not correctly matched ? B IAS Pre-2010

(a) Vertisols : Smectite (b) Oxisols : Vermiculite

(c) Histosols : Organic matter (d) Andisols : Allophane

564. Which one of the following pairs is not correctly matched? b IAS Pre-1997

(a) Expanding type ....Higher water of clay minerals holding capacity

(b) High calcium content in soil ....Iron chlorosis

(c)Water inundated ....High nitrogen Soils mineralization

(d) Sandy soils ....Split application of fertilizers

565. Which one of the following pairs of elements and the minerals from which they are obtained is not correctly matched? b IAS Pre-1997

(a) Sulphur ....Pyrite

(b) Boron ....Siderite

(c) Zinc ....Calamine

(d) Copper............Malachite

566. Which one of the following resources will continue to play the pivotal role in crop production activity to meet the challenging demand of food, fibre and fuel for exploding human population, fodder for animals, and industrial raw material for agro-Based industries in the country? A IAS Pre-2000

(a) Natural (b) Organic (c) Chemical (d) Artificial

567. Which one of the following sets of soil conditions is more suitable for plant growth? d IAS Pre-1997

(a) Sandy soils with high aeration and low water holding capacity

(b) Clay soils with high water holding capacity and low aeration

(c) Organic soils with high water holding capacity and low aeration

(d) Loamy soils with medium aeration and medium water holding capacity

568. Which one of the following sets shows the correct soil order in sequence of increasing age? A IAS Pre-2002

(a) Entisol, mollisol, alfisol. Ultisol (b) Entiso. Mollisol, ultisol. Affisol

(c) Ultisol, mollisol, entisol (d) Alfisol, mollisol, entiso, uttisol

569. Which one of the following soils no diagnostic pedogenic horizons? B IAS Pre-2004

(a) ultisols (b) Entisols (c) Alfisols (d) Histosols

570. Which one of the following values given in terms of redox-potential of soils (mV) represents a highly reduced conditions of the soil? D IAS Pre-2001

(a) -250 (b) -100 (c) +200 (d) +600

571. Which one statement of the following in reference to soil forming process is false ? 3 RPSC

(a) Humification is the process of decomposition of organic matter and synthesis of new organic substance. AAO-2018
(b) Biosphere is active soil forming factor.
(c) Thepodzolization is fimdarnentalsoil forming process.
(d) Parent material is passive soil forming factor.

572. Which one statement of the following in reference to soil forming process is false ? 3 RPSC, AAO-2019
(1) Humification is the process of decomposition of organic matter and synthesis of new organic substance
(2) Biosphere is active soil forming factor
(3) The podzolization is fundamental soil forming process
(4) Parent material is passive soil forming factor

573. Which process is responsible for accumulation of materials in B horizons ? b BHU PET-2015
(a) Eluviation (b) Illuviation (c) Carbonation (d) Oxidation

574. Which region of M.P. is rich in Black Cotton Soil? b MP PAT-2016
(a) Bundelkhand (b) Malwa plateau (c)Baghelkhand (d) None of the above

575. Which soil group occupies the largest area in Tamil Nadu ? 4 TN PSC Ag-II: 2001
(1) Black soil (2) Alluvial soil (3) Laterite soil (4) Red soil

576. Which soil group of India is covering largest area? 1 RPSC ACF Agri -2018
(1) Alluvial soils (2) Red soils (3) Laterite soils (4) Saline and Alkanie soils

577. Which soil has highest cation exchange capacity – d BHU PET-2011
(a) Alluvial sandy loam (b) Red clay loam
(c) Laterite loam (d) Black clayey soil

578. Which soil is highly permeable & excessively well drained with low water retention capacity thus need more frequent irrigation for successful crop growth than fine texture soil? **Ans.: Sandy soil** RRB SO-2021

579. Which soil is most suitable for the cultivation of cereals : a UPPSC Pre- 2009
(a) Alluvial soils (b) Red soils (c) Lateritic soils (d) Black soils

580. Which soil structure is most desirable for agriculture ? d School Lect. 2019
(a) Blocky (b) Platy (c) Columnar (d) Granular

581. Which soils have the highest cation exchange capacity – c BHU PET-2012
(a) Alluvial (b) Laterite soils (c) Black soils (d) Red soils

582. Which technique is used for quantitative analysis of Humic substances? 2 RPSC ARO Ag Chem - 2022
(1) IR Spectroscopy (2) UV Spectroscopy
(3) NMR Spectroscopy (4) ESR Spectroscopy

583. Which texture has very high surface area per unit mass : b UPPSC Pre- 2009
(a) Silt (b) Clay(c) Sand (d) Gravels

584. Which two new soil orders have been added in US Soil-Taxonomy after 1975 ? c BHU PET-2013
(a) Histosol & Andisol (b) Histosol and Gelisol
(c) Andisol & Gelisol (d) Humid tropics

585. Which type of soil auger is used in soils having higher amount of clay content? 1 RPSC

(1) Screw type auger (2) Tube auger (3) Dutch auger (4) Post hole auger ARO Ag Chem - 2022

586. Which type of soil covers maximum area in Rajasthan? 3 RPSC Sch Lect.2022
(A) Brown Sandy soil (2) Black soil (3) Sandy soil (4) Red Loamy soil

587. Which type of soil erosion is a major problem in arid Rajasthan ? a Raj JET-2013
(a) Wind (b) Water (c) Landslide (d) None of these

588. Which type of soil is commonly known as ' hungry and thirsty soil' ? 4 TN AO-2012
(1) Black soil (2) Alluvial soil (3) Laterite soil (4) Red soil

589. With increasing acidity, the availability of nutrients like ____ is limited. 2 TN PSC Ag-I:1999
(1) Nitrogen Phosphorous, Calcium (2) Phosphorous, Calcium, Magnesium
(3) Potassium, Calcium, Magnesium (4) Calcium, Magnesium, Sulphur

590. Yellow colour of soil is due to? B IBS,AFO-2014
(A)Iron (B) Silica (C) Zinc (D) Cobalt (E)Manganese

591. Diagnostic epipedon present in Alfisols is 4 Agri Pre PG-2016
(1) Spodic epipedon (2) Oxic epipedon
(3) Mollic epipedon (4) Ochric epipedon

592. Horizon in which redeposition of leached soil constituents occurs : b BHU PET-2016
(a)Horizon of eluviation (b)Horizon of illuviation
(c)Horizon of sedimentation (d) Horizon of precipitation

593. Horizon which is formed as a result of pedogenic processes and having distinct properties or features that can be described of measureable soil properties is called – b Agri Pre PG-2020
(a) C – horizon (b) Diagnostic horizon
(c) A – horizon (d) O- horizon

594. Recent soil with no diagnostic horizon other than octric epipedon and slight degree of profile development are classified as – 4 Agri Pre PG-2018
(1) Ultisol (2) Inceptisol (3) Oxisol (4) Entisol

CHAPTER- 139 : ESSENTIAL PLANT NUTRIENTS PYQ'S

1. "**Crop logging**" is a method of : UPPSC Pre- 1998 — b — UPPSC Pre- 2007

(a) Soil fertility evaluation
(b) Plant analysis for assessing the nutrient requirement of plant
(c) Assessing the crop damage (d) Testing suitability of fertilizers

2. ________nutrient elements have so for been found essential for plants :- — 2 — RPSC, AAO- 2009

(1) Thirty (2) Sixteen (3) Eighteen (4) Twenty

3. 'Mg' and 'S' are termed as – — d — RPSC, AAO- 2012

(a) Primary nutrients (b) Micronutrient
(c) Ultra- micronutrient (d) Secondary nutrient

4. .....is not an essential nutrient for normal development of plants — a — TNPSC Ag- 1995

(A) Lead (B) Molybdenum (C) Magnesium (D) Chlorine

5. ....is a constituent part of the enzyme nitrate reductase and nitrogenase : — a — BHU PET-2016

(a) Mo (b) B (c) Fe (d) None of the

6. .... is an immobile plant nutrient . — 4 — Agri Pre PG- 2019

(1) Zn (2) K (3) N (4) Ca

7. A critical soil test level refers to — c — TNPSC Ag- 1995

(A) Nutrient status of soil (B) Particular nutrient in soil
(C) Nutrient level below which response is obtained with added nutrient
(D) Routine process

8. A plant nutrient obtained from air is. — c — MP PAT-2013

(A) Nitrogen (B) Phosphorus (C) Carbon (D) Chlorine

9. According to the essentiality criteria of nutrients which one is correct (without it) : — a — ARO Agro-2016

(a) Plant can not complete life cycle (b) Plant can complete life cycle
(c) Plant can not grow (d) Plant can grow very well

10. Ammonia is transformed into nitrate by – — 2 — TN AO-2008

(1) Algae (2) Bacteria (3) Fungi (4) Actinomyces

11. Among the following the set of essential nutrient elements, which are absorbed as anions as by plants is — D — IAS Pre-2003

(a) Boron, Chlorine, Copper, Iron, Managenese
(b) Copper, Iron, Phosphorus, Sulphur, Zinc
(c) Potassium, Manganese, Molybdenum, Phosphorus, Zinc
(d) Boron, Chlorine, Molybdenum, Phosphorus, Sulphur

12. Among the various essential nutrients maximum nutrients come in which period of periodic table of the elements? — 3 — RPSC ARO Ag Chem -2022

(1) Second (2) Third (3) Fourth (4) Fifth

13. Among the various micronutrients the molybdenum comes in which period of periodic table of the elements? — 4 — RPSC ARO Ag Chem -2022

(1) 2nd Period (2) 3rd Period (3) 4th Period (4) 5th Period

14. Amount of Sulphur reaching the soil by rain is — 1 * — RPSC Sch Lect.2022

(1) 2-3 kg/ha (2) 7-8 kg/ha (3) 10-12 kg/ha (4) 13-15 kg/ha

Explanation: we can discuss it in terms of kilograms per hectare (kg/ha) annually, which is a unit commonly used for measuring atmospheric deposition. Here's a rough idea:

Range: The annual sulfur deposition through rain can vary significantly, typically ranging from **1 kg/ha to 50 kg/ha.**

Lower range (1-5 kg/ha): This is more common in remote areas with minimal human influence.

Higher range (10-50 kg/ha): This is more likely in areas closer to industrial sources or with higher rainfall.

15. An essential mineral nutrient which is present in oxidized form in biomolecules is — a — UPPSC Pre-2010
(a) S (b) N (c) P (d) Ca

16. An indigenous source of sulphur available in Rajasthan is — 2 — RPSC Pre-2007
(1) Rock phosphate (2) Gypsum
(3) Pyrite (4) Elemental sulphur

17. Anammox is one of the step of ? — e — IBS,AFO-2021
(a) Phosphorus cycle (b) Carbon cycle (c) Hydrological cycle
(d) Potassium cycle (e) Nitrogen cycle

18. Antagonism of Mn exists with ? — c — NSC MT P-2019
(a) Calcium (b) Boron (c) Iron (d) Copper

19. Apatite is a group of minerals which mainly contains — b — IAS Pre-1994
(a) sulphur (b) phosphorus (c) nitrogen (d) Titanium

20. Application of Mg increases uptake of : — a — UPPSC Pre-2005
(a) P in plants (b) K in plants (c) N in plants (d) S in plants

21. Application of potash increases: — A — IBPS SO-2017
A.Disease resistance in plants B.Resistance for water logging
C.Frost resistance in plants D.None of the above

22. Application of super digested compost to acidic calcareous and heavy soils increases the availability of — B — PPSC ADO-2020
a) N b) P c) K d) Ca

23. As plants grow to maturity, the concentration of plant nutrient changes. What king of change occurs in respect of N,P,K ca and Mg? — d — IAS Pre-1993
(a) conce-netration of all the five elements decreases
(b) Nand P decreases ,K, Ca and Mg increase
(c) N, p and K increase, Ca and Mg increase
(d) N, p and K decreases, Ca and Mg decreases,

24. At low pH which one of the following is affected – — 1 — TN AO-2008
(1) Phosphorus is precipitated (2) Potassium is accumulated
(3) Boron accumulates (4) Phosphorus leached out

25. At the pH 4.0 the predominant ionic form of phosphorus present is : — 2 — RPSC Pre-2003
(1)HPO_4^{2-} (2) $H_2PO_4^-$ (3) PO_4^{3-} (4) None of the above

26. Availability of phosphorus is maximum in soil pH range — c — UPPSC Pre-2009
(a) 3 to 4 (b) 5 to 6 (c) 6 to 7 (d) 7 to 8

27. Availability of plant nutrients in the soil can be assessed by extraction of the given nutrient from the soil by a specific chemical reagent. Match the nutrient in Lit I — B — IAS Pre-2007

with extracting reagent in List II and select the correct answer using the code given below the lists

List I (Plant Nutrient)	List II (Nutrient from soil)
A. Potassium	1. Sodium bicarbonate
B. Phosphours	2. Ammonium acetate
C. Zinc	3. DTPA
D. Molybdenum	4. Ammonium oxalate

	A	B	C	D		A	B	C	D
(a)	2	3	1	4	(b)	2	1	3	4
(c)	4	3	1	2	(d)	4	1	3	2

28. Availability of which form of P is highest at pH 6.7 — a — ICAR Gen Agri-2007
(A) H_2PO_4 (B) HPO_4 (C) PO_4 (D) None

29. Availability of Zn increases when it is applied as : — c — UPPSC Pre-2007
(a) Mixed with phosphatic fertilizers (b) Mixed with N.P.K. fertilizers
(c) Mixed with nitrogenous fertilizers (d) None of the above

30. Availabiltiy of phosphorus of maximum at pH – — 1 — TN AO-2008
(1) Neutral (2) Acidic (3) Alkaline (4) All of these

31. Available K is converted into K_2O by multiplying with - — 1 — RPSC ARO Ag Chem -2022
(1) 1.20 (2) 1.40 (3) 1.85 (4) 2.29

32. Available phosphorus of more than 25 kg/ha of soil considered as : — 3 — RPSC Pre-2003
(1) Low (2) Medium (3) High (4) Trace

33. Available soil nitrogen of less than 271 kg/ha is categorized as — 1 — RPSC Pre-2007
(1) Low (2) Medium (3) High (4) Very high

34. Average percentage of carbon in steel is – — b — BHU UET-2013
(a) 0.1-0.2 (b) 0.4-0.5 (c) 0.8-1.0 (d) 1.0-1.5

35. Besides the soil reservoir, components of integrated nutrient management include — d — IAS Pre-1999
(a) inorganic fertilizers and organic manures
(b) organic manures and biofertilizers
(c) biofertilizers and inorganic fertilizers
(d) inorganic fertilizers, organic manures and biofertilizers

36. Boron functions in plants in – — d — BHU PET-2014
(a) N-fixation (b) NO^-_3 reducation
(c) Fatty-acid synthesis (d) Sugar translocation

37. C/N ratio in Farmyard manure should be less than : — d — UPPSC Pre-2002
(a) 10 (b) 20 (c) 30 (d) 40

38. Ca equivalent of $CaCO_3$ is : — c — UPPSC Pre-2004
(a) 0.56 (b) 0.67 (c) 0.4 (d) 2.5

39. Ca, Mg and S are known as – — 2 — Raj JET-2018
(1) Primary nutrients (2) Secondary nutrients
(3) Micro- nutrients (4) Beneficial nutrients

40. Carbon is an essential element for plant growth plants take it from : — b — UPPSC Pre-1995
(a) Soil (b) Air (c) Water (d) Light

41. Carbon percentage in raw iron is – — b — BHU UET-2014

(a) 1.5 % (b) 3.5 % (c) 5.5 % (d) 7.5%

42. Cobalt is essential for Rhizobium to synthesize : b UPPSC Pre-2009

(a) Vitamin B_6 (b) Vitamin B_{12} (c) Vitamin C (d) Vitamin A

43. Consider the following C IAS Pre-2008

1. Phosphorus 2. Iron 3. Zinc 4. Molybdenum

Which of the above are the nutrient elements deficient in acid soils?

(a) 1and 2 (b) 1and 3 (c)1and 4 (d) 2,3 and 4

44. Consider the following chemical elements B IAS Pre-2003

1. Calcium 2. Chromium 3. Rubidum 4. Molybdenum

The beneficial elements among these are

(a) 1and 2 (b) 2and 3 (c) 3and 4 (d) 1and 4

45. Consider the following elements A IAS Pre-2001

1. Magnesium 2. Iron 3. Nitrogen 4. Manganese

The elements present in the porphyrin structure of chlorophyll molecule are

(a) 1and 3 (b) 1and 4 (c) 2and 3 (d) 2and 4

46. Consider the following elements: C IAS Pre-2007

1. Ca 2. Zn 3. P 4. Mg

The acidic soils are deficient in which of the above nutrient elements ?

(a) 1,2and 3 only (b) 2, 3 and 4 only

(c) 1, 3 and 4 only (d) 1,2 and 4 only

47. Consider the following statements a IAS Pre-1999

In crops, phosphorus

1. is essential for flowering, fruiting and seed formation
2. helps to regulate the opening of stomata in the leaves
3. is essential for root development and crop maturation
4. is essential for the synthesis of chlorophyll and enzymes

of these statements

(a) 1and 3 are correct (b) 2and 3 are correct

(c) 2and 4 are correct (d) 1 and 4 are correct

48. Consider the following statements b IAS Pre-1999

In rice silicon is a functional element and is required in large quantities for

1. increasing water use efficiency
2. disease and pest resistance
3. normal growth of plant and uptake of other nutrients
4. spikelet sterility control

Of these statements

(a) 1and 2 are correct (b) 3 and 4 are correct

(c) 1,2 and 3 are correct (d) 1,2,3 and 4 are correct

49. Consider the following statements B IAS Pre-2004

In crops, Magnesium is essential for

1.meristematic activity and formation of new tissues in the root tips
2. synthesis of chlorophyll
3. promoting transport of phosphorus particularly into the seeds

4. synthesis of cell wall

Which of the statements given above are correct?

(a) 1and 2 (b) 2and 3 (c) 3and 4 (d) 1and 3

50. Consider the following statements C TNPSC Ag-1998

Assertion (A) : Aluminium toxicity is probably the most important growth limiting actor in many acid soil, particularly those having pH levels below 5.0 to 5.5

Reason (R): Excess aluminium fixes phosphorus in less available forms.

Select your answer according to the coding scheme givenbelow

(A) Both (A) and (R) are false (B) (A) is true, but (R) is false

(C) Both (A) and (R) are true (D) (A) is false, and (R) is true

51. Consider the following statements c TNPSC Ag-1995

Assertion (A): Balanced and timely plant nutrition is vital for sufficient plant growth and development and that gives the higher yields

Reason (B): The crop thus invariably be supplied with inorganic fertilizers even under moisture stress condition

Select your answer

(a) A and R are true and (R) is the correct explanation of (A)

(b) (A) and (R) are true but (R) is not the correct explanation of (A)

(c) (A) is true and (R) is false

(d) (A) is false but (R) is true

52. Consider the following statements : D IAS Pre-2001

1 Mg is a co-factor for many enzymes activating phosphorylation in the glycolysis and tricarboxylic acid cycle

2.Mg limits the rate of photosynehttic process as it is requird to activate RUBP carboxylase

3. Protein synthеisis is dependent on the presence of Mg in plant.

Which of the above statements are correct?

(a) 1and 2 (b) 1and 3 (c) 2and 3 (d) 1,2 and 3

53. Consider The following statements : C IAS Pre-2009

1. Potassium is absorbed by plant as K^+ ions.

2. Potassium is essential to photosynthesis to take place.

3. Potassium is involved in activation of enzymes important to energy utilization.

Which of the statements given above are correct ?

(a) 1 and 2 only (b) 2 and 3 only (c) 1 and 3 Only (d) 1, 2 and 3

54. Consider the following statements : A IAS Pre-2010

1. High nitrogen content and low phosphorus content in soil reduce nitrogen fixation.

2. The amount of nitrogen fixed by Rhizobium with green gram is several times more than that fixed with Lucerne.

Wich of the statements given above is/are correct ?

(a) 1 only (b) 2 only (c) Both 1 and 2 (d) Neither 1 nor 2

55. Consider the following statements regarding the diagram given a IAS Pre-1998

Made a diagram ?

1. Nitrate is retained by the soil and hence the nitratenitrogen is temporarly immobilized during decomposition

2. Higher nitrate observed at the end of decomposition is due to the release of this nutrient by the soil

3. The peak level of CO^2 and (NO_3) observed in the diagram indicates the maximum activithy of microbes developed during decomposition

Of these statements

(a) 1,2 and 3 are correct (b) 1and 2 are correct

(c) 2and 3 are correct (d) 3 alone is correct

56. Consider the following statements regarding Zinc in soils: D IAS Pre-2001

1. Zinc is more soluble in acid soil and the solubility decreases as the soil pH increases.

2. Solubility of soil Zinc, native or applied, increases with the increase of native or added phosphate to the soil.

3. Zinc is practically immobile in the soil and hence leachate of the soil contains very little Zinc in it.

Which of the above statements are correct?

(a) 1,2 and 3 (b) 1and 2 (c) 2and 3 (d) 1 and 3

57. Conversion nitrogen to molecular nitrogens is known as – 1 TN AO-2012

(1) Denitrication (2) Nitrification (3) Nitrogen Fixation (4) Ammonification

58. Conversion of NO_3 – N to N_2 and N_2O us known as B IAS Pre-2005

(a) Oxidation (b) Denitrification (c) Mineralisation (d) Nitrification

59. Conversion of NO_3 into N_2 and N_2O is called. 1 Agri Pre PG-2016

(1) Denitrification (2) Nitrification (3) Mineralization (4) None of these

60. Conversion of protein to amino acid is called : c BHU PET-2016

(a) Carbonation (b) Deamination (c) Aminization (d)Amination

61. Criteria of essential plant nutrients was given by B ADA MP-2015

(A) Mendel & Cork (B) Arnon & Stout

(C) Bentham & Hukar (D) None

62. Criteria of essentiality of nutrients for plants were given by d IAS Pre-1994

(a) Arnon (b) Stout (c) Russel (d) Liebig

63. Criteria of essentiality of nutrients isgiven by ______: 2 RPSC ACF Agri -2018

(1) Brown 1954 (2) Amon 1954 (3) Blackman 1905 (4) Mitsherlich 1909

64. Critical limit of available phosphorus in soil for wheat crop by Olsen's method is : b UPPSC Pre-2002

(a) 5 kg/ha (b) 10 kg/ha (c) 15 kg/ha (d) 20 kg/ha

65. Critical limit of available sulphur in soil is 4 RPSC Pre-2007

(1) 10 ppm (2) 20 ppm (3) 30 ppm (4) 40 ppm

66. Critical level for hot water extractable B (ppm) in soil is A HPSC ADO-2022

(A) 0.1 – 2.0 (B) 2.0 – 5.0 (C)5.0 – 10.0 (D)10.0 15.0

67. Deficiency symptoms of immobile nutrients will appear first in: B PPSC ADO-2017

a) Plant roots b) Young, upper leaves c) Older, lower leaves d) Flowers

68. Dolomite is rich in-/ c MP PAT-2016
(a) Mo (b) Ag (c) Mg (d) K

69. Dolomite is rich in: c MP PAT-2016
1. Fe 2. B 3. Mg 4. Mo

70. Efficiency of phosphate utilization by cereal crops is about : a UPPSC Pre-2000
(a) 20% (b) 30% (c) 40% (d) 50%

71. Elements play direct role in Chlorophyll synthesis are 3 Agri Pre PG-2016
(1) P and K (2) Ca and Zn (3) N and Mg (4) Fe and S

72. Elements which are not universally essential but improve the growth of some plant species are – 2 Agri Pre PG-2018
(1) Zinc and Molybdenum (2) Cobalt and Vanadium
(3) Iron and Boron (4) Boron and Copper

73. Entry of potassium ions root hair in soils having a low potassium ion content in the soil is mediated through a IAS Pre-1996
(a) ion exchange through (b) mass flow phenomenon
(c) Donnan equilibrium process (d) utilization of metabolic energy

74. Essential element for plants, among the following is : d UPPSC Pre-2008
(a) Si (b) Se (c) Na (d) Ni

75. Essential elements are those c IAS Pre-1994
(a) Which could be replaced by other elements with similar properties
(b) which are required in large quantities
(c) Whose deficiency would prevent the completion of plant's life cycle
(d) which would promote plant growth

76. Essential elements needed for plants are – 3 TN AO-2008
(1) 5 (2) 6 (3) 16 now 17 (4) 21

77. Essential micro-nutrient is: d NSC S T-2019
(a) Potassium (b) Calcium (c) Sulphur (d) Manganese

78. Essential nutrients need not to be applied as they are presents in abundance – d Agri Pre PG-2017
(a) Carbon and Oxygen (b) Oxygen and Hydrogen
(c) Carbon and Hydrogen (d) Carbon, Hydrogen and Oxygen

79. Excess uptake of which element is known as luxury consumption : c UPPSC Pre-2002
(a) N (b) P (c) K (d) Zn

80. For 92 kg Nitrogen, how much quantity of urea is required ? B ADA MP-2015
(A) 120 kg (B) 200 kg (C) 46 kg (D) None

81. For calculating value of P, P_2O_5 is multiplied by : c UPPSC Pre-2000
(a) 3.258 (b) 2.146 (c) 0.437 (d) 0.125

82. For Crop growth potash released in the soil by the weathering of the minerals D TNPSC Ag-1998
(A) Apatite (B) Montmotillonite (C) Tourmaline (D) Feldspar

83. For which nutrient element, plants depend strongly on chelation the improve availability and transport from soil to plant root surfaces? C IAS Pre-2007
(a) Ca (b) Mg (c) Fe (d) B

84. Form of zinc adsorbed by plants is: b NSC S T-2019

(a) Zn^{+} (b) Zn^{++} (c) Zn^{+++} (d) None of These

85. From Q/I relationship described by Beckett (1964) a high PBC^{k} indicates that A IAS Pre-2001
(a) availability of potassium in the soil is excellent
(b) the soil needs potassium fertilization
(c) the soil has been recently limed (d) the soil needs fiming

86. General recommendation of N,P,K fertilizer doses for chickpea in Rajasthan : 2 RPSC Pre-2007
(1) 15-50-0 (2) 20-40-0 (3) 30-20-20 (4) 20-40-20

87. Group of minerals which are the original source of 'K' in soils are : d UPPSC Pre-2006
(a) Dolomite and Mica (b) Apatite and Feldspars
(c) Brolite and Dolomite (d) Feldspars and Mic

88. Highly mobile element is- b MP PAT-2016
(a) Boron (b) Phosphorous (c) Calcium (d) None of these

89. How many elements have so far been found essential for plant growth ? c UPPSC Pre-1994
(a) 20 (b) 30 (c) 16 (d) 18
Now 17 elements is essential. New element is **Nickel.**

90. Identify the beneficial nutrient among the following nutrients? b Agri Pre PG-2022
(a) Calcium (b) Sodium (c) Magnesium (d) Sulphur

91. Identify the nutrient which is function as secondary messenger? c Agri Pre PG-2022
(a) Sodium (b) Potassium (c) Calcium (d) Magnesium

92. If a soil contains 0.6 percent organic carbon, what will be the level of nitrogen ? c UPPSC Pre-2009
(a) Very low (b) Low (c) Medium (d) High

93. Immobilization of sulphur takes place when the 'S' content of organic matter is less than : b UPPSC Pre-2001
(a) 0.60% (b) 0.45% (c) 0.30% (d) 0.15%

94. In acid soil, toxicity of the following nutrient/s dose not hampers plant growth — 4 RPSC ARO Agro-2022
(1) Hydrogen (2) Manganese (3) Aluminium (4) Carbon

95. In gypsum nutrients present are – a BHU UET-2013
(a) calcium and sulphur (b) calcium and iron
(c) iron and sulphur (d) iron and manganese

96. In leguminous crop pink colour of root nodules is due to – d BHU UET-2011
(a) nitrogen (b) calcium (c) sulphur (d) leg haemoglobin

97. In natural soils, crops absorb added phosphates as – c BHU PET-2010
(a) $H_2PO_4^-$ (b) HPO_4^{2-} (c) $H_2PO_4^- + HPO_4^{2-}$ (d) PO_4^{3-}

98. In the process of nitrogen mineralization, the first step is called :- 1 AARO Agro-2016
(1) Aminization (2) Nitrification
(3) Ammonification (4) Immobilization

99. In urease enzyme activity which micronutrient plays an important role? 3 RPSC ARO Ag Chem -2022
(1) Zinc (2) Copper (3) Nickel (4) Boron

100. In which soil zinc availability to crop is higher : a UPPSC Pre-2002
(a) Acidic soil (b) Alkaline soil (c) Calcareous soil (d) Waterlogged soil

101. Integrated nutrient management involves – 4 TN AO-2012
I. Biofertilizers

II. Chemical fertilizers

III. Crop residues

IV. Organic manures

(1) I, II and IV of the above (2) I, III and IV of the above

(3) I, II, and III of the above (4) I, II, III and IV of the above

102. Iron form mines is known as – **d** BHU UET-2013

(a) pig iron (b) cast iron (c) rot iron (d) iron ore

103. It is an indicator used for determination of Ca+Mg – **2** Agri Pre PG-2019

(1) Phenolphthalein (2) Erochrome Black – T

(3) Methyl orange (4) Methyl red

104. Langbeinite is a unique source of plant nutrients, it contains three essential nutrients, namely - **4** RPSC ARO Ag Chem -2022

(1) N, p, K (2) K, Mg, Ca (3) P, K, S (4) K, Mg, S

105. Leaf Colour Chart (LCC) indirectly tells us the status of: **A** PPSC ADO-2017

a) Nitrogen in rice plants b) Phosphorus in rice plants

c) Sulphur in rice plants d) Micronutrients in rice plants

106. Leghaemoglobin is a red plant pigment : **d** UPPSC Pre-1998

(a) Red chillies (b) Ripe fruits of tomato

(c) Roots of carrot (d) Root nodules of leguminous plants

107. Loss of ammonia occurs through volatilisation when : **d** UPPSC Pre-2007

(a) Urea is applied on soil surface (b) Soil is alkaline

(c) Temperature is high (d) All above are correct

108. Luxury consumption is generally associated with : **c** UPPSC Pre-2008

(a) Nitrogen (b) Phosphorus (c) Potassium (d) Zinc

109. Magnesium and iron are needed for plants in the : **1** RPSC Pre-1994

(1) synthesis of chlorophyll pigments in leaves

(2) translocation of carbohydrates from leaves to the stem

(3) energy transfer concerned with photosynthesis and respiration

(4) mechanism of stomatal opening and closure

110. Magnesium is absorbed in plants in the form of – **4** Ag Sup JAU 2017

(1) Maganus (2) Maganeic (3) Both A & B (4) None of the above

111. Match List I with List 2II and select the correct answer using the code given below the lists **D** IAS Pre-2006

Lists I (Available nutrients)	List II (Extractants used)
A. Potassium	1. Neutral normal ammonium acetate
B. Boron	2. 0.005 M DTPA (pH = 7.3)
C. Iron	3. Hot water
D. Molybdenum	4. Ammonium oxalate (pH = 3.3)

	A	B	C	D		A	B	C	D
(a)	1	2	3	4	(b)	4	3	2	1
(c)	4	2	3	1	(d)	1	3	2	4

112. Match List – I (Minerals) List – II (Functions) and choose correct answer. **3** RPSC FSO-2019

List – I List – II

(A) Calcium (i) Blood coagulation

(B) Sodium (ii) Maintenance of electrical equilibrium between intracellular fluid

(C) Iron (iii) Anaemia

(D) Iodine (iv) Formation of Thyroid hormone

(1) A-iv, B-i, C-ii, D-iii

(2) A-iii, B-iv, C-ii, D-i

(3) A-i, B-ii, C-iii, D-iv

(4) A-ii, B-iii, C-i, D-iv

113. Match List (micronutrients) with List ll (typical deficiency symptoms)and select the correct answer: b IAS Pre-1994

List I	List II
A. Manganes	1. Speckled yellow of sugarbeet
B. Molybdenum	2. White bud of maize
C. Zinc	3. Whiptail in cauliflower
D. Copper	4. Reclamation disease of cereal

114. Match List I (Compound/material) with List II (Nutrient/Activity) and select the correct answer using the codes given below the lists d IAS Pre-1999

Lists I	*List II*
A. Thiourea	1. Calcium
B. Serpentine	2. Nitrification inhibitor
C. Oxamide	3. Slow release N fertilizer
D. Rock phosphate	4. Magnesium

	A	B	C	D		A	B	C	D
(a)	2	4	1	3	(b)	4	2	3	1
(c)	4	2	1	3	(d)	2	4	3	1

115. Match List I (*Nutrient Element*) with List II (*Source in soil*) and select the correct answer using the codes given bellows the lists D IAS Pre-2005

List I	Lists II
A. calcium	1. Apatite
B. Nitrogen	2. Dolomite
C. Phosphorus	3. feldspar
D. potassium	4. Organic

	A	B	C	D		A	B	C	D
(a)	2	1	4	3	(b)	3	4	1	2
(c)	3	1	4	2	(d)	2	4	1	3

116. Match list I correctly with list II and select your answer using the codes given below- b TNPSC Ag-1996

List-I **List-II**

(A) critical nutrient status in soil (1) Mass per unit vol. consisting of solid and gas phase

(B) Hidden hunger in crops (2) Negative log of hydrogen ion concentration

(C) Bulk density (3) Range of concentration of nutrients at which growth is reduced

(D) pH of soil solution (4) deficiency of nutrients reduced yield even without apparent symptoms

Codes

	a	b	c	d
(A)	2	3	4	1
(B)	3	4	1	2
(C)	1	2	3	4
(D)	4	1	2	3

117. Match List I List II and select the correct answer using the code given below the lists B IAS Pre-2008

List I (Micronutrient) **ListII (Mineral)**

A. Zn 1. Wulfenite

B. Mo 2. Pyrite

C. Cu 3. Smithsonite

D. Mn 4. Malachite

5. Pyrolusite

	A	B	C	D		A	B	C	D
(a)	2	1	4	3	(b)	3	1	4	5
(c)	2	4	1	3	(d)	3	4	1	5

118. Match List with List second and select the correct answer: a IAS Pre-1995

List firs List second

A. Nitrogen 1. Reduction of nitrate

B. Phosphorus 2. Root growth

C. Potassium 3. Acceleration of vegetative growth

D. Molybdenum 4. Translocation of photosynthesis

	A	B	C	D		A	B	C	D
a)	3	2	4	1	b)	4	2	1	3
c)	4	3	2	1	d)	3	1	4	2

119. Match List-I with List-II and select the correct answer using the code given below the Lists : B IAS Pre-2010

List-I (*Nutrient element*) **List-II** (*Chief source in the soil*)

A. Nitrogen 1. Apatite

B. Phosphorus 2. Pyrite

C. Potassium 3. Organics

D. Sulphur 4. Mica

Code :

	A	B	C	D		A	B	C	D
(a)	2	4	1	3	(b)	3	1	4	2
(c)	3	4	1	2	(d)	2	1	4	3

120. Match the following using the codes 3 TN AO-2012

List I List II

A. Calcium	1. Major nutrient
B. Molybdenum	2. Micro element
C. Phosphours	3. Micronutrient
D. Silicon	4. Secondary nutrient

Codes :

	A	B	C	D
(1)	3	4	1	2
(2)	1	2	3	4
(3)	4	3	1	2
(4)	2	3	4	1

121. Methods for estimation of nitrogen are – 3 RPSC FSO-2019

(1) Dumas and Carius method (2) Kjeldahi's and Carius method
(3) Dumas and Kjeldahi's method (4) Carius method

122. Micro nutriant use efficiancey is more when these are applied :- b ARO Agro-2016

(a) Through sprinkler (b) Foliar spray
(c) Soil application (d) Through drip irrigation

123. Micro nutrients are always required in very little amounts but play a very important role in the physiological processes of the crop plants. Which of the following is micro nutrient? A IBS,AFO-2018

(A) Iron (B) Zinc (C) Nickle (D) Manganese (E) Sulphur

124. Micro-nutrients of plants are : 4 RPSC Pre-1993

(1) nitrogen, phosphorus, potash (2) urea, silica, chlorophyll
(3) water, carbon dioxide (4) magnesium, zinc, iron

125. Mineral which provides Boron in soil is : b UPPSC Pre-2006

(a) Malachite (b) Trumaline (c) Glauconite (d) Montmorillonite

126. Molybdenum is required by plants because it is a cofactor for b IAS Pre-1994

(a) cytochrome oxidase (b) nitrate reductase
(c) nitrite reductase (d) phosphates

127. Molybdenum is required by plants, because itis a cofactor for - 4 RPSC ARO Ag Chem -2022

(1) Cytochrome oxidase (2) Phosphatase
(3) Nitrite reductase (4) Nitrate reductase

128. More availability of calcium and magnesium at pH? B IBS,AFO-2014

(A) 6-7.5 (B)7.5-8.5 (C) 8.5-10 (D) 3.5-5 (E)All of these

129. More than _____ percentage of the nutrient value of FYN losses through leading and volatilization . 3 TN AAO-2019

(1) 10 (2) 25 (3) 50 (4) 75

130. Most available form of P for plant is 1 RPSC Pre-2010

(1) $H_2PO_4^-$ (2) HPO_4^{2} (3) PO_4^{3-} (4) None of these

131. Most of the plants obtain nitrogen from the soil in the form as :- 3 RPSC, AAO-2009

(1) Nitrite (2) Free Nitrogen gas (3) Nitrate (4) Nitric acid

132. Movement of P and K from soil to the root surface take place due to - 3 RPSC ARO Agro-2022

(1) Mass flow (2) Root interception (3) Diffusion (4) Osmosis

133. Nitrogen is a major nutrient because : d UPPSC Pre-

(a) It is available in soil more (b) It is constituent of proten 1995

(c) It is available in atmosphere more (d) It is required by plants more

134. Nitrogen is absorbed by plants in which form of the following ? a Raj JET-2014

(a) NH_4^+ and NO_3 (b) N_2O and NO (c) HNO_3 (d) NO_2 and N

135. Nitrogen is fixed in leguminous crops by b UPPSC Pre-2005

(a) Azotobacter (b) Rhizobium (c) Nitrobacter (d) Blue green algae

136. Nitrogen is taken by plants in the form of – c BHU UET-2012

(a) chloride (b) oxide (c) nitrate (d) nitrate acid

137. Non-essential but beneficial element to plant is : c UPPSC Pre-1995

(a) Calcium (b) Potassium (c) Sodium (d) Magnesium

138. Non-essential but useful nutrients for plants would include c IAS Pre-1998

(a) carbon and vanadium (b) vanadium and chlorine

(c) vanadium and sodium (d) sodium and chlorine

139. Number of essential elements required for plant growth is 2 RPSC Pre-2010

(1) 112 (2) 16 (3) 20 (4) 10

Now 17 elements is essential. New element is **Nickel.**

140. Number of essential nutrient element is : b UPPSC Pre-2002

(a) 17 (b) 16 (c) 22 (d) 25

Now 17 elements is essential. New element is **Nickel.**

141. Nutrient element acts as "energy currency" within plants is :- c ARO Agro-2016

(a) calcium (b) Potassium (c) Phosphorus (d) Nitrogen

142. Nutrient Input a TNPSC Ag-1995

(1) Potassium is essential for flowering, fruiting and seed formation

(2) Zinc application increase the flowering, fruiting and seed formation of plant

(3) Phosphorus uptake to plants results good flowering, fruiting and seed formation

(4) Nitrogen is used by the plants and produce good flowering , fruiting and seed formation

Of these statements

(A) 1 alone is correct (B) 2 alone is correct

(C) 3 and 4 are correct (D) 4 alone is correct

143. Nutrient Magnesium found in 2 RPSC Pre-2007

(1) Gypsum (2) Dolomite (3) Rock Phosphate (4) None of these

144. One kilogram nitrogen is equivalent to : b UPPSC Pre-1999

(a) 1.22 kg urea (b) 2.22 kg urea (c) 1.84 kg urea (d) 1.95 kg urea

145. One kilogram Nitrogen is equivalent to following amount of urea : c UPPSC Pre-2009

(a) 4.25 kg (b) 6.75 kg (c) 2.22 kg (d) 6.75 k

146. One of the following is a micronutrient required for plant growth – 2 TN AO-2018

(1) Nitrogen (N) (2) Manganese (Mn) (3) Phosphorous (P) (4) Potassium (K)

147. One of the linkages of Agriculture and livestock is used of fertilizer which of following nutrient is highest in poultry manure? **Ans.: Nitrogen** RRB SO-2018

148. Opening of stomata is related with… 2 RPSC Pre-1995

(1) Calcium (2) Potassium (3) Magnesium (4) Iron

149. Organic carbon content in the soil is a measure of : a UPPSC Pre-2009
(a) Available Nitrogen (b) Available Phosphorus
(c) Available Potash (d) Available Calcium

150. Organic matter of soil decreases the fixation of – 3 RPSC AAO-2022
(1) Nitrogen (2) Potassium (3) Phosphorus (4) None of the Above

151. Our soils are deficient in ____ micronutrient . 1 TN PSC Ag-II: 2001
(1) Zn (2) Cu (3) Mn (4) Mo

152. Out of 17 nutrients that are recognized by universally, essential for growth & development of plant, which is Macronutrient? **Ans.: Potassium** RRB SO-2021

153. Paddy takes nitrogen in the form of – 3 TN AO-2012
(1) NO_2^- (2) N_2 (3) NH_4^+ (4) NO_3^-

154. Phosphate containing mineral is : b UPPSC Pre-2007
(a) Dolomite (b) Apatite (c) Marble (d) Pyrites

155. Phosphate fixation is maximum at pH range of : b UPPSC Pre-2010
(a) 8.5 to 9.5 (b) 4.5 to 5.5 (c) 7.5 to 8.5 (d) 6.5 to 7.5

156. Phosphate fixation is maximum in the pH range of : a UPPSC Pre-2004
(a) 8.5 to 9.5 (b) 4.5 to 5.5 (c) 7.5 to 8.5 (d) 6.5 to 7.5

157. Phosphate fixation pushes the ZPC towards the…….pH.- 2 RPSC ARO Ag Chem -2022
(1) higher (2) lower (3) first increases than decreases (4) not affected

158. Phosphorus fixation refers to the phenomenon of c IAS Pre-1997
(a) absorption of phosphorus by the plant and synthesis of biological compounds
(b) leaching of phosphorus from soil by percolating waters
(c) conversion of soluble phosphorus into plant unavailable forms
(d) anion exchange with colloidal constituents of soil

159. Phosphorus is a necessary participant in – 4 TN ACF-2012
(1) Photosynthesis (2) Synthesis of starch, fasts and proteins
(3) Glycolysis (4) All these processes

160. Phosphorus is necessary for b Agri Pre PG-2014
(a) Shoot growth (b)Root development
(c) Bacterial growth (d)Fungal growth

161. Phosphours movement from soil to root is mainly through – c Gujrat AO-2017
(a) Diffusion (b) Mass flow
(c) Root interception (d) Osmosis

162. Phsophoric acid is mainly helpful in – 4 TNPSC – Ag: 1999
(1) Tillering (2) Emergenece (3) Germination (4) Grain formation

163. Pick the beneficial element of plant growth: B ADA MP-2015
(A) Fe (B) Si (C) Cobalt (D) Molybdenum

164. Pink colour of nodule in legumes is assoicated with a UPPSC Pre-2008
(a) Fe (b) Mn (c) Cu (d) Zn

165. Plant available potassium refers to: A PPSC ADO-2017
a) Exchangeable K plus soluble K b) Exchangeable K
c) Solution K d) Fixed K

166. Plant nutrient increasing disease resistance in plants is: c NSC S T-2019

(a) Nitrogen (b) Phosphorus (c) Potassium (d) None of these

167. Plants absorb nickel in the form of: B PPSC ADO-2017

a) Ni^{+} b) Ni^{2+} c) Ni^{3+} d) Ni^{-}

168. Plants absorb nitrogen from the soil solution in the from – d Agri Pre PG-2017

(a) Organic matter (b) Organic carbon (c) N_2O (d) NO_3

169. Plants absorb nitrogen in which form ? c Raj JET-2013

(a) NO_3^- (b) NH_4^+ (c) Both 1 & 2 (d) None of the above

170. Plants take most of the phosphorus in form of b Agri Pre PG-2014

(a) PO_4^{3-} (b)$H_2PO_4^-$ (c) HPO_4^{2-} (d)H_3PO_4

171. Postassium is absorbed by plants in the ionic form – b BHU PET-2012

(a) K (b) K^+ (c) K^{++} (d) KaO

172. Potassium (K*) is present in crop plants as – b BHU PET-2014

(a) Cell wall (b) Cell Sap (c) Mitochondria (d) Nucleus

173. Potassium content is maximum in : a UPPSC Pre-2001

(a) Feldspar (b) Pyroxine (c) Amphibole (d) Olivine

174. Primary inorganic form of phosphorus in mineral soils are - 2 RPSC ARO Ag Chem -2022

(1) Iron and aluminium phosphate minerals (2) Apatite

(3) Augite (4) Anorthite

175. Primary source of Nitrogen for plant is C ADA Guj-2013

(A) Soil (B) Water (C) Air (D) Manures and fertilizers

176. principal element of glass is – b BHU UET-2013

(a) lead (b) calcium silicate (c) magnesium (d) iron

177. Propounding of the essentiality of following elements for plants was made in different years : d UPPSC Pre-1995

(a) Nitrogen (b) Zinc (c) Manganese (d) Copper

178. Read the following statements and marks your answer according to the code given below : a UPPSC Pre-2002

Molybdenum is an important element in N-fixation by grain legumes because of the following :

I. Structural component of leghaemoglobin.

II. Essential component of nitrate reductase.

Ill. Essential component of nitrogenase enzyme.

IV. Component of chlorophyll.

Answer Code :

(a) I and II are correct (b) II and III are correct

(c) 111 and IV are correct (d) All four are correct

179. Recommended does of zinc sulphate for foliar application in paddy crop is : b UPPSC Pre-2009

(a) 2.5 kg/ha (b) 5.0 kg/ha (c) 7.5 kg/ha (d) 10.0 kg/ha

180. Relatively immobile element in the soil system is – b BHU PET-2012

(a) Nitrogen (b) Phosphorus (c) Potassium (d) Boron

181. Salts in the xylem ducts of the root are carried upward with B IAS Pre-2002

(a) photosynthesis (b) transpiration stream (c) respiration (d) guttation

182. Size of K^+ ion is similar to that of - 3 RPSC ARO Ag

(1) Zn^{2-} (2) Na^{+} (3) NH^{4+} (4) Mg^{2+} Chem -2022

183. Soil with high pH are generally deficient in — a — IAS Pre-1997
(a) Zn and Mn (b) B and Fe (c) Cu and Mo (d) Ca and Mg

184. Sulphur deficiency. occurs in soils when its level reaches to : — d — UPPSC Pre-2006
(a) 15-20 ppm (b) 12-14 ppm (c) 11-11 ppm (d) 8-10 ppm

185. Sulphur is an essential – — a — Gujrat AO-2017
(a) Secondary nutrient (b) Micro nutrient
(c) Macro nutrient (d) Non essential but beneficial nutrient

186. The 17th nutrient added to the list of essential elements is BHU PET-2016 — 4 — (RPSC (AO)-2009
(1) boron (2) molybdenum (3) chlorine (4) nickel

187. The availability of molybdenum is more at : — c — UPPSC Pre-1997
(a) pH -5.0 (b) pH 7.5 (c) pH 7.0 (d) pH 9.0

188. The availability of phosphorous is higher : — b — UPPSC Pre-1999
(a) Between 4.0 - 5.0 pH (b) Between 6.0 –7.0 pH
(c) Between 7.5 – 8.5 pH (d) between 9.0 – 9.5 pH

189. The availability of zinc is reduced when zinc sulphate is mixed with : — c — UPPSC Pre-1994
(a) Nitrogenous fertilizers (b) Potassic fertilizers
(c) Phosphatic fertilizers (d) All above

190. The available nitrate and ammonium form is only ……% of the total nitrogen: — a — BHU PET-2016
(a) 1-2 (b)2-4 (c) 4-6 (d) 6-8

191. The cake of which one of the following materials prepared with the comparable processing technology, contains the largest percentage of 'N' plant nutrient among all the materials given in the list? — B — BOD AO-2008
(A) Coconut (B) Neem (C) Palm nut (D) Mahua (E) Karanj

192. The carbon, hydrogen and oxygen constitutes nearly what percentage of the dry matter of the crop plants? — 3 — RPSC ARO Agro-2022
(1) 85-86 (2) 89-90 (3) 95-96 (4) 97-98

193. The concept of Q/I relationship was developed by — C — IAS Pre-2003
(a) Mitscherlich (b) Beckett (c) Schofield (d) Martin

194. The conversion factor for calculating P from P_2O_5 ? — d — IFFCO T -2019
(a) P_2O_5 x 2.29 (b) P x 0.44 (c) P x 2.29 (d) P_2O_5 x 0.44

195. The conversion factor to convert % P to %P_2O_5- — 1 — RPSC ARO Ag Chem -2022
(1) 2.29 (2) 1.29 (3) 2.90 (4) 0.29

196. The criteria of essentiality of nutrients in plants was given by — 2 — RPSC Pre-2003
(1) D J Nicholas (2)Arnon & Stout (3)J S Kanwar (4)Rajendra Prasad

197. The criteria of essentiality was finally refined and established by — 1 — (RPSC (AO)-2009
(1) Arnon (1954) (2) Theodore de Saussure (1804)
(3) Justus von Liebig (1840) (4) Maze (1915)

198. The criterion of essentiality of a plant nutrient was proposed by – — 2 — TN PSC Ag-I:1999
(1) Nicholas (2) Arnon (3) Malburt (4) Toffee

199. The critical concentrations of N, P and K nutrients in rice plant below which deficiency symptoms may develop are respectively. — 2 — TN PSC Ag-I:1999

(1) 3.5%, 1.0%, 1.5% (2) 2.5%, 0.1% , 1.0%

(3) 2.8% , 0.5% , 1.0% (4) 3.0%, 1.0% , 0.1%

200. The element normally deficient for plants in acidic soils is : **b** UPPSC Pre-2008

(a) Zn (b) Mo (c) Mn (d) Boron

201. The element which does NOT enter into permanent organic combination in plants is **D** IAS Pre-2001

(a) Nitrogen (b) Phosphorus (c) Magnesium (d) Potassium

202. The end product of nitrification is : **b** UPPSC Pre-1999

(a) N_2gas (b) N_2 and N_2O gases (c) NO_2 gas (d) NH_3 gas

203. The essential macro elements to plants : **1** RPSC Pre-1994

(1) P, K, Ca, Mg and S (2) Fe, Mn, Zn, Cu, B and Mo

(3)CAN, As, Gypsum (4) none of above

204. The essential nutrient elements for plant growth are : **4** RPSC Pre-2007

(1)Ten (2)Nine (3)Twenty (4) Seventeen

205. The essentiality for Fe (iron) in plants is discovered by………………… **c** Agri Pre PG-2022

(a) C. Sprengel in 1839 (b) J.S Mc Hargue in 1922

(c) E. Gris in 1843 (d) K. Warington in 1923

206. The following figure shows the relationship between nutrient concentration in the plants and yield of cops: **c** IAS Pre-1996

Drawing Nutrient concentration in tissues

Which portion (s) of the curve fall (s) in hidden hunger zone?

(a) A and B (b) B and C (c) B and C (d) A alone

207. The formula for balanced salt solution of mineral elements for plant growth was given by **1** MP PG PAT-2016

(1) Knop (2) Hoagland (3) Watson (4) Hill

208. The immobility of phosphorus in soils is primarily a result of orthophosphates **C** IAS Pre-2006

(a) reacting with Ca in acid soils and Fe and Al in neutral and basic soils

(b) being immobilized in organic matter

(c) reacting with Fe and al in acid soils and ca in neutral and basic soils

(d) reacting with K in acid soils and Ca in neutral and basic soils

209. The maximum P availability in most of the soil is near pH of - **2** RPSC ARO Agro-2022

(1) 6.0 (2) 6.5 (3) 7.0 (4) <5.0

210. The Metal atom present in chlorophyll is **b** Agri Pre PG-2014

(a)Manganese (b)Magnesium (c) Copper (d) Zinc

211. The micronutrient available in the alkaline pH is – **4** TNPSC – Ag: 1999

(1) Fe (2) Zn (3) B (4) Mo

212. The micronutrient which is a constituent of vitamin B_{12} is : **B** IAS Pre-2006

(a) Copper (b) Cobalt (c) Zinc (d) Boron

213. The micronutrient which is not available under acidic soil – **4** TN PSC Ag-I:1999

(1) Zinc (2) Iron (3) Mangenese (4) Molybdenum

214. The mineral chlorite has an extra layer of **d** IAS Pre-1994

(a) montmorillonite (b) illite (c) gibbsite (d) brusite

215. The most efficient use of phosphorus is achieved by : **c** UPPSC Pre-

(a)Broadcasting at the sowing time (b) Top dressing 21 days after sowing 1994
(c) basal placement at the time of sowing (d) foliar spray

216. The nitrogen content of leaf litter varies from: c Agri Pre PG-2021
(a) 50-150 kg (b) 500-1000 kg (c) 150-300 kg (d) > 1000 kg

217. The Nitrogen present in a 5 gram soil sample, is estimated by the modified Kjeldahl's method and the NH_3 evolved is absorbed in 4% boric acid solution the back titration value of 0.1 Normal Standard H_2SO_4 is 10 ml. the percentage of nitrogen in the soil sample will work out to be C IAS Pre-2001
(a) 0.10 (b) 0.14 (c) 0.28 (d) 0.36

218. The number of essential elements for plant growth is : b UPPSC Pre-1995
(a) 8 (b) 16 now 17 (c) 12 (d) 20

219. The number of essential elements required for the growth of higher plants is d IAS Pre-1995
(a) 3 (b) 6 (c) 8 (d) 16 (now-17)

220. The optimum temperature range for nitrification in soil is - 4 RPSC ARO Agro-2022
(t) 15-25°C (2) 20-25^{0}C (3) 36-40°C (4) 25-35°C

221. The organic P is mostly located in whichfraction of the soil humus? 2 RPSC ARO Ag Chem -2022
(1) Humic acid (2) Fulvic acid (3) Humin (4) Hymetomelanic acid

222. The phosphorus availability in a soil is moderate in the pH of – 2 TN PSC Ag-I:1999
(1) 4.0 to 4.5 (2) 5.0 to 5.5 (3) 6.0 to 6.5 (4) 7.0 to 7.5

223. The phosphorus content as pin the plough layer of one hectare of soil containing 0.1%P2O5 is a IAS Pre-1995
(a) 430kg (b) 860kg (c) 1290kg (d) 1500kg

224. The plant indicator which shows the presence of gold in soil is A IBS,AFO-2016
A. *Vallozia candida* B. *Astragalus species*
C. *Viscaria alpina* D. *Eriogonium ovalifolium* E. Salsola nitrate

225. The principal way in which P ank K ions move from the soil to the root of field crops : b UPPSC Pre-2001
(a) Root interception (b) Mass flow (c) Diffusion (d) None

226. The relative proportion of three major plant nutrient, keeping the percentage of nitrogen as one in a fertilizer is called : c UPPSC Pre-1998
(a) Fertilizer ratio (b) Fertilizer mixture (c) Fertilizer grade (d) None of the above

227. The secondary plant element is : c UPPSC Pre-1997
(a) Nitrogen (b) Zinc (c) Calcium (d) Boron

228. The seventeenth essential nutrient, Nickel essentiality was first recognized by the - 4 RPSC ARO Ag Chem -2022
(1) Amon& Stout (2) Sommer, Lipman&Mckinney
(3) Warington (4) Brown, Welch & Cary

229. The soils having 20 kg p/ha are classified as : c UPPSC Pre-2005
(a) High in P (b) Low in P (c) Medium in P (d) None of the above

230. The source of slowly available K in soils for crops is : c UPPSC Pre-2004
(a) Mineral K (b) Exchangeable K (c) Non exchangeable K (d) K in soil solution

231. The sufficiency range of the iron in plant tissue is (ppm) – 2 RPSC ARO Agro-2022
(1) 25-150 (2) 50-250 (3) 100-300 (4) 150-300

232. The threshold limit of micronutrients in plant parts is : 1 RPSC Pre-1994

(1) less than 1ppm (2) less than 50 ppm
(3) more than 50 ppm but less than 75 ppm
(4) more than 76 ppm but less than 100 ppm

233. There is a definite relationship between the extent of accumulation of a particular metal ion and the extent of stomatal opening. The metal ion in question is — c — IAS Pre-1994
(a) calcium (b) magnesium (c) potassium (d) sodium

234. This is a beneficial element for the plant — D — AO SDAU-2015
A. Zn B. Bo C. Ca D. Si

235. Total essential nutrients of plant ? — B — IBS,AFO-2013
(A) 10 (B) 17 (C) 14 (D) 12 (E)15

236. Water-logged soils are deficient : — a — UPPSC Pre-2008
(a) Available Zn (b) Available Fe (c) Available Mn (d) Available P

237. What is the form in which zinc is absorbed by the plants : — c — UPPSC Pre-1997
(a) Zn^{+} (b) Zn^{+++} (c) Zn^{++} (d) None of these

238. What is the form of sulphur (S) nutrient for plant absorption? — C — IBS,AFO-2017
A. SO_3^{+} B. SO C. SO_3 and SO_4 D. SO_2 E. SO_3

239. What is the predominant mechanism of transport of Zn to plant roots ? — b — IAS Pre-2009
(a) Mass flow (b) Diffusion
(c) Contact exchange (d) Root interception

240. What would be the connection of nutrients in plants when they are suffering from hidden hunger? — c — IAS Pre-1997
1. Above deficiency symptom zone 2. Below profitable yield zone
3. Below deficiency symptom zone 4. Above profitable yield zone
Select the correct answer using the codes given below
(a) 1and 4 (b) 2and 3 (c) 1and 2 (d) 3 and 4

241. Which among the following is a macro nutrient? **Ans.: Potassium** — PSB AO-2019

242. Which element has greater significance in biological nitrogen fixation: — d — UPPSC Pre-2001
(a) Nickel (b) Sulphur (c) Potassium (d) Molybdenum

243. Which element is a part of cytochrome oxidase? — 2 — MP PG PAT-2016
(1) Mg (2) Fe (3) Mo (4)All of these

244. Which element is added as essential nutrient in the year 1987? — D — AO KTPSC-2021
(A) Cadmium (B) Chromium (C) Iron (D) Nickel (E) Answer not known

245. Which element is associated with nitrogen fixation – — c — BHU PET-2011
(a) Potassium (b) Zinc (c) Molybdenum (d) Iron

246. Which element is common to nucleic acids, phospholipids, ATP and ADP? — 4 — MP PG PAT-2016
(1) Ca (2) B (3) Zn (4) P

247. Which element is immobile in plants… — 3 — RPSC Pre-1995
(1)Nitrogen (2)Potassium (3) Calcium (4) Phosphorus

248. Which element is maximum in black soil ? — c — NSC MT P-2019
(a) Nitrogen (b) Phosphorus (c) Potash (d)Sulphur

249. Which element is not phytotoxic : — 1 — RPSC Pre-1998
(1)Boron (2)Lithium (3) Fluorine (4) Selenium

250. Which enzyme helps to convert Amide form of nitrogen to ammoniacal nitrogen ? — c — UPPSC Pre-

(a) Nitrogenase (b) ratalase (c) Urease (d) Hydrogenase 2009

251. Which form of nitrogen absorbed by plant is toxic c Agri Pre PG-2013

(a) NH_4^+ (b)NO_3^- (c) NO_2^- (d)Amide

252. Which form of phosphate ions are absorbed by plants c BHU PET-2016

(a) $H_2PO_4^-$ (b) HPO_4^{-2} (c) $H_2PO_4^-$ and HPO_4^{-2} (d) PO_4^{-3}

253. Which group is required for chlorophyll synthesis 1 MP PG PAT-2016

(1) Fe, Mg (2) Mo, Ca (3) Cu, Ca (4) Ca, K

254. Which group of micronutrients is taken by plants in anionic form? 2 RPSC ARO Ag Chem -2022

(1) Zn, Cl, B (2) B, Mo, Cl (3) Fe, CI, Cu (4) Mn, Mo, B

255. Which is formed in aminization ? 4 Agri Pre PG-2019

(1) NO_3^- (2) NO_2^- (3) NH_4^+ (4) $R\text{-}NH_2$

256. Which is not a micro nutrient? C IBS,AFO-2015

(A) Copper (B) Zinc (C) Calcium (D) Chlorine (E) Boron

257. Which is not essential for plants? b MP PAT-2016

1. K, Ca 2. Na, Ni 3. Zn, B 4. Fe, Ca

258. Which is the beneficial element for rice: 2 RPSC Pre-2008

(1) Sodium (2)Silicon (3) Vanadium (4) Iodine

259. Which is the boron containing mineral? 2 RPSC ARO Ag Chem -2022

(1) Chalcopyrite (2) Tourmaline (3) Pyrite (4) Serpentine

260. Which is the secondary nutrient for plant growth ? 4 RPSC Pre-2010

(1) Ca (2) Mg (3) S (4) All of these

261. Which is the secondary nutrient? 1 RPSC Sch Lect.2022

(1) Sulphur (2) Phosphorus (3) Boron (4)Zinc

262. Which micro nutrient increases, if pH is increased C AO SDAU-2013

A Ca B. Mg C.Mo D. Cu

263. Which nitrogen transformation process is responsible for causing a decrease in nitrate –N under anaerobic condition? C IAS Pre-2007

(a) Mineralization (b) Nitrification (c) Denitrification (d) Immobilization

264. Which nutrient is highly available in acidic soil – 1 Ag Sup JAU 2017

(1) Iron (2) Molybdenum (3) Boron (4) Calcium

265. Which nutrient is highly available in alkaline soil – 1 Ag Sup JAU 2017

(1) Molybdenum (2) Boron (3) Magnesium (4) Sulphur

266. Which nutrient is important for nitrogen fixation in legumes ? d BHU UET-2010

(a) Cl (b) P_2O_5 (c) K_2O (d) Mo

267. Which nutrient uptake is reduced in plants due to manganese toxicity (Mn) ? 1 Raj JET-2020

(1) Ca (2) P (3) N (4) Zn

268. Which of the following are critical elements? 1 MP PG PAT-2016

(1) N, P, K (2) O, N, H (3) Zn, Fe, Cu (4) Cl, Fe, H

269. Which of the following are the criteria for determining the essentiality of nutrient elements? b IAS Pre-1998

1. A deficiency of the particular elements makes it impossible for the plant to grow normally or complete its life cycle

2. The deficiency symptoms can be corrected only by supplying the nutrient in

question

3. The nutrient is abundantly present in the soil for rapid plant absorption

4. The elements is directly involved in the plant metabolism

(a) 1and 3 (b) 1,2 and 4 (c) 2,3 and 4 (d) 1,2,3 and 4

270. Which of the following are the criteria used to designate an element as "essential element" in plants? C IAS Pre-2004

1. It should have a clear physiological role

2. Its absence prevents the plants from completing its life-cycle

3. It is required for all metabolic processes in plants

4. Its absence cannot be satisfied by supplementing with another essential element

Select the correct answer using the codes given below

(a) 1,2 and 3 (b) 1and 4 (c) 1,2 and 4 (d) 3and 4

271. Which of the following element is 'Energy currency' of Cell ? 2 Raj JET-2018

(1) Potassium (2) Phosphorus (3) Boron (4) Zinc

272. Which of the following elements is called as nanonutrient element ? d BHU PET-2015

(a) Zinc (b) Copper (c) Iron (d) Molybdenum

273. Which of the following elements is not essential element for plants but proves to be beneficial for some ? 4 RPSC, AAO-2009

(1) Copper (2) Iron (3) Sulphur (4) Sodium

274. Which of the following elements is not essential element of plants but proves to be beneficial for some ? b UPPSC Pre-1994

(a) Copper (b) Sodium (c) Boron (d) Iodine

275. Which of the following elements is not micronutrient ? c BHU UET-2011

(a) Copper (b) Boron (c) Sulphur (d) Iron

276. Which of the following elements play an important role in nitrogen metabolism ? B TO MPUAT-2014

(A) Fe (B) Mo (C) Mg (D) Mn

277. Which of the following essential elements are regarded as oxidation –reduction regulators? 4 RPSC Pre-2008

(1) Hydrogen, Oxygen, carbon

(2) Nitrogen, Phosphorous, Sulphur

(3) Potassium, Calcium, Sodium, Magnesium

(4) Iron, Manganese, Molybdenum, Copper, Boron, Zinc

278. Which of the following fertilizers supply both N and P to plants simultaneously 4 TN AO-2008

I. Ammonium phosphate

II. Basic slag

III. Nitrophosphate

IV. Urea

(1) I and II (2) II and III (3) III and IV (4) I and III

279. Which of the following groups belongs to the macro- nutrients – 4 TN AO-2008

(1) C, H, O (2) Ca, Mg, S (3) Zn, Mn, S (4) N, P, K

280. Which of the following is a constituent element of chlorophyll ? 2 Ag sup 2018

(1) Mn (2) Mg (3) Mo (4) K

281. Which of the following is a micronutrient : c UPPSC Pre-

(a)Calcium (b) Nitreogen (c) Zinc (d) Phosphorus 1994

282. Which of the following is a micronutrient ? 4 RPSC, AAO-2009
(1) Magnesium (2) Potassium (3) Phosphorus (4) Manganese

283. Which of the following is an essential plant nutrient ? 2 Agri Pre PG-2015
(1) Al (2) Cu (3) Cd (4) Pb

284. Which of the following is an extremely toxic heavy metal for plants 1 Agri Pre PG-2015
(1) cadmium (2) mercury (3) copper (4) nickle

285. Which of the following is correct : a UPPSC Pre-2002
(a) P_2O_5 x 0.44 = P (b) P_2O_5 x 2.29 = P (c) P_2O_5 x 0.83 = P (d) P_2O_5 x 1.20 = P

286. Which of the following is macro nutrient ? e IBS,AFO-2020
(a) Iron (b) Calcium (c) Boron (d) Sodium (e) Potassium

287. Which of the following is not a micronutrient for plants? B IBS,AFO-2017
A. Iron B. Nitrogen C. Copper D. Boron E. Zinc

288. Which of the following is not an essential element for plant 2 RPSC Pre-2007
(1) Iron (2) Copper (3) Sodium (4) manganese

289. Which of the following is not an essential Plant nutrient element ? b Raj JET-2017
(a) Cl (b) I (c) Mo (d) Mn

290. Which of the following is not considered as fertilizer nutrient : 1 RPSC Pre-2003
(1) C (2) N (3) S (4) Zn

291. Which of the following is not correct regarding fertilizer ? **Ans.: soil having same available nutrient may not supply same amount of nutrient even if to the same crop** RRB SO-2020

292. Which of the following is the richest source of nitrogen? b MP PAT-2016
(a) Onion (b) Dried blood (c) Fish manure (d) None of above

293. Which of the following micronutrients is especially tightly held by organic matter that its availability to crop plants can be very low in organic soils? C IAS Pre-2007
(a) Zinc (b) Iron (c) Copper (d) Manganese

294. Which of the following mineral elements is essential for nitrogen metabolism in green plants ...? 3 RPSC Pre-1995
(1)P (2)K (3) Mo (4) Zn

295. Which of the following nutrient element is immobile in plants:- 3 RPSC, AO-2016
(1) P (2) S (3) Ca (4) Mn

296. Which of the following nutrient is absorbed in both cationic and anionic form by crop plants ? 1 Raj JET-2020
(1) Nitrogen (2) Potassium (3) Iron (4) Molybdenum

297. Which of the following nutrient is cycled in the soil through atmosphere ? 3 RPSC, AAO-2009
(1) Phosphorous (2) Zinc 3) Nitrogen (4) Potash

298. Which of the following nutrient is fast mobile – a BHU PET-2010
(a) Nitrogen (b) Calcium (c) Sulphur (d) Potassium

299. Which of the following nutrient is lowest in cattle manure? **Ans.: Sulphur** RRB SO-2018

300. Which of the following nutrient plays an important role to activate various enzymes and also plays a major role in transport of water? E IBS,AFO-2017
A. Nitrogen B. Phosphorus C. Copper D. Calcium E. Potassium

301. Which of the following nutrients are involved in redox reactions ? 2 Agri Pre PG-2019
(1) B and Si (2) Cu and Zn (3) Cl and Mn (4) Fe and Mg

302. Which of the following nutrients is absorbs in combined form by the plants? b MP PAT-2013
(A) Potassium (B) Phosphorus (C) Zinc (D) Iron

303. Which of the following nutrients is beneficial but not essential to plants? b NSC S T-2019
(a) Calcium (b) Sodium (c) Iron (d) Boron

304. Which of the following nutrients is known as oxidation reduction regulator 1 RPSC Pre-1999
(1) Iron (2) Sulphur (3)Pottasium (4) Carbon

305. Which of the following nutrients plays an important role in root growth and promotes the establishment of younger plants? E IBS,AFO-2017
A. Calcium B. Potassium C. Nitrogen D. Copper E. Phosphorus

306. Which of the following nutruient is cycled in the soil through atmosphere ? d UPPSC Pre-1994
(a) Phosphorus (b) Zinc (c) Potash (d) Nitrogen

307. Which of the following pairs are correctly matched? a IAS Pre-1994
1. Copper.....'Die back' disease of citrus
2. Manganese ......'Water core' in turnip
3. Boron.....'Heart rot' of sugarbeet
(a) 1,2,3 (b) 1,2 (c) land 3 (d) 2 and 3

308. Which of the following pairs related to nutrient deficiency symptoms is not correctly matched ? 3 RPSC, AAO-2019
(1) Ca – Deficiency symptoms appear on terminal bud and it dries with time
(2) S – Chlorosis symptoms appear on younger leaves
(3) Fe – Chlorosis symptoms appear on older leaves
(4) N – Chlorosis symptoms appear on older leaves

309. Which of the following plant essential element is contained in tourmaline ? 2 RPSC Pre-1999
(1) Zinc (2) Boron (3) Molybdenum (4) Copper

310. Which of the following scientists proposed the Critical level concept for nutrients in soil? B IAS Pre-2005
(a) Jackson (b) Cate and Nelson (c) Stem (d) Schofield

311. Which of the plants obtain nitrogen from the soil in the form : c UPPSC Pre-1994
(a) Nitrite (b) Free nitrogen gas (c) Nitrate (d) Nitric acid

312. Which of these groups of nutrient elements are structure elements / 4 RPSC Pre-2007
(1) Nitrogen, Phosphorus, Potassium (2) Calcium, Magnesium, Sulpur
(3) Boron, Manganese, Molybdenum (4) Carbon, Hydrogen, Oxygen

313. Which one of following is a manganese containing mineral ? D IAS Pre-2002
(a) Magnetite (b) Tourmaline (c) Apatite (d) Pyrolusite

314. Which one of the following element is not essential for plant growth is: B PPSC ADO-2017
a) Nickle b) Sodium c) Manganese d) Zinc

315. Which one of the following elements is a micronutirent – a RPSC, AAO-2012
(a) Boron (b) Nitrogen (c) Phosphorus (d) Magnisium

316. Which one of the following elements is non-essential but useful for plants ? b UPPSC Pre-2007
(a) Magnesium (b) Sodium (c) Chlorine (d) Copper

317. Which one of the following elements is nonessential but useful for crops ? b UPPSC Pre-

(a) Magnesium (b) Sodium (c) Chlorine (d) Copper 2006

318. Which one of the following essential nutrient elements is absorbed both as an anion and a cation by some plants? A PPSC ADO-2017

a) Nitrogen b) Potassium c) Calcium d) Sulphur

319. Which one of the following formulage gives the phosphate potential ? B IAS Pre-2006

(a) $pCa - \frac{1}{2}pHPO_4$ (b) $\frac{1}{2}PCa + pH_2PO_4$

(c) $\frac{1}{2}pCa - pH_2PO_4$ (d) $pCa + \frac{1}{2}pH_2PO_4$

320. Which one of the following groups of nutrients is absorbed by plants only in anionic form ? B IAS Pre-2007

(a) Nitrogen, Manganese and Phophours (b) Phosphours, Sulphur and boron

(c) Copper, Zinc and Iron (d) Molybdenum, potassium and manganese

321. Which one of the following has organic form of sulphur? B IAS Pre-2002

(a) Purine (b) Cysteine (c) RNA (d) Phytin

322. Which one of the following is a micronutrient 2 RPSC Pre-2010

(1) Magnesium (2) Manganese (3) Calcium (4) Potassium

323. Which one of the following is a micronutrient – a Agri Pre PG-2017

(a) Mn (b) S (c) Ca (d) Mg

324. Which one of the following is a micronutrient for plants ? 1 Raj JET-2020

(1) Fe (2) Ca (3) Mg (4) S

325. Which one of the following is correct in relation to Ca and B : c UPPSC Pre-1998

(a)Highly mobile in soil (b)Moderately mobile in soil

(c)Less mobile in soil (d)Immobile in soil

326. Which one of the following is correctly matched ? 2 TN PSC Ag-I:1999

(1) K - Is more available in vertisol

(2) S - Is mirco nutrient

(3) P - Is very volatile substance

(4) N - Controls stomatal opening

327. Which one of the following is essential element for crops ? c UPPSC Pre-2007

(a) Silica (b) Vanadium (c) Sodium (d) Nickel

328. Which one of the following is essential element to the plants B PPSC ADO-2020

a) Strontium (Sr) b) Nickel (Ni) c) Chromium (Cr) d) Arsenic (As)

329. Which one of the following is micronutrient anion ? 1 Agri Pre PG-2018

(1) B (2) Fe (3) Mn (4) Zn

330. Which one of the following is not a micronutrients ? 2 RPSC ACF Horti -2018

(1) Molybdenum (2) Magnesium (3) Boron (4) Zinc

331. Which one of the following is not a criterion for essentiality of plant nutrient 2 RPSC Pre-2010

(1) Plant can not complete life cycle (2) Can not be substituted

(3) Directly involved in metabolism (4) Is present in the plant

332. Which one of the following is not a critical method of soil fertility evaluation? A IAS Pre-2004

(a) Nutrient deficiency symptoms (b) Soil testing

(c) Field experiments (d) Plant tissue tests

333. Which one of the following is not a micronutrient 2 RPSC Pre-2010

(1) Chlorine (2) Sulphur (3) Boron (4) Copper

334. Which one of the following is not a micronutrient : — b — UPPSC Pre-1996

(a) Copper (b) Sulphur (c) Boron (d) Manganese

335. Which one of the following is not essential plant nutrient — 3 — RPSC Pre-2010

(1) Calcium (2) Magnesium (3) Sodium (4) Iron

336. Which one of the following is the micronutrient that favours uptake of Calcium and its translocation to different plant organs? — B — IAS Pre-2008

(a) Molybdenum (b) Boron (c) Zinc (d) Manganese

337. Which one of the following manures has the narrowest C/N ratio : — a — UPPSC Pre-2002

(a) Bigas slurry (b) Groundnut cake (c) Farmyard manure (d) Compost

338. Which one of the following micronutrient elements is concerned with the regulation of oxidation reduction potential within the cells? — B — IAS Pre-2002

(a) Boron (b) Copper (c) Manganese (d) Zinc

339. Which one of the following minerals is the main source of boron in soils? — b — IAS Pre-1994

(a) Pyrolusite (b) Tourmaline (c) Haematite (d) Hemimorphy

340. Which one of the following nutrient elements is involved in osmotic regulations and maintenance of turgor pressure in plant cell? — C — IAS Pre-2004

(a) Nitrogen (b) Phosphorus (c) Potassium (d) Sulphur

341. Which one of the following nutrients has been added as 17th essential plant nutrient ? — c — Raj JET-2014

(a) Silicon (b) Chromium (c) Nickel (d) Selenium

342. Which one of the following nutrients is known as Ultramicronutrien- — c — Raj JET-2014

(a) Manganese (b) Zinc (c) Molybedenum (d) Iron

343. Which one of the following nutrients is most immobile in soil — 1 — RPSC Pre-2010

(1) Nitrogen (2) Phosphorus (3) potassium (4) Sulphur

344. Which one of the following nutrients promotes root growth, keeps the soil reaction neutral and improves the soil structure? — C — IAS Pre-2006

(a) Sulphur (b) Potassium (c) Calcium (d) Magnesium

345. Which one of the following pairs of plant nutrients other than phosphorus re present in superphosphate? — C — IAS Pre-2002

(a) Calcium and iron (b) Sulphur and nitrogen
(c) calcium and sulphur (d) Calcium and potassium

346. Which one of the following plants nutrients is useful in increasing resistance to disease and insect pests? — d — IAS Pre-1997

(a) Calcium (b) Phosphorus (c) Nitrogen (d) Potassium

347. Which one of the following sets of nutrients is beneficial for plant growth ? — c — UPPSC Pre-2006

(a) Na, Pb, Cd, Ni (b) Si, Co, Cr, Zn (c) Si, Na, Co, Se (d) Si, V, Hg, Co

348. Who gave the concept of essential elements in higher plants – — b — BHU PET-2012

(a) Stout and Rain (b) Arnon and Stout
(c) Hoagland and Plant (d) Epstein and Mettler

349. Who proposed the criteria of essentiality of plant nutrients: — 1 — RPSC Pre-2008

(1) D.I.Arnon (2)E A Mischerlich
(3) Theosphrastus (4) D.A.Russel

350. Who suggest the term functional nutrients? c Agri Pre PG-2021

(a) Criss (b) Leibig (c) Nicholus (d) Arnon

351. Zinc is absorbed by the plant from the soil in the ionic form – c BHU PET-2014

(a) Zn (b) Zn^{+++} (c) Zn^{++} (d) ZnO

352. Zinc is antagonistic with – c Gujrat AO-2017

(a) Available nitrogen (b) Potassium availability

(c) Available Phosphorus (d) Available copper

353. Zinc, iron, copper, boron, manganese and molybdenum are called micronutrients because they are c IAS Pre-1993

(a) Nutrients of microscopic significance

(b) nutrients which produce microscopic effects

(c) Essential nutrients but are required in minute quantities

(d) nutrients required by micro-organisms

CHAPTER- 140 : PLANT NUTRIENT DEFICIENCY PYQ'S

1. **'Khaira'** disease in paddy is caused by : 2 RPSC Pre-1999
(1) Phanenogamous (2) Zinc deficiency
(3)Cuscuta (4) Manganese deficiency

2. **"Browning of cauliflower"** disease is attributed to the plant deficiency of the micronutrient a BHU PET-2013
(a) Boron (b) Molybdenum (c) Copper (d) Zinc

3. a situation in which a crop needs more of a given element, yet has shown no deficiency symptoms is referred as - 3 RPSC, AAO-2018
(1) quantitative deficiency (2) bare economic deficiency
(3) hidden hunger (4) essential hungar

4. Chlorosis, necrosis, reddening, stunting, new growth cessation etc, of plants are characterized as – b Agri Pre PG-2020
(a) Visual nutrient toxicity symptoms (b) Visual nutrient deficiency symptoms
(c) Visual frost injury symptoms (d) Visual water stress symptoms

5. Copper deficiency causes : 3 RPSC Pre-2008
(1) 'white bud' in maize (2)'Grey speck' in oat
(3) Ergot in Bajra (4) 'Khaira' in rice

6. Critical deficiency level (mg Kg^{-1}) of available zinc (DTPA-Zn) in alluvial soils of Indo Gangetic plain is : c BHU PET-2013
(a) 0.20 (b) 0.45 (c) 0.60 (d) 3.50

7. Deficiency of Mo causes: c MP PAT-2016
1. Wilting 2. Chlorosis
3. Necrosis and mottling 4. None of these

8. Deficiency of which element causes *Khaira* disease in rice ? d BHU PET-2017
(a) Ca (b) Mg (c) B (d) Zn

9. Deficiency of which element in soil causes chlorosis in plants - 2 MP PG PAT-2016
(1) Iron (2) Magnesium (3) Carbon (4) Sodium

10. Deficiency of which of the following elements cause 'white bud' of maize 1 RPSC Pre-1999
(1) Zinc (2) Copper (3) Iron (4) Sulphur

11. Deficiency symptom of sulphur first appears on ? a BHU UET-2015
(a) younger leaves (b) older leaves (c) middle leaves (d) None of these

12. Deficiency symptoms of which nutrient element appears in terminal buds of the plant ? a BHU PET-2017
(a) Boron (b) Copper (c) Iron (d) Zinc

13. Excess amount of which of the following nutrients in soil causes iron and zinc deficiency in plants ? b BHU PET-2017
(a) Nitrogen (b) Phosphorus (c) Potassium (d) Calcium

14. Iron deficiency is normally shown on crop plant parts : a Raj JET-2015
(a) New and upper leaves (b) Old and lower leaves
(c) Lowest leaves (d) None of the above

15. *Khaira* disease in rice is caused due to deficiency of d Agri Pre PG-

(a) Magnesium (b) Calcium (c)Boron (d)Zn 2014

16. **Khaira** disease is associated with – **b** BHU UET-2012

(a) wheat (b) paddy (c) maize (d) barley

17. Khaira disease of rice is caused by : **3** Agri Pre PG-2018

(1) Rhizoctonia Spp (2) Aspergillus Spp

(3) Deficiency of Zinc (4) Xanthomonas Spp

18. **Khaira** disease of rice is due to deficiency of – **a** RPSC, AAO-2012

(a) Zinc (b) Iron (c) Nitrogen (d) Calcium

19. Match the Column – I with Column – 2 and choose the correct answer using the codes given below : **1** RPSC, AAO-2019

Column – I	Column – 2
Nutrients	Physiological functions/ deficiency symptoms
1. P	i. plays important role in water tolerance
2. K	ii. Involved in energy transfer
3. B	iii. deficiency causes KHAIRA disease in rice
4. Zn	iv. plays vital role in pollen germination and pollen tube growth

Codes :

	1	2	3	4
(1)	ii	i	iv	iii
(2)	i	iii	ii	iv
(3)	iii	ii	i	iv
(4)	iv	i	ii	iii

20. Name of the element responsible for Jhulsa disease in plant is – **b** BHU UET-2013

(a) sulphur (b) zinc (c) iron (d) calcium

21. Pica disease in animals is caused by the deficiency of – **d** BHU UET-2010

(a) potassium (b) calcium (c) manganese (d) phosphorus

22. Premature leaf fall is due to deficiency of **2** Agri Pre PG-2016

(1) Phosphorus (2) Nitrogen (3) Iron (4) Calcium

23. Symptoms of iron deficiency in plants are.............. **2** RPSC Pre-1995

(1) Yellowing of lower leaves

(2) Yellowing of young growing leaves

(3) Yellowing of whole plant (4) Drying of lower leaves

24. The '*Khaira disease*' of rice is caused due to the deficiency of the following micronutrient – **b** BHU PET-2017

(a) Boron (b) Zinc (c) Molybdenum (d) Nickel

25. The deficiency of nitrogen in plants first appears on **2** RPSC Pre-2010

(1) Stems (2) Older leaves (3) Roots (4) Younger leaves

26. The most deficient micro- nutrient in Indian soil is – **a** RPSC, AAO-2012

(a) Zn (b) Fe (c) Mn (d) N_2

27. Which micro nutrient deficiency is maximum in Gujarat – **d** Gujrat AO-2017

(a) Molybdenum (b) Copper (c) Manganese (d) Zinc

28. Which micronutrient is most deficient in Indo Gangetic alluvium soils: **3** RPSC Pre-1998

(1)Iron (2)Copper (3) Zinc (4)Manganese

29. Which of the following crop is used as indicator crop for the deficiency of nitrogen, phosphorus and zinc? **4** RPSC, AAO-2018

(A) Potato (B) Cauliflower (C) Rice (D) Maize

30. Which of the following deficiency is observed in young leaves ? **c** Gujrat AO-2017

(a) Nitrogen (b) Phosphorus (c) Iron (d) Zinc

31. Which one of the following is correctly matched ? **1** RPSC Pre-1994

(1) manganese : gray speck of oats

(2) molybdenum : white bud if maize

(3) zinc : heart rot of sugarbeet

(4) boron : whiptail of cauliflower

32. Which one of the following pairs is not correctly matched ? **4** AARO Agro-2016

(1) Magnesium - Green veins in old leaves

(2) Iron - Green veins in new leaves

(3) Copper - Yellow veins in new leaves

(4) Manganese - Yellow veins in old leaves

33. White irregular spots between veins of upper leaves of maize plant shows the deficiency of : **3** RPSC Pre-2003

(1) Copper (2) Molybdenum (3) Manganese (4) Boron

34. Zinc deficiency in rice cause the disease : **1** RPSC Pre-2003

(1) Khaira (2) Bacterial leaf blight

(3) Bacteria leaf streak (4) Blast

35. The deficiency of copper in plants causes which disease? **2** RPSC AAO-2022

(1) Whiptail disease (2) Die-back disease

(3) Early blight disease (4) Khaira disease

36. Interveinal cholorosis fo the younger leaves of the plants is the characteristic symptom of **c** IAS Pre-1993

(a) Boron deficiency (b) Zinc deficiency

(c) Iron deficiency (d) phosphorus deficiency

37. Consider the following symptoms: **d** IAS Pre-1995

1. Younger leaves show signs of deficiency first.

2. High amide and nitrate nitrogen

3. Effect more pronounced on shoots when compared to roots and cruciferous plants develop narrow leaf lamina

4. Blockage of the synthesis of cystine, methionine etc.

Development of the above mentioned symptoms is attributable to the deficiency of

(a) calcium (b) magnesium (c) nitrogen (d) sulphur

38. Match List first (Symptoms) with List second (causes) and select the correct answer: **d** IAS Pre-1995

List firstList second

A. Khaira disease of rice 1. Phosphorus deficiency

B. Browning of cauliflower 2. Molybdenum deficiency

C. Purple colouration of maize leaves 3. potassium deficiency

D. Firing of tobacco leaves 4. Zinc deficiency

	A	B	C	D		A	B	C	D
a)	2	4	3	1	b)	2	4	1	3
c)	4	2	3	1	d)	4	2	1	3

39. Consider the following symptoms of iron deficiency : **c** IAS Pre-1999

1. Leaves turning entirely white 2. Entirely leaves developing chlorosis

3. Young leaves developing interveinal chloriosis

The correct sequence in which these symptoms develop is

(a) 1,2,3 (b) 3,1,2 (c) 3,2,1 (d) 2,3,1

40. Match List I (Deficiency disease) with List II (Remedy) and select the correct answer using the codes given below the lists **c** IAS Pre-1999

List I	*List II*
A. Reclamation disease of cereals	1. Ammonium molybdate
B. White bud of Maize	2. Borax
C. Whiptail of cauliflower	3. Copper sulphate
D. Hollow heart of groundnut	4. Ferrous sulphate
	5. Zinc sulphate

	A	B	C	D		A	B	C	D
(a)	3	4	2	5	(b)	2	4	3	
(c)	3	5	1	2	(d)	4	5	1	2

41. Potato is an indicator plant for which one of the following soil deficiencies? **a** IAS Pre-1999

(a) Potassium (b) Calcium (c) Nitrogen (d) Phosphorus

42. The plateau with little growth-grate and continuing accumulation of nutrient element in the plants can be defined as **D** IAS Pre-2001

(a) severe deficiency range (b) toxic range

(c) moderate deficiency range (d) sufficiency range

43. Match List I with List II and select the correct answer **B** IAS Pre-2002

List I (Micrountrients)	**ListII (Deficiency symptoms)**
A. Copper	1. Heart rot of sugarbeet
B. Calcium	2. Exanthema
C. Zinc	3. Little leaf in citrus
D. Boron	4. Blossom end rot in tomato

	A	B	C	D		A	B	C	D
(a)	4	3	1	2	(d)	3	4	1	2
(c)	4	3	2	1	(d)	3	4	2	1

44. Consider the following disorders in crops **B** IAS Pre-2003

1. Heart rot of sugarbeet 2. Speckled yellow of sugarbeet

3. Grey speck disease of oats 4. Pahala blight of sugarcane

Which of these are caused due to Mn-deficiency?

(a) 1,2 and 3 (d) 2,3 and 4 (c) 1,2 and 4 (d) 1,3 and 4

45. The deficiency of which one of the following causes Khaira disease? **D** IAS Pre-2005

(a) Copper (b) Iron (c) Phosphorus (d) Zinc

46. The deficiency of which one of the following causes lime induced chlorosis? **D** IAS Pre-2008

(a) Iron (b) Zinc (c) Boron (d) Magnesium

47. Consider the following pairs **D** IAS Pre-2008

1. Molybdenum deficiency ....Whip-tail disease of cauliflower

2. Zinc deficiency ....Little leaf in mango

3. Boron deficiency .... Brown rot of cauliflower

Which of the pairs given above are correctly matched

(a) 1and 2 (b) 2and 3 (c) 1and 3 (d) 1,2 and 3

48. The P-deficiency symptom visible on foliage of cereal crops is **d** IAS Pre-2009

(a) General yellowing of young leaves

(b) Development of reddish brown or purple colour on older leaves

(c) Marginal scorching of older leaves

(d) Interveinal chlorosis of young leaves

49. Severity of '**Club root**' of crucifers a\can be reduced by the application of- **b** Agri Pre PG-2022

(a) Gypsum (b) Lime (c) Fertilizer (d) Wood chips

50. Interveinalchlorisis on new leaves remains unfolding & veins remain green with full chlorosisbackground ? **e** IBS,AFO-2020

(a)Manganese (b) Magnesium (c) Nitrogen (d)Sulphur (e) Iron

51. Which among the following nutrient deficiency symptom is major veins remain green, top veins become short and slender and chlorosis on new leaf? **a** IBS,AFO-2019

(a) Fe (b) Mn (c) Cu (d) Bo (e) Zn

52. Symptoms of which nutrient deficiency appears first on older leaves and then advance up the stem to younger leaves? **A** IBS,AFO-2016

A. Nitrogen deficiency B. Phosphorus deficiency

C. Potassium deficiency D. Magnesium deficiency E. Calcium deficiency

53. Symptoms of iron deficiency in plants are **D** ADA Guj-2013

(A) Yellowing of whole plant (B) Drying of lower leaves

(C) Yellowing of lower leaves (D) Yellowing of young growing leaves

54. Deficiency symptoms of potassium first appeared on? **B** ADA MP-2015

(A) upper leaf / new leaf (B) leaf /older leaf

(C) flower (D) (A) & (C) both

55. Potassium deficiency symptoms in plants appear In first in **A** AO GPSC-2013

(A) Lower most leaves (B) Upper most leaves

(C) Middle leaves (D) All of these

56. Deficiency symptom of potassium occurs on **C** AO SDAU-2013

A. Older leaves B. Lower leaves

C.Both A and B D. None of these

57. Marginal leaf burning is due to **C** AO SDAU-2015

A. Nitrogen B. Phosphorus C. Potash D. All of these

58. Yellowing of older leaves occur due to deficiency of **B** AO SDAU-2015

A. Phosphorus B. Nitrogen C.Potash D.Calcium

59. Scorching of burning on margins of bottom leaves manifests the deficiency of : **d** UPPSC Pre-

(a)Nitrogen (b) Copper (c) Zinc (d) Potassium 1995

60. Deficiency sympotms of calcium on plants are first noticed at : c UPPSC Pre-1997

(a)Lwer leaves (b) Terminal leaves (c) Middle leaves (d) All leaves

61. Iron deficiency is prominent in : b UPPSC Pre-1999

(a) Neutral soil (b) Calcareous soil (c) Acidic soil (d) Water logged soil

62. Sodium molybdate corrects whiptail disease of cauliflower as it contains : b UPPSC Pre-2000

(a) 25% Mo (b) 39% Mo (c) 54% Mo (d) 60% Mo

63. Nitrogen deficiency symptoms is plants first appear on : 2 UPPSC Pre-2003

(1) middle leaves (2) lower leaves (3) upper leaves (4) all of the above

64. Zinc deficiency in soil is aggravated due to : d UPPSC Pre-2006

(a) Higher availability of phosphorous (b) Higher availability of iron

(c) Saline reaction (d) All of the above

65. Deficiency symptoms of calcium on plants are first noticed at : c UPPSC Pre-2006

(a) Lower leaves (b) Middle leaves (c) Terminal leaves (d) All leaves

66. Top sickness of tobacco is due to deficiency of : a UPPSC Pre-2007

(a) Boron (b) Manganese (c) Copper (d) Molybdenum

67. Match List-I with List-II and select the correct answer using the codes given below : a UPPSC Pre-2007

List-I (Deficient Nutrients)	List-II (Indicator Plants)
A. Nitrogen	1. Rape Seed
B. Phosphorus	2. Potato
C. Potassium	3. Cauliflower
D. Boron	4. Sugar beet

Code :

	A	B	C	D
(a)	3	1	2	4
(b)	4	3	1	2
(c)	2	3	1	4
(d)	I	2	3	4

68. Deficiency symptoms of calcium on plants are first noticed at : c UPPSC Pre-2007

(a) Lower leaves (b) Middle leaves (c) Terminal leaves (d) All leaves

69. Browning in cauliflower is corrected by : b UPPSC Pre-2007

(a) Ammonium molybdate (b) Boric acid (c) Zinc Sulphate (d) Urea

70. Interveinal chlorosis occurs due to deficiency of : d UPPSC Pre-2008

(a) Nitrogen (b) Potassium (c) Zinc (d) Fe

71. Excess of Ca availability in soil causes : b UPPSC Pre-2010

(a) Nitrogen deficiency (b) Phosphorus deficiency

(c) Potassium deficiency (d) All the above

72. Calcium deficiency causes toxicity of ? b NSC MT P-2019

(a) Iron (b) Manganese (c) Boron (d) None of these

73. Blue chaff disease of oats is due to deficiency of ? b NSC MT P-2019

(a) Copper (b) Molybdenum (c) Boron (d) Manganese

74. Purple pigmentation in Brassicas is due to ? **d** NSC MT P-2019
(a) Deficiency of Iron (b) Excessive nitrogen
(c)Pottassium deficiency (d) Phosphorus deficiency

75. Copper deficiency is a problem in which part of India ? **b** NSC MT P-2019
(a) North (b) South (c) East (d) West

76. Boron deficiency causes ? **d** NSC MT P-2019
(a) Blue chaff disease (b) Die back disease
(c) Gray speck disease (d) Brown heart disease

77. Typical nitrogen deficiency symptoms in crop plants under high nitrogen content is due to the deficiency of **A** HPSC ADO-2022
(A) Mo (B) B (C) Zn (D) Mn

78. Crop symptom due to nitrogen deficiency in soil is – **4** TN AO-2008
(1) Bronzing (2) Browning (3) Reddening (4) Yellowing

79. Yellow spots on the leaves of grape indicates the deficiency – **1** TN PSC Ag-I:1999
(1) Boron (2) Zinc (3) Iron (4) None of these

80. The zinc deficiency in rice causes – **4** TN PSC Ag-2003
(1) Bacterial leaf streak (2) Bacterial leaf blight
(3) Sheath blight (4) Khaira

81. Deficiency of ________ causes 'whiptail' in cauliflower. **2** TN PSC Ag-2003
(1) Magnesium (2) Molybdenum (3) Manganese (4) Zinc

82. The characteristic symptoms of iron deficiency – **4** TN PSC Ag-II: 2001
(1) Stunted growth (2) Yellowing of leaves
(3) Burning of leaf margin (4) Interveinal chlorosis

83. Top sickness of tobacco is due to the deficiency of – **2** TNPSC – Ag: 1999
(1) Iron (2) Boron (3) Copper (4) Chloride

Top sickness of tobacco, also known as **"budworm disease"** or "top rot," is a physiological disorder in tobacco plants. It is characterized by the failure of terminal buds to develop properly, leading to stunted growth and deformed leaves at the top of the plant. This condition is primarily caused by the deficiency of boron.

84. Khaira disease of rice is due to the deficiency of the minor element **B** TNPSC Ag-1998
(A) Copper (B) Zinc (C) Iron (D) Molybdenum

85. Which of the following pairs related to nutrient deficiency symptoms is not correctly matched ? **3** RPSC AAO - 2018
(a) Ca - Deficiency symptoms appear on terminal bud and it dries with time
(b) S - Chlorosis symptoms appear on younger leaves
(c) Fe - Chlorosis symptoms appear on older leaves
(d) N - Chlorosis symptoms appear on older leaves

86. Copper deficiency causes : **1** RPSC ACF Agri -2011
(a) 'Ergot' in bajra (b) "Grey speak' in oat
(c) 'Khaira' in rice (d) 'White bud' in maize

87. The interveinal chlorosis on older leaves is deficiency symptom of : **1** RPSC ACF Agri -2018
(1) Magnesium (2) Molybdenum (3) Potassium (4) Phosphorus

88. Deficiency symptoms of sulphur first appears on : **1** RPSC ACF

(1) Young leaves (2) Older leaves (3) Middle leaves (4) None of these — Horti -2018

89. The Itai - Itai and Minamata diseases arecaused due to toxicity of - **2** RPSC ARO Ag Chem -2022

(1) Cd and Ni (2) Cd and Hg (3) Zn and Hg (4) Zn and Ni

90. Hypokalemia in animals is causes due to deficiency of - **3** RPSC ARO Ag Chem -2022

(1) Calcium (2) Magnesium (3) Potassium (4) Copper

91. White bud of maize disease is caused due to deficiency of **1** RPSC ARO Ag Chem -2022

(1) Zn (2) Mn (3) Fe (4) Cu

92. The deficiency of copper in plants causes which disease? **2** RPSC AAO Ag -2022

(1) Whiptail disease (2) Die-back disease

(3) Early blight disease (4) Khaira disease

93. ' Little leaf of cotton occurs due to the deficiency of which nutrient ? **2** RPSC AO Ag - 2021

(1) Mn (2) Zn (3) B (4) Ca

94. Exanthema disease is caused by deficiency of **d** ICAR Gen Agri- 2007

(A) MN (B) Zn (C) Fe (D) Cu

95. The region in India where boron deficiency is mostly occurs **d** ICAR Gen Agri- 2005

(A) Coastal region (B) Central region (C) Southern region (D) NW region

96. The low availability of following nutrient reduces Ca translocation in the groundnut which causes hollow heart - **3** RPSC ARO Agro-2022

(1) Sulphur (2) Zinc (3) Boron (4) Iron

97. Yellow spot in citrus in due to? **C** IBS,AFO-2013

(A) Cobalt (B) Magnesium (C) Molybdenum (D) Copper (E)Zinc

98. Deficiency of which of the following element causes general yellowing and poor growth of the plant : **c** UPPSC Pre- 1994

(a) Phosphorus (b) Calcium (c) Nitrogen (d) Boron

99. Deficiency of mobile element appears first on : **b** UPPSC Pre- 2010

(a) Younger leaves (b) Older leaves (c) Roots (d) Stem

CHAPTER-141 : SOIL ORDER PYQ'S

1. Major caharacteristics of entisols is: **4** RPSC Pre-2008

(1) High organic C content (2)High salt content

(3) Low soil moisture (4) Recently formed

2. Major characteristics of alfisol soil is – **c** MP PAT-2013

(A) Recently formed (B) Low organic carbon content

(C) High organic carbon content (D) Low soil moisture

3. Majority of soils of Gujarat falls under – **a** Gujrat AO-2017

(a) Inceptisols (b) Aridisols (c) Vertisols (d) Entisols

4. Match List – I with List –II and select the correct answer by using codes given below **3** RPSC, AAO-2019

List – I	List – II
Soil Orders	Formative Elements in the name of orders
1. Entisols	A. ept
2. Vertisols	B. ent
3. Inceptisols	C. ert
4. Spodosols	D. od

Codes :

	A	B	C	D
(1)	4	1	2	3
(2)	2	3	1	4
(3)	3	1	2	4
(4)	1	3	4	2

5. Name of the soil type occupying maximum are in the country **1** RPSC Pre-2010

(1) Alluvial soil (2) Black soil (3) Red soil (4) Lateritic soil

CHAPTER- 142 : SOIL ROCKS PYQ'S

1. ___ of igneous rock is found in earth crust. **d** IFFCO T - 2019
(a) 45% (b) 65% (c) 75% (d) 95%

2. An igneous rock **d** TNPSC Ag- 1995
(A) Slate (B) Sandstone (B) Conglomerate (D) Granite

3. Consider the following rocks **d** IAS Pre-2008
1. Diorite 2. Basalt 3. Breccia
Which of the following is/are igneous rocks?
(a) 1and 2 (b) 2only (c) 1and 3 (d) 1,2 and 3

4. Dominant mineral in igneous rock is : **2** UPPSC Pre- 2003
(1) Feldspar (2) Quartz (3) Apatite (4) Mica

5. Intermediate textured rock is – **3** TN AO-2018
(1) Granite (2) Diorite (3) Ryolite (4) Felsite

6. Match List-I with List-II and select the correct answer using the code given below the Lists : **b** IAS Pre-2010

List-I (*Type of mineral/rock*)	List-II (*Specific example*)
A. Primary mineral	1. Quartz
B. Clay mineral	2. Sandstone
C. Sedimentary rock	3. Marble
D. Metamorphic rock	4. Illite

Code :

	A	B	C	D		A	B	C	D
(a)	1	4	2	3	(b)	1	2	4	3
(c)	3	4	2	1	(d)	3	2	4	1

7. Pumice is which type of rock, having very light weight and specific gravity is lower than water? **1** RPSC ARO Ag Chem - 2022
(1) Igneous rock (2) Sedimentary rock
(3) Metamorphic rock (4) All of the above

8. Rocks containing more than 65% of SiO_2 are : **c** UPPSC Pre- 2007
(a) Neutral (b) Alkaline (c) Acidic (d) None of the above

9. Rocks containing more than 65% SiO_2 are : **c** UPPSC Pre- 2002
(a) Neutral (b) Alkaline (c) Acidic (d) Calcareous

10. Sandstone and limestone are – **a** School Lect. 2019
(a) Sedimentary rocks (b) Metamorphic rocks
(c) Primary rocks (d) ligneous rocks

11. Sedimentary rocks are formed by : **2** RPSC Pre- 1993
(1) increase in pressure (2) cementation of broken part
(3) the force of compaction (4) solidification of lava

12. SiO_2 content (%) of sub-basic igneous rocks is – **c** BHU PET- 2010
(a) <55 (b) 55-60 (c) 60-55 (d) >65

13. Slate is metamorphosed – **d** BHU PET-

(a) Sand Stone (b) lime stone 2013
(c) Mica Schists (d) Shales and mud stones

14. Soil forming factor in which altitude and slope determine accumulation of soil is – 3 Raj JET-2020
(1) Parent rock (2) Soil organic matter
(3) Relief (4) Soil organisms

15. The chemical formula of the liming compound "Dolomite" is – c BHU PET-2014
(a) $CaCo_3$ (b) $MgCO_3$ (c) $CaMg(CO_3)_2$ (d) CaO

16. The crystal units of montmorillonite are held together by – a BHU PET-2015
(a) O-O linkage (b) O-H linkage (c) H-bonding (d) NH-bond

17. The mineral weathering and clay formation are rapid where the climate is : 3 RPSC Pre-1998
(1)Warm and moist (2)Warm and dry
(3) Cold and moist (4) Cold and dry

18. The most resistant mineral to weathering is – a Raj JET-2014
(a) Quartz (b) Muscovite (c) Feldspar (d) Calcite

19. The unconsolidated material on the underlying rock called a IAS Pre-1996
(a) regolith (b) soil (c) solum (d) earth

20. Which of the following is an igneous rock…… 4 RPSC Pre-1995
(1)Lime stone (2)Slate (3) Marble (4) Basalt

21. Which of the following is correctly matched ? c TNPSC Ag-1996
(A) Percentage of water soluble phosphorus in super phosphates --- 8%
(B) Granite rock—Basic rock (C) Sonara 64- Mexico
(D) Invitro- culture – Haplontic sterility

22. Which of the following rock does not belong to sedimentary rocks? e IBS,AFO-2021
(a) Basalt (b) Sand stone (c) Lime stone (d) Shale (e)Granite

23. Which one is sedimentary rock ? a BHU PET-2014
(a) Sandstone (b) Basalt (c) Quartzite (d) Diorite

24. Which one of the following is the correct sequence of transformation of igeous rock to kaolinite? d IAS Pre-2001
(a) Igneous rock __ Montmorillonite Smectite Halloysite Kaolinite
(b) Igneous rock __ Montmorillonite __ Metahalloysite Halloysite Kaolinite
(c) Igneous rock __ Montmorillonite __ Halloysite __ Metahalloysite Kaolinatie
(d) Igneous rock __ Halloysite Metahalloysite __ Montmorillonite __ Kaolinite

25. Which one of the following is the primary mineral that occurs predominatly in igneous rocks? b
(a) Micas (b) Feldspars (c) Quartz (d) Pyroxenes

26. Which one of the following minerals is LEAST weather able in soil? b IAS Pre-1996
(a) Olivine (b) Quartz (c) Calcite (d) Biotite

CHAPTER- 143: SOIL PH PYQ'S

1.	As pH drops from 5.5 to 4.5, dissolved Al is how much times greater at pH 4.5 than that of pH 5.5? (1) 5 times (2) 10 times (3) 100 times (4) 1000 times	4	RPSC ARO Ag Chem - 2022
2.	At what pH value, phosphate availability is highest in the soil ? (A) 5 - 5 (B) 6 – 5 (C) 7 - 5 (D) 8 - 5	B	ADA Guj- 2013
3.	Availability of iron to plants is relatively high at the following pH range : (1) 6.0 to 6.5 (2) 6.6 to 7.0 (3) 7.1 to 7.5 (4) 7.6 to 8.0	1	RPSC Pre- 1995
4.	Availability of phosphorus to crop plants is most affected by : (1) Soil pH (2) Soil Moisture Stress (3) Temperature (4) Biological Factors	1	RPSC Pre- 1995
5.	Crop which is sensitive to soil alkalinity ESP less thanl5: **Ans.: Maize**		RRB SO- 2019
6.	Each unit change in pH represents a change in activity of H^+ ions by : (1) One fold (2) Ten fold (3) Hundred fold (4) Thousand fold	2	UPPSC Pre- 2003
7.	How many times H+ ion concentration increases when the pH of a solution is reduced from 6 to 4 ? (a) 10 times (b) 20 times (c) 50 times (d) 100 times	d	UPPSC Pre- 2009
8.	If a soil has pH 6.5 and this pH is lowered to pH 5.5, the acid content becomes ___ times greater acidic? A. 100 B. 0.1 C. 10 D. 50 E. 1	C	IBS,AFO- 2017
9.	If soils have pH 4.5 than which type soil required more amount of lime for reclamation? (a) Clay (b) Loamy (c) Silty (d) Sandy	a	Agri Pre PG- 2021
10.	In the statement if soil A has a pH of 5 and soil B has a pH of 7, then the acidity of soil A will be X times that of soil B.' X stands for (a) 2 (b) 5 (c) 10 (d) 100	b	IAS Pre-1999
11.	In which pH range phosphate availability in soil is maximum : (a) 4 to 5 (b) 5 to 6 (c) 6 to 7 (d) 7 to 8	c	UPPSC Pre- 2002
12.	Measurement of pH of a soil indicates – (a) total acidity (b) active acidity (c) residual acidity (d) salt-replaceable acidity	b	BHU PET- 2017
13.	Most suitable soil pH for crop production is : (a) 4 - 5 (b) 5 – 6 (c) 6 - 7 (d) 7 - 8	c	UPPSC Pre- 2008
14.	Non environmental physical character of soil? (A) pH (B) Water (C) Air (D) Humus (E)Sunlight	A	IBS,AFO- 2014
15.	None saline-alkali soils usually have P^H range between :- (1) 7.5-8.5 (2) 8.5-10.0 (3) 10-12 (4) 12-14	2	RPSC, AO- 2016
16.	Normal pH range of soil at which plant nutrient availability and microbial activity is at maximum is : (a) 6.5 to 8.5 (b) 7.5 to P1.5 (c) 8.5 to 9.5 (d) 6.5 to 7.5	d	UPPSC Pre- 2010
17.	On the basis of pH measurements , the nearly neutral-soils have pH value between :	2	RPSC Pre-

	(1) 6.1 to 6.5 (2) 6.6 to 7.5 (3)7.6 to 8.5 (4) 5.6 to 6.0		1993
18.	P fixation in acid soil starts below the pH :- (a) 7.0 (b) 7.5 (c) 6.5 (d) 3.5	c	ARO Agro-2016
19.	pH is measured based on – (a) Ohm's law (b) Darcy law (c) Wheatstone bridge (d) redox principle	d	BHU PET-2011
20.	Phosphorus availability in soil increases with increase in pH :- (a) >8.0 (b) >8.2 (c) >8.4 (d) >8.5	*	ARO Agro-2016
21.	Soil pH indicates : (a) Total acidity (b) Active acidity (c) Residual acidity (d) Salt-replaceable acidity	b	UPPSC Pre-2004
22.	Soils with high pH are generally deficient in – (a) Zn and Mn (b) Cu and Mo (c) B and Fe (d) Ca and Mg	a	BHU UET-2010
23.	The base saturation percentage of a soil containing 7.0 cmol $P^+ kg^{-1}$ of Ca^{2+} , 1.0 cmol $p^+ kg^{-1}$ of Mg^{2+}, 0.25 cmol $P^+ kg^{-1}$ of K^+, 0.75 cmol $P^+ kg^{-1}$ of H^+ and 1.0 cmol $p^+ kg^{-1}$ of Al^{3+}, will be (a) 82.5 (b) 90 (c) 92.5 (d) 100	A	IAS Pre-2002
24.	The capacity of a soil to resist appreciable change in pH value is called (a) cation-exchange capacity (d) buffering capacity (c) percentage base saturation (d) anion-exchange capctity	B	IAS Pre-2001
25.	The concept of pH was invented by – (1) Sorensen (2) Whitney (3) Dokuchaev (4) Buckmen	1	Ag Sup JAU 2017
26.	The critical value of soil ECe for germination of seed of crop is :- (1) Up to 2 ds/m (2) 2-4 ds/m (3) 4-6 ds/m (4) 6-8 ds/m	1	RPSC, AO-2016
27.	The given chart shows the classification fo irrigation water Irrigation water having Na^+ =15me/litre, (Ca^2+Mg^2) = 8 me/litre and conductivity = EC x106 =2300 umho/cm can be classified as Drawing Salinity hazard (a) C^4-S^2 (b) C^3-S^3 (c) C^4-S^3 (d) C^1-S^1	a	IAS Pre-1996
28.	The gypsum equivalent of iron pyrite used for reclamation of sodic soils is – (a) 0.85 (b) 0.19 (c) 1.29 (d) 0.63	c	RPSC, AO-2012
29.	The hydrogen ion toxicity in crops may occurs in soil having pH of - (1) <4 (2) <5 (3) <6 (4) <7	1	RPSC ARO Agro-2022
30.	The increase of pH from 6.0 and above, the availability of molybdenum : (1) increase (2) decrease (3) remains unaffected (4) becomes constant	1	RPSC Pre-1993
31.	The most productive normal soils have pH : (1)4-6 (2)5-7 (3) 6-8 (4) 7-9	3	RPSC Pre-1998
32.	The p^H of 0.1NHCl solution is ……. (a)0 (b) 1 (c) 2 (d) 3	b	BHU PET-2016
33.	The pH of saline soil is - (a) > 8.5 (b) < 7 (c) > 10.0 (d) 14	a	MP PAT-2016
34.	The pH of saline soil is:	2	RPSC Pre-

(1) <7.5 (2)<8.5 (3) >8.5 (4) >10 | 2008

35. The pH value of alkali soil is — **E** IBS,AFO-2016

A. 0 B. 3 C. 5 D. 7 E. 8

36. The saline, alkali soils has the value of : — **1** RPSC Pre-1993

(1) E.C. > 4 m. mhos/cm, E.S.P. >15, pH < 8.5

(2) E.C. < 4 m. mhos/cm, E.S.P. > 15, pH < 8.5

(3) E.C. > 4 m. mhos/cm, E.S.P. < 15, pH < 8.5

(4) E.C. < 4 m. mhos/cm, E.S.P. > 15, pH > 8.5

37. The salt index of urea is :- — **1** AARO Agro-2016

(1) 1.61 per unit of N (2) 2.99 per unit of N

(3) 3.25 per unit of N (4) 6.00 per unit of N

38. The sodic soils need treatment with amendments like – — **c** School Lect. 2019

(a) Zinc sulphate (b) HCO_3^- (c) Gypsum (d) Carbonates

39. There are some crops which are either salt tolerance or semi salt tolerance. which of the following crop is a salt sensitive? **Ans.: Apple** — RRB SO-2018

40. Tolerance to soil salinity of the given set of crops is such that — **a** IAS Pre-1997

(a) barley > wheat > upland paddy > beans

(b) barley > wheat > beans > upland paddy

(c) wheat > barley > beans > upland paddy

(d) wheat > barley> upland paddy> beans

41. Total dissolved solids in water having EC of 5 ds/m will be about : — **3** RPSC Pre-1998

(1) 3200ppm (2) 3600ppm (3) 4000ppm (4) 4400ppm

[i.e. if EC more than 5 than TDS=5*800]

42. Under high P.H. soil a successfully grown crop is : — **c** UPPSC Pre-1996

(a) Pea (b) Sorghum (c) Barley (d) Bajra

43. Unit of pH is – — **d** Agri Pre PG-2020

(a) Percent (b) Molar litre $^{-1}$ (c) dS m^{-1} (d) Unit less

44. What happens when an saline alkali soil is leached with water ? — **1** RPSC Pre-1998

(1)pH and EC both decreases (2)pH and EC both increases

(3) pH increases and EC decreases (4) pH decreases and EC increases

45. What is the effect of nitrification on soil pH:- (1) Increases (2) Decreases — **3** AARO Agro-2016

(1) Codes 1,2 and 3 (2) Codes 1 and 3

(3) Code 2 only (4) Codes 1 and 2

46. What is the pH for maximum inorganic phosphorus availability in soil ? — **B** IAS Pre-2010

(a) Above 7.0 (b) 6.0 to 7.0 (c) 4.0 to 6.0 (d) Below 4.0

47. What is the pH of acidic soil? — **a** IBS,AFO-2019

(a) **Less than 5.5** (b) 7.0 (c) 8 (d) 11 (e) 7.5

48. When pH under 3.5 ? — **C** IBS,AFO-2015

(A) Slightly acid soil (B) Saline alkaline soil (C) Ultra acidic soil

(D) Alkaline soil (E) Saline soil

49. When soil pH changes from 7.0 to 6.0 , its H-ion concentration increases ……..times? (RPSC (AO)-2009 — **b** BHU PET-2016

(a)1 (b) 10 (c)100 (d) 1000

50. Where the pH will be highest and the EC will be lowest — **1** — RPSC, AAO-2009
(1) Soil : Water = 1:2 (2) Soil : Water = 1:3
(3) Soil : Water = 1:6 (4) Soil : Water = 1:8

51. Which crop sensitive for saline soil? — **C** — IBS,AFO-2014
(A) Whaet (B) Lentil (C) Potato (D) Soybean (E)All of these

52. Which fruit tree is sensitive to aridity and salinity : — **4** — RPSC Pre-1998
(1)Phalsa (2)Aonla (3) Guava (4) Plum

53. Which generally used for correcting soil acidity — **2** — RPSC Pre-2003
(1) Gypsum (2)Lime (3)Iron sulphate (4)Both (1) and (2)

54. Which of the following crops causes maximum reduction in soil alkalinity : — **a** — UPPSC Pre-2000
(a) Cowpea (b) Maize (c) Paddy (d) Wheat

55. Which of the following is highly salt tolerant fruit crop? — **a** — ICAR Gen Agri-2009
(A) Date palm (B) Mango (C) Apple (D) Citrus

56. Which of the following is not a highly salt tolerant crop ? — **4** — Agri Pre PG-2019
(1) Rice (2) Lucerne (3) Barley (4) Linseed

57. Which of the following is the pH value of alkali soils? **Ans.: >8.5** — NABAR-2019

58. Which one is the most tolerant crop to Soil Sodicity ? — **d** — BHU PET-2013
(a) Pearl millet (b) Cotton (c) Barley (d) Rice

59. Which one of the following graphs describes soil pH? — **B** — IAS Pre-2001

Map a Graphs ?

(a) [H+] (b) – log [H+] (c) log [H+] (d) – log [H+]

60. Which one of the following statements is correct in respect of saline soils ? — **c** — UPPSC Pre-2005
(a) pH more than 8.5 electrical conductivity less than 4.0 dsm^{-1}, granular structure, white colour.
(b) Electrical conductivity more than 4.0 dsm^{-1}. pH less than 8.5 hard structure, black colour
(c) pH less than 8.5. Electrical conductivity more than 4.0 dsm^{-1}' granular structure, white colour.
(d) Black colour, pH more than 8.5 Electrical conductivity less than 4.0 dsm^{-1}'', hard structure.

61. With reference to salt-tolerance of crop plants, consider the following pairs : — **E** — IAS Pre-2009

Crop		Degree of salt-tolerance
1. Potato	:	Tolerant
2. Maize	:	Semi-tolerant
3. barley	:	Sensitive

Which of the pairs given above is/are correct ?
(A) 1 only (b) 2 and 3 only (c) 2 only (d) 1, 2 and 3 (e)

Given this information, the degrees of salt-tolerance for each crop should be as follows:
Potato: Moderately sensitive (not tolerant)
Maize: Moderately sensitive (not semi-tolerant)
Barley: Tolerant (not sensitive)

Thus, none of the pairs given are correct.

The correct answer is: **None of the pairs are correct.**

CHAPTER- 144; SOIL SURVEY PYQ'S

1. A soil survey undertaken to prepare resource inventory of large areas is called as — 1 — RPSC, AAO-2018
   (A) Reconnaissance soil survey (B) Detailed soil survey
   (C) Semi- detailed survey (D) Detailed reconnaissance survey

2. Collection of data about objects which are not in contact with collecting data is known as — 2 — Agri Pre PG-2016
   (1) Soil survey (2) Remote sensing (3) Telegraphy (4) None for these

3. For district level planning by semi-detailed survey, the distance between field observations should be – — 2 — RPSC ARO Ag Chem - 2022
   (1) 100 meter (2) 500 meter (3) 800 meter (4) 1000 meter

4. Reconnaissance is a kind of – — 3 — TN ACF-2012
   (1) Soil conservation (2) Soil sampling (3) Soil survey (4) Soil testing

5. Reconnaissance soil survey carried out to produce maps for planning in all the states of the country at the scale of — 4 — RPSC, AAO-2018
   (A) 1:8000 (B) 1.12000 (C) 1:20000 (D) 1:250000

6. The height of aircraft for aerial photographic soil survey depends upon – RPSC AAO - 2018 — 3 — RPSC, AAO-2019
   a. Scale of aerial photography b. Type of camera
   c. Focal length of camera d. Area of photography
   Select the correct answer from above
   (1) a & b (2) b & c (3) a & c (4) c & d

7. The low intensity soil survey is – — 2 — TN PSC Ag-2003
   (1) Exploratory (2) Reconnaissance (3) Semi detailed (4) Detailed

8. The modern soil-surveying techniques include the use of — d — MP PAT-2014
   (A) ERIS (B) LANDSAT (C) GIS (D) All of the above

9. The objectives of the……………….soil survey are to have a broad idea about the major soil groups. — b — Agri Pre PG-2022
   (a) Detailed (b) Reconnaissance
   (c) Detailed reconnaissance (d) None of the above

10. Which scale is used in detailed soil survey? — 4 — RPSC ARO Ag Chem - 2022
    (1) 1:10,000 (2) 1:8,000 (3) 1:5,000 (4) All of the above

CHAPTER- 145: SOIL EROSION PYQ'S

1. A subdivision on the basis of some important deviations such as surface texture, erosion, slope and stoniness is called as — A — HPSC ADO-2022
(A) soil phase (B) soil series (C) soil family (D) soil order

2. According to '**universal soil loss equation**' the factors on which rate of erosion depends are : — 1 — RPSC Pre-1993
(a) rainfall, soil erodibility and slope length
(b) slop gradient, crop management, erosion control practice
(c) rainfall, wind velocity, crop management
(d) soil erodibility, soil type crop management
(1) a & b (2) a & c (3) b & c (4) d

3. Arrange the following types to erosion in order of 'first to advance stages'- — 4 — RPSC AAO Ag -2022
(a) Gully erosion (b) Sheet erosion
(c) Rill erosion (d) Splash erosion
Order of first to advance stages-
(1) d, b, a, c (2) b, a, c, d (3) b, d, c, a (4) d, b, c, a

4. Choose correct cause of soil erosion – — 2 — TN PSC Ag-2003
(1) Cultivation (2) Deforestation (3) Nature of soil (4) Plants

5. Consider the following types of erosion — c — IAS Pre-1998
1.Gully erosion 2. Splash erosion 3. Normal erosion 4. Rill erosion
5. Sheet erosion
The correct sequence in terms of the INCREASING order of soil loss from the filed due to these types of erosion is
(a) 2,3,4,5,1 (b) 2,3,5,4,1 (c) 3,2,4,1,5 (d) 3,2,5,4,1

6. First stage of water erosion? — D — IBS,AFO-2015
(A) Gully erosion (B) Rill erosion (C) Sheet erosion
(D) Splash erosion (E) All of these

7. Geological erosion is also known as : — c — UPPSC Pre-1995
(a) Accelerated erosion (b) Soil erosion (c) Natural erosion (d) Water erosion

8. Gully erosion is an advance stage of ? — 1 — Ag sup 2018
(1) Rill erosion (2) Splash erosion (3) Sheet erosion (4) Wind erosion

9. In the universal soil loss equation — b — IAS Pre-1999
A = RKLSP K stands for
(a) slope length (b) soil erodibility (c) rainfall (d) cover and management

10. In universal soil loss equation, A=RKLSCP, K denotes — 3 — RPSC, AAO-2018
(A) Soil conservation practice (B) Soil roughness
(C) Soil erodibility (D) None of these

11. In Which type of soil erosion, soil matrix is lost but remains undetected for long period ? — 2 — Ag sup 2021
(1) Gully erosion (2) Sheet erosion (3) Stream bank erosion (4) Rill erosion

12. Loss of soil by water is known as — B — AO SDAU-2013
A. Soil erosion B. Water erosion C. Wind erosion D. None of these

13. Materials transported and deposited by water are called as? — a — IFFCO T-2019
(a) Alluvium (b) Colluvium (c) Loess (d) Aeolian

14. Most damaging form of soil erosion is : — b — UPPSC Pre-2008
(a) Rill erosion (b) Sheet erosion (c) Splash erosion (d) Water-fall erosion

15. Muddy runoff from the field is an indicator of: — b — Agri Pre PG-2021
(a) Splash erosion (b) Gully erosion (c) Rill erosion (d) Sheet erosion

16. Name the first phase of water erosion : — c — UPPSC Pre-1995
(a) Sheet erosion (b) Rill erosion (c) Splash erosion (d) None of these

17. Out of these which mechanism is not related to wind erosion ? — 2 — Agri Pre PG-2015
(1) saltation (2) siltation (3) suspension (4) surface creep

18. Saltation .process is related to : — 4 — RPSC ACF Agri -2011
(a) Geological erosion (b) Simple erosion (c) Water erosion (d) Wind erosion

19. Soil erosion and deposition by a river greatly depends on its – — 2 — TN PSC Ag-2003
(1) Length (2) Speed (3) Depth (4) Span

20. Soil loss equation A = RKLSCP K Stands for? — B — BOM AO-2021
a. Soil erosivity b. Soil erodibility c. Soil covering d. Soil conservation

21. Splash Erosion is otherwise called as — A — HPSC ADO-2022
(A) rain drop erosion (B) sheet erosion (C) rill erosion (D) gully erosion

22. The cross slope ditch system is used for drainage of — 3 — RPSC ACF AE -2018
(a) Flat land (b) Pounded land (c) Slopping land (d) Undulating land

23. The erosion of soil particles between 0.1 to 0.5 mm diameter by wind is termed as : — 1 — RPSC AAO -2018
(a) Saltation (b) Suspension (c) Surface creep (d) Interruption

24. The following terms "Saltation, suspension" and "surface creep" are related to — b — TNPSC Agri-1997
(A) Gully erosion (B) Water erosion (C) Wind erosion (D) Geologic erosion

25. The least effective vegetation for protecting the soil from erosion is — A — AO GPSC-2013
(A) Tall tree crops (B) Dense grass
(C) Low light crops with big leaves (D) Grain crops

26. The mushroom rocks remnants in the Aravalli regions are formed due to - — 1 — RPSC ARO Ag Chem -2022
(1) Wind erosion (2) Water erosion (3) Exfoliation (4) Moraine

27. The process of closing the tile gaps and covering them by placing loose top soil materials in setting tile-drain, is called : — 1 — RPSC ACF AE -2018
(a) Blinding (b) Bedding (c) Blocking (d) Breaking

28. The soil carried in saltation consists of particle size : — a — UPPSC Pre-2002
(a) 0.1 to 0.5 mm (b) 0.1 to 0.2 mm (c) 0.5 to 1.0 mm (d) None of the above

29. Water erosion is distinguished by — D — ADA Guj-2013
(A) Sheet erosion (B) Rill erosion
(C) Gully erosion (D) All of the above

30. When there is rainfall and rapidly running water produces fingershaped grooves or rills over the area, it is called ? — b — IBS,AFO-2020
(a)Splash erosion (b) Rill erosion (c)Pedestrial erosion
(d) Sheet erosion (e) Ravine

31. Which is the correct sequence of soil erosion? A TO MPUAT-2014
(A) Sheet - Rill – Gulley (B) Sheet - Gulley - Rill
(C) Rill- Sheet - Gulley (D) Gulley - Sheet - Rill

32. Which of the following factors is not taken into consideration while computing soil loss by 'universal soil loss' equation ? d UPPSC Pre-2010
(a) Rainfall (b) Slope length (c) Crop management (d) Fertilizer management

33. Which of the following is not a type of soil erosion caused by water- a Agri Pre PG-2022
(a) Sand Dunes (b) Rain Drop (c) Sheet (d) Rill

34. Which of the following is not used for preventing soil erosion? 2 RPSC Pre-1993
(1) reclamation of ravine lands (2) deforestation
(3) terracing (4) contour bonding

35. Which of the following is the most dominant factor of soil degradation in semi-arid zones in India? **Ans.:Soil erosion** NABARD-2020

36. Which one of the following method is most appropriate to check the soil erosion on steep – 3 Raj JET-2020
(1) Shelter belt (2) Mulching (3) Terrace cultivation (4) Contour barrier

CHAPTER- 146 : LAND CAPABILITY CLASSIFICATION PYQ'S

1. According to land capability classification, the soils which are not suitable for agriculture and silviculture belong to : 4 RPSC Pre-1993
(1) class 1 (2) class 5 (3) class 8 (4) class 7 & 8

2. As per guidelines of FAO (1977), gently undulating land surface has a slope of – 2 Agri Pre PG-2018
(1) 6-10 per cent (2) 2-5 per cent
(3) 11-15 percent (4) Less than 2 per cent

3. Land capability class VIII in maps is represented by the colour :- 3 AARO Agro-2016
(1) Green (2) Brown (3) Purple (4) Red

4. Land use of Class VIII land is restricted to – d Agri Pre PG-2017
(a) Plantation Crops (b) Arid Crops
(c) Short duration Vegetable Crops (d) Secretion and Wild life

5. the colour of land capability classes for class 1 and class 8 on map are respectively 2 RPSC, AAO-2018
(1) light green and red (2) lighr green and purple
(3) dark green amd purple (4) yellow and orange

6. The land capability class II is shown by – 1 Agri Pre PG-2018
(1) Yellow (2) Pink (3) Brown (4) Green

7. The land capability class which may be used for cultivation with intensive soil conservation measures is – b BHU PET-2010
(a) Class II (b) Class III (c) Class V (d) Class VI

8. The usual diameter classes used in India are – c Agri Pre PG-2020
(a) 5, 10, 15 cm (b) 1, 3, 5 cm (c) 2, 5, 10 cm (d) 10, 20, 30 cm

9. What is the lowest unit of soil classification ? d BHU PET-2015
(a) Family (b) Type (c) Phase (d) Series

10. Land capability classification scheme was developed by : 4 RPSC ACF Agri -2011

(a) China (b) India (c) Japan (d) USA

11. Match the following with respect to classes of erosion by water : 2 RPSC ACF AE - 2018

Column-A	Column-B
(i) Class-I	(a) More than about 75% of the original A horizon and part of all the B horizon lost
(ii) Class-II	(b) Up to about 25% of the original A horizon removed
(iii) Class-III	(c) Soil profiles have been destroyed except in small areas between gullies
(iv) Class-IV	(d) Approximately 25% to 75% of the original A horizon has been lost

The correct matching is

(1) (i) — (a), (ii) — (c). (iii) — (d), (iv) — (b)

(2) (i) (b), (ii) — (d), (iii) — (a), (iv) — (c)

(3) (i) — (c), (ii) — (a), (iii) — (b), (iv) — (d)

(4) (i) — (d), (ii) — (b), (iii) — (c), (iv) — (a)

12. According to land capability classification, the class VI denoted by the colour on map is- 4 RPSC ARO Ag Chem -2022

(1) Dark grey (2) Green (3) Yellow (4) Orange

CHAPTER- 147 : PROBLEMATIC SOILS PYQ'S

1. A major cause for formation of saline and sodic soil is — **d** — IAS Pre-2009
   (a) Intensive use of the land
   (b) Inadequate presence of gypsum in soil
   (c) Inadequate presence of lime in soil
   (d) Poor soil drainage (both surface and internal)
2. A saline soil is a non sodic soil containing sufficient soluble salt to adversely affect the growth of most crop plants ,What is the Electrical conductivity of Saline Soil ? — **A** — IBS,AFO-2018
   (A) >4 dsm (B) 6 dsm (C) 7 dsm (D) 5 dsm (E) nome of above
3. A soil sample indicating pH = 7.5 ECe 4.8 dS/m, exchangeable sodium percentage = 12, may be categories as which one of the following? — **B** — IAS Pre-2007
   (a) Alkaline soil (b) Saline soil
   (c) Saline alkaline soil (d) Normal fertile soil
4. Acid soil can be managed by — **4** — RPSC Pre-2010
   (1) Adding lime material (2) Using basic fertilizer
   (3) Growing acid tolerant crop (4) All of these
5. Acid soils are amended by – — **b** — Delhi PGT-2014
   (a) Gypsum (b) Lime (c) Sulphuric acid (d) $CaCl_2$
6. Acid soils are characterized by pH of – — **1** — TN AO-2012
   (1) < 6 (2) 7 to 8 (3) 8 to 10 (4) > 10
7. Acid soils can be reclaimed by — **a** — Agri Pre PG-2014
   (a) Adding lime material (b)Using basic fertilizers
   (c) Growing acid tolerant crops (d)None of the above
8. Acid soils can be reclaimed by… — **2** — RPSC Pre-1995
   (1)Gypsum (2) Lime (3) Compost (4) Green manure
9. Acid sulphate soils are found in — **2** — RPSC Pre-2008
   (1) Desert areas (2)Coastal areas (3) Hilly areas (4) Tarai areas
10. Acid sulphate soils are found in – — **3** — TN PSC Ag-I:1999
    (1) Arid region (2) Semi-arid region
    (3) Coastal region (4) Himalayan region
11. Acid Sulphate soils are found mostly in — **c** — MP PAT-2016
    1. Desert areas 2. Tarai areas 3. Coastal areas 4. None of the above
12. Addition of the following material makes it possible to lake good crop in sodic soil — **D** — ADA Guj-2013
    (A) FYM (B) Green manure (C) Gypsum (D) All of the above
13. Alkali soil can be reclaimed by the addition of : — **1** — UPPSC Pre-2003
    (1) Gypsum (2) Lime (3) Basic slag (4) Dolomite
14. Alkali soil is reclaimed by : — **d** — UPPSC Pre-2000
    (a) CaO (b) $Ca(OH)_2$ (c) $CaCO_3$ (d) $CaSO_4.2H_2O$
15. Alkali soil is reclaimed by which of the following practices — **b** — IBS,AFO-2021
    (a) Lime (b) Gypsum (c) Calcium carbonate (d) Press mud

(e)Sodium bicarbonate

16. Alkali soils are treated with gypsum to correct the deficiency of : **3** RPSC Pre-1998

(1)Sulphur (2)Calcium

(3) Magnesium (4) Zinc (Exp.: It maintain the Ca-Mg ratio)

17. Alkali soils have wide spread deficiency of : **(b)** UPPSC Pre-2006

(a) Nitrogen (b) Phosphorus (c) Potassium (d) Sulphur

18. Alkaline soil can be reclaimed by applying ? **3** Raj JET-2018

(1) Lime (2) Potassium Sulphate

(3) Gypsum (4) Zinc Sulphate

19. Alkaline soil is less soluble than acidic or neutral soil, availability of nutrients is often limited. What is the pH of Alkali soil? **C** IBS,AFO-2018

(A) 7 (B) 7-8 (C) >8.2 (D) none of above

20. Alkalinity in soil is due to **3** RPSC Pre-2010

(1) sodium salt in soil solution (2) presence of Na clay

(3) Both (1) and (2) (4) None of these

21. Amendment used to reclaim acid soil **B** AO KTPSC-2021

(A) Gypsum (B) Lime (C) Pyrite (D) Sulphur (E) Answer not known

22. Among the following sources of salts in soils, which one is the primary source? **D** IAS Pre-2008

(a) Ground water (b) Organic manures

(c) Canal irrigation (d) Rock weathering

23. Among various classes of salt affected soils, the highest soil permeability is recorded by – **a** BHU PET-2010

(a) Saline soils (b) Alkali soils

(c) Saline-alkali soils (d) Degraded-alkali soils

24. Among varlous classes of salt affected soils, the most permeable one is – **a** BHU PET-2014

(a) Saline (b) Saline Sodic

(c) Non-Saline Sodic (d) Degraded Sodic

25. Black alkali is formed due to the presence of **b** TNPSC Agri-1997

(A) Organic matter (B) Sodium (C) Organic matter + Sodium (D) Calcium

26. $CaCO_3$ (lime) is added for the reclamation of: **c** MP PAT-2016

1. Saline soil 2. Alkali soil 3. Acidic soil 4. None of the above

27. $CaCO_3$ is added to reclaim what type of land ? **b** BHU UET-2010

(a) alkali (b) acidic (c) saline (d) latrite soil

28. Calcareous soil give effervescence visibly when treated with diluted 0.1 N HCL due to release of? **A** BOM AO-2021

a. CO_2 b. NO_2 c. CH_4 d. NH_3

29. Cheapest way of treating alkaline soil is by adding: **a** MP PAT-2016

1. Gypsum 2. NaOH 3. NPK 4. None of these

30. Choose the correct sequence in relation to saline soil - **3** RPSC AO Ag - 2021

(1) pH > 8.5, EC (dSm^{-1}) < 4, SAR < 13, ESP < 15

(2) pH < 8.5, EC (dSm^{-1}) > 4, SAR > 13, ESP < 15

(3) pH < 8.5, EC ($dSrri^{-1}$) > 4, SAR < 13, ESP < 15

(4) pH < 8.5, EC (dSm^{-1}) > 4, SAR < 13, ESP > 15

31. Exchangeable sodium percentage (ESP) is used in the classification of saline and alkali soils or to determine if a sodium hazard exists. What is the Exchangeable Sodium Percentage of Saline - Alkali Soil? **D** IBS,AFO-2018

(A) 5 (B) 10 (C) <15 (D) >15 (E)None

32. For reclamation of alkaline soil we use – **a** BHU UET-2017

(a) gypsum (b) lime (c) urea (d) murate of potash

33. For reclamation of saline-sodic soils which the following is appropriate reclamation technology – **d** Gujrat AO-2017

(a) Gypsum application (b) Organic matter application/green manuring

(c) Drainage provision (d) Combination of all

34. Free Al3+ ions contribute to **B** IAS Pre-2010

(a) native acidity (b) potential acidity

(c) active acidity (d) nascent acidity

35. Gypsum is commonly used for reclamation of **C** AO SDAU-2015

A. Acidic soil B. Saline soil C Sodic soil D. None of these

36. Gypsum is used as an reclamation of : **2** RPSC Pre-1999

(1) Calcareous alkali soils (2) Non- calcareous alkali soils

(3) Non calcareous saline soils (4) Calcareous saline soils

37. Gypsum is used for reclamation of which soil type ? **2** RPSC AAO-2022

(1) Water logged (2) Sodic (3) Saline (4) Acidic

38. Gypsum is used for reclamation of which soil type ? **2** RPSC AAO Ag -2022

(1) Water logged (2) Sodic

(3) Saline (4) Acidic

39. Highest area under salt degraded soil in which state-**Gujarat** **B** IBS,AFO-2018

(A) MP (B) Gujrat (C) UP (D) Haryana (E) Rajasthan

40. Hill soils are generally : **1** UPPSC Pre-2003

(1) Acidic (2) Alkaline (3) Neutral (4) Saline

41. Hydraulic conductivity of soil is very low in case of : **(d)** UPPSC Pre-2000

(a) Acid soils (b) Saline soil (c) Loam soil (d) Alkali soils

42. In acid soils Phosphorus gests precipitated as – **c** Gujrat AO-2017

(a) Calcium phosphate (b) Sodium phosphate

(c) Iron and Aluminium phosphates (d) Magnesium phosphate

43. In acid soils, availability of the nutrient is quite low – **d** BHU PET-2010

(a) Fe (b) Mn (c) Zn (d) Mo

44. In acidic soil, phosphorus absorbed by plant in which form ? **C** ADA MP-2015

(A) PO_4^{++} (B) $P_2O_3^{+}$ (C) $H_2PO_4^{-}$ (D) FF^{+}

45. In alkali soils, the form of phosphorus that predominates is :- **1** AARO Agro-2016

(1) Calcium phosphate (2) Iron phosphate

(3) Aluminum phosphate (4) Nitro phosphate

46. In alkaline soils, loss of nitrogen as gaseous NH3 is known as **B** IAS Pre-2000

(a) denitrification (b) volatilization
(c) ammonification (d) nitrate reduction

47. In saline- alkali soil the electrical conductivity is – **3** TN ACF-2012
(1) 8 dsm^{-1} (2) 6 dsm^{-1} (3) 4 dsm^{-1} (4) 2 dsm^{-1}

48. In saline soils crop growth is mainly affected due to **c** TNPSC Ag-1996
I) High concentration of soluble salts and exchangeable sodium
II) High concentration of chlorides and sulphates
III) Low infiltration, poor percolation and poor aeration
IV) High concentration of some micronutrients
Select the most appropriate answer
(A) I alone is correct (B) II alone is correct
(C) I and II are correct (D) II and IV are correct

49. In saline soils major problem is due to ……….. **3** RPSC Pre-1995
(1) High pH (2) High exchangeable sodium
(3) High content of soluble salts (4) Low soil pH

50. In sodic soil, the soil structure is – **2** TN ACF-2012
(1) Blocky (2) Columnar (3) Single grained (4) Prismatic

51. Iron deficiency usually occurs in soils in the pH range of : **2** RPSC Pre-2003
(1) 5.4-6.5 (2) 7.4-8.5 (3) 9-9.5 (4) 9.6-10.1

52. Lime is added to reclaim **2** Agri Pre PG-2016
(1) Alkali soil (2) Acid soil (3) Saline soil (4) Laterite soil

53. Micro nutrient which is not available in acid soils is **b** TNPSC Agri-1997
(A) Fe (B) Mo (C) Mn (D) Zn

54. Most salinity tolerant crop among the seed spices is :- **b** ARO Agro-2016
(a) Coriander (b) Cumin (c) Fennel (d) Fenugreek

55. Name the chemical used for reclamation of acidic soils **2** RPSC Pre-2010
(1) Gypsum (2) Lime
(3) Ammonium sulphate (4) Super phosphate

56. Name the chemical used for reclamation of alkali soils **2** RPSC Pre-2010
(1) Lime (2) Gypsum (3) Rock phosphate (4) Sodium nitrate

57. Near the canal bank soils become : **(a)** UPPSC Pre-1994
(a)Alkaline (b) Netural (c) Acidic (d) Well drained

58. pH of saline soils is – **a** RPSC, AAO-2012
(a) 8.5 (b) 9.5 (c) 10.5 (d) 11.5

59. pH value of the saline alkali soil will be – **b** BHU UET-2015
(a) > 8.5 (b) < 8.5 (c) = 8.5 (d) None of these

60. Rock phosphate is applied in? **a** IBS,AFO-2022
(a) Acidic soil (b) Neutral (c) Alkaline (d) Saline (e) Arid soils

61. Saline- Alkali soils have pH, Electric conductivity (EC) and Exchangeable Sodium Percentage (ESP) respectively are – **a** Raj JET-2015
(a) pH>8.5;EC>4 ds/m; ESP> 15% (b) pH>8.5;EC<4 ds/m; ESP> 15%
(c) pH<8.5;EC<4 ds/m; ESP < 15% (d) pH>8.5' EC> 4ds/m; ESP < 15%

62. Saline sodic soil reclamation includes – **b** Gujrat AO-2017
(a) Application of amendment (b) Drainage with leaching
(c) Appropriate cropping (d) All the above

63. Saline soil also called as **1** RPSC Pre-2010
(1) White alkali soil (2) Brown alkali soil (3) Both (1) and (2) (4) None of these

64. Saline soil are reclaimed by – **3** TN PSC Ag-2003
(1) Addition of gypsum (2) Addition of lime
(3) Leaching of soluble salts (4) Addition of pyrates

65. Saline soil is reclaimed by – **3** Raj JET-2020
(1) Use of lime (2) Use of basic fertilizers (3) Leaching (4) All of the above

66. Saline soils are formed – **2** TNPSC – Ag: 1999
(1) Due to accumulating of soluble salts and hydroxides of sodium
(2) Due to accumulation of soluble salts
(3) Due to accumulation of hydroxides of sodium
(4) Due to accumulation of hydroxides of potassium

67. Saline soils are reclaimed by – **a** Delhi PGT-2014
(a) Addition of gypsum (b) Addition of lime
(c) Leaching of soluble salts (d) Addition of pyrite

68. Saline soils are reclaimed by – **3** TN AO-2008
(1) Addition of gypsum (2) Addition of lime
(3) Leaching of soluble salts (4) Addition of pyrites

69. Saline soils are those which have – **c** Raj JET-2013
(a) EC>4 m mhos/cm, pH>8.5, ESP > 15
(b) EC<4 m mhos/cm, pH>8.5, ESP > 15
(c) EC>4 m mhos/cm, pH<8.5, ESP,< 15
(d) EC<4 m mhos/cm, pH<8.5, ESP < 15

70. Saline soils can be improved by – **1** Ag sup 2018
(1) Leaching (2) Pyrite Application
(3) Gypsum Application (4) Lime Application

71. Saline soils could be improved by **a** ARO Agro-2016
(a) Leaching (b) Gypsum application
(c) Pyrite application (d) Sulphur application

72. Saline-Alkali soils are generally deficient in : **(a)** UPPSC Pre-2009
(a) Nitrogen and Zinc (b) Nitrogen and Phosphorus
(c) Nitrogen and Sulphur (d) Phosphorus and Sulphur

73. Salinization of soil is a great problem in **1** Agri Pre PG-2015
(1) arid and semi arid regions (2) humid regions
(3) freezing climate (4) sub-humid climate

74. Salt affected soils of the arid zone are classified under which soil order? **2** RPSC AAO-2022
(1) Ultisols (2) Aridisols (3) Mollisols (4) Spodosols

75. Salt affected soils of the arid zone are classified under which soil order? **2** RPSC AAO Ag

(1) Ultisols (2) Aridisols (3) Mollisols (4) Spodosols 2022

76. SAR is used to assess the alkali related hazards of the water. Which of the following SAR range is termed as SAR class S2? **Ans.: 11-18** RRB SO-2018

77. Sodic soil can be reclaimed by – **4** TN PSC Ag-II: 2001
(1) Leaching (2) Gypsum (3) Lime + Leaching (4) Gypsum + Leaching

78. Sodic soils are characterized by : **(d)** UPPSC Pre-1999
(a) High solunle salt concentration and low pH
(b) High soluble salt concentration
(c) Low pH and high exchangeable sodium
(d) high pH exchangeable sodium and high pH

79. Sodic soils can be made more productive by adding – **b** RPSC, AAO-2012
(a) Boron (b) Calcium (c) Phosphorus (d) Sodium

80. Soil – amendment used to reclaim barren land (usarland) : **1** RPSC, AAO-2009
(1) Calcium sulphate (2) Gully erosion
(3) Potassium sulphate (4) Sodium sulphate

81. Soil acidity is attributed to **A** TNPSC Ag-1998
(A) Hydrogen and aluminium (B) Hydrogen and iron
(C) Hydrogen alone (D) Aluminium alone

82. Soil having ESP (Exchangeable Sodium Percentage) greater than 15 are **b** ICAR Gen Agri-2009
(A) Saline soils (B) Alkali soil (C) Acid soils (D) None of these

83. Soil-amendment used to reclaim user (barren) land is : **(a)** UPPSC Pre-1995
(a) Calcium sulphate (b) Potassium sulphate
(c) Sodium sulphate (d) Calcium carbonate

84. Soils of India are abundant in – **2** TNPSC – Ag: 1999
(1) Nitrogen (2) Potash (3) Phosphours (4) None of these

85. Solubility of gypsum in alkali soils is : **(a)** UPPSC Pre-2008
(a) 0.5 % (b) 2.0 % (c) 4.0 % (d) 8.0 %

86. The alkalinity in the alkali soils depends upon the relative concentration of………….and partial pressure of CO_2 in the soil solution. **d** Agri Pre PG-2022
(a) $MgCO_3$ and $CaCO_3$ (b) $Mg(HCO_3)$ and $CaCO_3$
(c) Na_2Co_3 and $CaCO_3$ (d) $Na2CO_3$ and $NaHCO_3$

87. The chemical characteristic feature of non saline alkali soil is …… **1** RPSC Pre-1995

	EC ds/m	ESP	pH
(1)	<4	>15	>8.5
(2)	<4	<15	>8.5
(3)	>4	>15	>8.5
(4)	>4	<15	<8.5

88. The ESP of the saline soil will be (Percentage) – **1** TN PSC Ag-2003
(1) < 15 (2) 15-30 (3) 30 – 45 (4) 45 – 50

89. The extent of land degradation in India is estimated about – **2** TN PSC Ag-I:1999
(1) 165 million hectare (2) 175 million hectare

(3) 185 million hectare (4) 180 million hectare

90. The organism which can withstand a wider range of salinity is known as? **c** IBS,AFO-2022

(a) Oligohaline (b) Estuarine **(c) Euryhaline** (d) Stenohaline

(e) Tecno-hyaline

91. The pH and ESP of saline sodic soil are respectively – **2** TN PSC Ag-II: 2001

(1) < 8.5 and < 15 (2) < 8.5 and > 15 (3) > 8.5 and > 15 (4) > 8.5 and > 15

92. The saline soils have an electrical conductivity of ….. **a** Agri Pre PG-2022

(a) > 4 mmho/cm (b) < 1.25 mmho/cm (c) 1.25 mmho/cm (d) 2.5 mmhp/cm

93. The salt affected soils are divided in how many classes depending upon electrical conductivity and sodium contents of their solution extract : **(c)** UPPSC Pre-1995

(a) Two (b) Four (c) Three (d) Five

94. The soil more suitable for application of rock phosphate and basic slag is – **1** TNPSC – Ag: 1999

(1) Acid soil (2) Neutral soil (3) Saline soil (4) Alkali soil

95. The term 'Residual Acidity' in soil refers to **B** IAS Pre-2004

(a) Acidity which is determined after taking a crop

(b) Acidity that can be neutralized by alkaline a crop

(c) Activity of hydrogen ion in the aqueous phase

(d) Acidity due to exchangeable hydrogen and aluminium

96. The term residual acidity refers to **c** IAS Pre-1999

(a)soil acidity that can be neutralized by alkaline material

(b) acidity of hydrogen ion in the aqueous phase

(c) acidity due to exchangeable hydrogen and aluminium

(d) acidity which is determined after taking a crop

97. The toxicity found in acid soil is of **A** AO SDAU-2013

A. Fe B. Ca C. P D.. N

98. The waterlogged saline soils can be reclaimed through : **4** RPSC Pre-1998

(1) Chemical Amendments (2) Farmyard Manure

(3) Fertilizers (4) Bio-drainage

99. What is the cost of reclamation of acidic soils under RKVY? **a** IBS,AFO-2019

(a) 15000 (b) 30000 (c) 40000 (d) 50000 (e) 60000

100. Which among the following state has highest alkaline soil? **a** IBS,AFO-2019

(a) UP (b) Gujarat (c) Punjab (d) West Bengal (e) Odisha

101. Which fertilizer most beneficial for alkali soils: **2** RPSC Pre-1998

(1)Urea (2)Ammonium sulphate

(3) Calcium ammonium sulphate (4) Ammonium Nitrate

102. Which is NOT correct about Saline soil? **Ans.: In saline soil due to precipitation Salt content increase** RRB SO-2020

103. Which method is used for reclamation of saline soil ? **B** AO SDAU-2013

A. Lime B. Leaching C. Gypsum D. All of these

104. Which of the following corresponds to saline-alkali soil : **b** UPPSC Pre-1998

	EC (mm hos/cm)	ESP	pH
(a)	>4	<15	<8.5
(b)	>4	>15	<8.5

(c) <4 >15 <10

(d)<4 <15 <10

105. Which of the following is a technique for reclamation of saline sodic soils? **C** IBS,AFO-2016

A. GIS B. SRI C. HFT D. FIRB E. All of these

106. Which one of the following anions is highly absorbed in acid soils? **D** IAS Pre-2000

(a) Chlorides (b) Nitrates (c) Sulphates (d) Phosphates

107. Which one of the following is correctly matched ? **3** TN PSC Ag-I:1999

Problematic soil		Amendment
(1) Calcareous sodic soil	-	Iron sulphate
(2) Non- calcareous sodic soil	-	Elemental sulphur
(3) Saline soil	-	Gypsum
(4) Saline sodic soil		Agriculture lime

108. Which one of the following is responsible for the failure of crop in saline soil? **A** IAS Pre-2004

(a) High osmotic potential (b) poor aeration

(c) Low permeability (d) Poor physical condition

109. Which one of the following is the chemical property of saline soil ? **3** TN PSC Ag-I:1999

(1) pH < 7.0, EC > 4 dSm^{-1}, ESP > 15%

(2) EC > 4 dSm^{-1}, ESP > 15%, pH > 8.5

(3) EC > 4 dSm^{-1}, ESP < 15%, pH < 8.5

(4) pH < 6.0, EC > 4 dSm^{-1}, ESP > 15%

110. Which one of the following pairs is not correctly matched? **B** IAS Pre-2005

(a) Acid soils	:	Ai toxicity
(b) Saline alkali soils	:	K toxicity
(c) Water logged soils	:	Methane emission
(d) Sandy soils	:	Nutrient leaching

111. Which soil ameliorants are used in sodic soil reclamation which is cheaper and easily available? **d** IBS,AFO-2022

(a) Iron pyrite (b) Ammonium nitrate (c) Lime **(d) Gypsum**

(e) Ammonium sulphate

CHAPTER- 148 : DENSITY OF SOILS PYQ'S

1. Advantage of bulky organic manures over inorganic fertilizer is — 4 — RPSC Pre-2010
   (1) Supply micronutrients (2) Improve soil physical condition
   (3) Increase available nutrient (4) All of these
2. Bulk density is higher of — d — Agri Pre PG-2014
   (a) Clay soil (b)Clay loam soil (c) Silt loam soil (d)Sandy soil
3. If a soil has bulk density 1.5 Mg/m³ and particle density 2.5 Mg/m³, what will be the percent porosity of soil — b — ARO Agro-2016
   (a) 30% (b) 40% (c) 50% (d) 60%
4. If bulk density of a soil is 1.4 g/cm^3 and particle density is 2.65 gm/cm^3, What will be the porosity (%) ? — 3 — Raj JET-2020
   (1) 43 (2) 53 (3) 47 (4) 57
5. The bulk density will be lowest in – — c — Gujrat AO-2017
   (a) Sandy soil (b) Loamy soil (c) Clayey soil (d) Gravelly soil
6. The percentage of total pore space in soil can be calculated by the formula : — 3 — RPSC Pre-1993
   (1) pore space = 100 – % solid space
   (2) % pore space = – particle density ÷ bulk density ×100
   (3) % pore space = 100 – bulk density ÷ particle density × 100
   (4) pore space = + % solid space
7. The bulk density of a soil with particle density of 2.65g/cc and pore space 405 would be — c — IAS Pre-1998
   (a) 1.29 g/cc (b) 1.45 g/cc (c) 1.59 g/cc (d) 1.72 g/cc
8. The % pore space in a soil having a bulk density of 1.16 mg m-3 and the particle density of 2.62 mg m-3 is — C — IAS Pre-2003
   (a) 26.2 (b) 44.3 (c) 55.7 (d) 81.7
9. Which one of the following soil properties does not change by cropping and cultivation? — B — IAS Pre-2005
   (a) Bulk density (b) Particle density (c) Porosity (d) Permeability
10. A sample of soil weighs 110 g and contains 15% moisture. If the volume of the soil is 75 cm^3, what is the bulk density of the soil? — C — IAS Pre-2008
    (a) 1.80 g/cm^3 (b) 1.52 g/cm^3 (c) 1/47 g/cm^3 (d) 1/28 g/cm^3
11. What is the pore space (%) in a soil having bulk density of 1.1 Mg m^{-3} and particle density of 3.1 Mg m^{-3} ? — D — IAS Pre-2008
    (a) 34.5 (b) 35.4 (c) 4.5 (d) 64.5
12. Which one of the following is the formula for calculating "percentage pore space" ? — a
    (a) $100 - \left(\frac{\text{Bulk density}}{\text{Particle density}} \times 100\right)$ (b) $\frac{\text{Bulk density}}{\text{Particle density}} \times 100$
    (c) $100 - \left(\frac{\text{Particle density}}{\text{Bulk density}} \times 100\right)$ (d) $\frac{\text{Particle density}}{\text{Bulk density}} \times 100$
13. Bulk density of soil is expressed as — C — ADA MP-2015
    (A) mg/ km (B) kg/ m^2 (C) Mg/ m^3 (D) kg/m
14. Bulk density of soil normally varies between — D — TO

(A) 2.60 - 2.75 mg/ m^3 (B) 2.75 - 2.90 mg/m^3 MPUAT-
(C) 2.00 - 2.20 mg/ m3 (D) 1.00 - 1.80 mg/ m^3 2014

15. When organic matter is added to the soil then : b UPPSC Pre-1998
(a) Bulk density is increased (b) Bulk density is decreased
(c) Bulk density does not change (d) None of the above

16. True principle density of most mineral soils is usually : 3 UPPSC Pre-2003
(1) 1.35 g/cm^3 (2) 1.65 g/cm^3 (3) 2.65 g/cm^3 (4) 3.50 g/cm^3

17. Bulk density of one soil weighing 1.4 is : b UPPSC Pre-2004
(a) 1.3 g/cm^3 (b) 1.4 g/cm^3 (c) 1.5 g/cm^3 (d) 1.35g/cm^3

18. Particle density of soil refers to : d UPPSC Pre-2008
(a)massof soil/volume of soil (b)mass of soil/pore volume
(c) mass of soil solids/pore volume (d)mass of soil solids/volume of soil solids

19. Bulk density of one m3 soil weighing 1.4 Mg is : c UPPSC Pre-2008
(a) 1.30 g/cm^3 (b) 1.35 g/cm^3 (c) 1.40 g/cm^3 (d) 1.50 g/cm^3

20. Particle density of mineral soil is usually : b UPPSC Pre-2009
(a) 3.4 g/cm^3 (b) 2.65 g/cm^3 (c) 1.65 g/cm^3 (d) 1.35 g/cm^3

21. The average bulk density of the normal soil is A AO KTPSC-2021
(A) 1- 1.60 Mg/m^3 (B) 2-2.50 Mg/m^3 (C) < 1 Mg/m^3
(D) > 3 Mg/m^3 (E) Answer not known

22. Bulk density of organic matter is ? b IFFCO T-2019
(a) 0.3 g/cc (b) 0.5 g/cc (c) 0.6 g/cc (d) 1.0 g/cc

23. A soil is having bulk density of 1.5 then the pore space (%) will be: C PPSC ADO- 2017
a) 41 b) 42 c) 43 d) 44

24. The major component of biogas generated from cow-dung is – d BHU PET-2012
(a) H_2 (b) CO_2 (c) N_2 (d) CH_4

CHAPTER- 149 : CATION EXCHANGE CAPACITY (CEC)

PYQ'S

1. Cation exchange capacities (C mol/kg. of soil) of humus, vermiculite, montmorillonite and illite at high soil pH values more or less are in the order of : 2 RPSC Pre-1994
(1) 30, 100, 150 and 200 (2) 200, 150, 100 and 30
(3) 100, 30, 200 and 150 (4) 150, 100, 200 and 30

2. Cation Exchange capacity (centimole/kg) of humus ranges between : 4 RPSC Pre-1999
(1) 25-50 (2) 50-100 (3)100-150 (4) 150-200

3. Electrical conductivity of a saturation extract (ECe) of a soil is greater than 4 decisiemens per meter (dS/m), exchangeable sodium percentage less than 15 per cent and pH usually less than 8.5, such soil is called : 4 RPSC Pre-1994
(1) saline alkali (2) non-saline alkali (3) acidic (4) saline

4. The approximate relationship between Total Dissolved Solids (TDS) and Electrical Conductivity (EC) of waters having EC less than 5 ds/m is expressed as 3 RPSC, AAO-2019
(1) TDS (mg/L) = 425 × EC (ds/m) (2) TDS (mg/L) = 515 EC (ds/m)
(3) TDS (mg/L) = 640 × EC (ds/m) (4) TDS (mg/L) = 720 EC (ds/m)

5. The approximate value of cation exchange capacity of organic colloid is___C mole (p^+) kg^{-1} soil:- 4 RPSC, AO-2016
(1) 80-150 (2) 3-10 (3) 10-40 (4) More than 200

6. The C.E.C. (m.e./100g) fo humic colloids is – d BHU PET-2010
(a) 3-50 (b) 20-80 (c) 50-120 (d) 100-300

7. The cation exhange capacity (in units of milli equivalents per 100 gram of soil) of kaolinite clay varies between a IAS Pre-1995
(a) 3 and 15 (b) 16 and 40 (c) 41 and 80 (d) 81and 100

8. Which one of the following is a measure of the net positive charge held on soil exchange complex? B IAS Pre-2005
(a) Anion exchange capacity (b) Cation exchange capacity
(c) Base exchange capacity (d) Electrical conductivity

9. If the contents of Ca^{++} Mg^{++}, Na^{+} and H^{+} are 13,4,3,2 and 2 mol (p^+) respectively and the CEC of soil is 25 mol (p^+) kg^{-1} what is the base saturation (%) ? D IAS Pre-2008
(a) 68 (b) 80 (c) 88 (d) 96

10. Which one of the following has the highest Cation Exhange Capacity? C IAS Pre-2008
(a) Kaolintie (b) Illite (c) Humus (d) Montmorillonite

11. Cation exchange capacity generally increases as the soil pH b IAS Pre-2009
(a) Stabilizes (b) Increases (c) Decreases (d) Attains neutrality

12. Cation exchange capacity is maximum in : d UPPSC Pre-2010
(a) Podzol soil (b) Laterite soil (c) Gley soil (d) Chernozem soil

13. The CEC of montmorillonite soil is – 3 TN PSC Ag-I:1999
(1) 3-10 m.e/100 g (2) 10-30 m.e / 10g (3) 80-100 m.e/100 g(4) > 150 m.e/100 g

CHAPTER- 150: CLAY MINERALS PYQ'S

1. Clay mineral illite has C.E.C. (cmol. (P*)kg-1) values ranging between – **b** BHU PET-2014
(a) 3-15 (b) 20-40 (c) 50-80 (d) 80-120

2. Diameter of Colloid Particles in soil is **d** MP PAT-2016
1. 0.51mm 2. 5100mm 3. 12mm 4. less than 2μm

3. Montmorillonite clay has silica and alumina layers, respectively in the following proportion : **1** RPSC, AAO-2009
(1) 2:1 (2) 1:2 (3) 3:2 (4) 2:3

4. Negative Charges on organic colloids originates due to presence of – **b** BHU PET-2017
(a) ketone and aldehyde groups (b) carboxyl and phenolic groups
(c) exposed crystal edges (d) isomorphrous substitution

5. Nutrient ion liable to be fixed in 2 : 1 clay mineral is – **c** BHU PET-2014
(a) $H_2PO^-_4$ (b) Fe^{++} (c) NH_4^+ (d) Zn^{++}

6. Chlorite belongs to the **a** IAS Pre-1994
(a) 2:2 type (b) 1:1 type (c) 2:1type (d) amorphous type

7. Kaolinitic clays are able to satisfy the Ca^{2+} requirement of most plants at calcium saturation value of **b** IAS Pre-1999
(a) 40 to 50% (b) 50 to 60% (c) 60 to 70% (d) 70 to 80%

8. 2:1:1 type of clay mineral consists of **C** IAS Pre-2000
(a) two layers of silica tetrahedron, one layer of alumina octahedron and one layer of magnesium octahedron called brucite
(b) two layers of alumina octahedron, one layer of silica tetrahedron and one layer of magnesium octahedron called brucite
(c) two layers of magnesium octahedron called brucite, one layer of silica tetrahedron and one layer of alumna octahedron
(d) two layers of silica tetrahedron, one layer of alumina octahedron and one layer of organic matter

9. Negative charge on silicate clays may be on account of and/or dependent on **C** IAS Pre-2000
(a) exposed crystal edges and isomorphous substitution
(b) isomorphous substitution and pH
(c) pH exposed crystal edges and isomorphosu substitution
(d) exposed crystal edges and pH

10. The process of replacement of one atom by another atom of similar size, in a crystal lattice of a soil clay, without disrupting or changing the crystal structure of the mineral is termed as **C** IAS Pre-2001
(a) ion exchange (b) isomerism
(c) isomorphic substitution (d) polymorphism

11. Consider the following clay minerals: **C** IAS Pre-2002
1. Montmorillonite 2. Illite 3. Kaolinite 4. Vermiculite
The arrangement of these clay minerals in descending order in terms of their CEC would be
(a) 2,14,3 (b) 4,2,3,1 (c) 4,1,2,3 (d) 3,2,4,1

12. The clay mineral that has high CEC is **D** IAS Pre-2006

(a) Kaolinite (b) Illite (c) Montmorillonite (d) Vermiculite

13. Which one of the following solid particles will form a soil suspension exhibiting high colloidal properties? **B** IAS Pre-2007

(a) Kaolinite (b) Vermiculite (c) Illite (d) Hematite

14. The specific surface area of clay minerals in soil varies from one to another, especially for the following clay minerals : **a** IAS Pre-2009

1. Kaolinite 2. Montmorillonite 3. Illite 4. Vermiculite

In terms of specific surface area of the above clay minerals in soil, in descending order, what is the correct sequence ?

(a) 4 – 2 – 3 – 1 (b) 1 – 3 – 2 – 4 (c) 4 – 3 2 – 1 (d) 1 – 2 – 3 – 4

15. Anion exchange is significant in soils high in **a** IAS Pre-2010

(a) 2 : 1 clay and hydrous oxides of Fe and Al

(b) 1 : 1 clay and hydrous oxides of Fe and Al

(c) 2 : 1 clays (d) 2 : 1 : 1 clays

16. Which one of the following pairs is correctly matched ? **d** IAS Pre-2010

(a) Dickite : 2: 1 non-expanding crystal lattice

(b) Illite : 2 : 1 expanding crystal lattice

(c) Nacrite : 2 : 2 non-expanding crystal lattice

(d) Saponite : 2 : 1 expanding crystal lattice

(a) Dickite: Dickite is a clay mineral with a 1:1 crystal lattice structure, meaning it consists of one tetrahedral sheet and one octahedral sheet. It does not typically expand upon hydration.

(b) Illite: Illite is a clay mineral with a 2:1 crystal lattice structure, meaning it consists of two tetrahedral sheets sandwiching one octahedral sheet. Illite can exhibit some degree of expansion upon hydration, but it is generally considered non-expanding.

(c) Nacrite: Nacrite is a clay mineral with a 1:1 crystal lattice structure, similar to dickite. It does not typically expand upon hydration.

(d) Saponite: Saponite is a clay mineral with a 2:1 crystal lattice structure. It is known for its expanding crystal lattice, meaning it can swell and increase in volume upon hydration.

17. Which one of the following clay minerals is formed under very advanced stage of weathering ? **d** IAS Pre-2010

(a) Chlorite (b) Illitc (c) Monotmorillonite (d) Kaolinite

18. Which clay mineral has highest phosphate adsorbing capacity ? **B** AO GPSC-2013

(A) Illite (B) Kaolonite (C) Montmorillonite (D) Chlorite

19. Montmorillonite clay has silica and alumina layers respectively in the following proportion : **a** UPPSC Pre-1997

(a)2 : 1 (b)3 : 2 (c)1 : 2 (d)2 : 3

20. Vermiculite is an aluminosilicate soil clay belonging to the type (aluminium : silicate ratio of) : **b** UPPSC Pre-2010

(a) 1:1 (b) 2:1 (c) 2 : 2 (d) 2 : I : 1

21. Cation exchange capacity of Kaolinite is — **C** — AO KTPSC-2021

(A) 8-100 Cmol (P^+) kg^{-1} (B) 15-40 Cmol (P^+) kg^{-1} (C) 3-15 Cmol (P^+) kg^{-1}
(D) 10-40 Cmol (P^+) kg^{-1} (E)Answer not known

22. A non expanding type of clay mineral is – — **4** — TN AO-2012

(1) Chlorite (2) Illite (3) Kailinite (4) Montomrillionite

23. An example for 2:1 expanding type of clay mineral is – — **4** — TN PSC Ag-I:1999

(1) Allophane (2) Illite (3) Kaolinite (4) Montmorillonite

24. Isomorphous substitution is a major source of negative charge in- — **1** — TN PSC Ag-I:1999

(1) 1:1 type clays (2) 2:1 type clays (3) Organic matter(4) Sesqul – oxide clays

25. Use of Kaolinic clay in pest control is classified under – — **1** — TN PSC Ag-I:2001

(1) Physical method (2) Chemical method
(3) Prophylactic method (4) None of these

26. Anion exchange capacity is more in – — **4** — TN PSC Ag-II: 2001

(1) Montmorillonite (2) Illite (3) Biotyte (4) Kaolinite

27. K availability is more in alluvial soils because of presence of – — **3** — TN PSC Ag-II: 2001

(1) Illite (2) Montmorillonite (3) Vermiculite (4) Kaolinite

28. Fixation is more in the following type of minerals. — **1** — TN PSC Ag-II: 2001

(1) 2 : 1 (2) 1 : 1 (3) 2 : 1 : 1 (4) None of these

29. Which two secondary silicate clay minerals have similar cation exchange capacity? — **4** — RPSC ARO Ag Chem -2022

(1) Kaolinite — Chlorite (2) Kaolinite – Illite
(3) Mite – Montmorillonite (4) Mite - Chlorite

CHAPTER-151 : SOIL COLLOIDS PYQ'S

1. Size of colloidal clay particle is less then : **4** UPPSC Pre-2003

   (1) o.2 mm (2) 0.02 mm (3) 0.02 mm (4) 0.0002 mm

2. Size of the colloidal particle is : **a** UPPSC Pre-2002

   (a) 10^{-4} to 10^{-7} cm (b) 10^{-5} to 10^{-8} cm (c) 10^{-6} to 10^{-8} cm (d) 10^{-4} to 10^{-7} cm

3. Soil colloidal particle shows the phenomena? **d** IFFCO T-2019

   (a) Plasticity(b) Adhesion and cohesion (c) Flocculation (d) All of the above

4. The ability of common ions to flocculate soil colloids is in the order of **A** IAS Pre-2010

   (a) Al > Ca = H > Mg > K > Na (b) Al = Ca = H > Mg > K > Na

   (c) Ca > Al = H > Mg > K > Na (d) Ca ≤ Al = H > Mg > K ≤ Na

5. The bulk of the…………………………… powers is concentrated in the crystalline clay minerals of the soil colloids. **c** Agri Pre PG-2022

   (a) Flocculation (b) Membrane potential

   (c) Cation exchange (d) Resilication potential

6. The chief inorganic colloidal fraction in soil is – **a** BHU PET-2011

   (a) Aluminosilicate layer lattec clays

   (b) Hydrous oxides and hydroxides of Fe, Al, Si and Mn in clay size dimension

   (c) Amorphous silicates (d) Clay sized primary minerals

7. The scattering of light by colloid is called – **2** RPSC ARO Ag Chem - 2022

   (1) Brownian movement (2) Tyndall effect (3) Dialysis (4) Coagulation

8. The size of the colloidal particle is : **a** UPPSC Pre-2007

   (a) 10^{-4} to 10^{-7} cm (b) 10^{-5} to 10^{-8} cm (c) 10^{-6} to 10^{-8} cm (d) 10^{-4} to 10^{-7} cm

9. Types of Soil colloids are: **c** MP PAT-2016

   1. Inorganic 2. Organic 3. Both of the above 4. None of these

CHAPTER- 152 : SOIL WATER PYQ'S

1. ______ is used for measuring percolation and leaching losses from a column of soil under controlled conditions. **B** PPSC ADO-2017
a) Infiltrometer b) Lysimeter c) Irrometer d) Porometer

2. A farmer wants to prepare basins of 2.5 m X 2.0 m size. How many basins can be formed in one hectare ? **3** TN AO-2008
(1) 100 (2) 1000 (3) 2000 (4) 3000

3. A soil having bulk density of 1.65 g/cc , exhibits 20.5 per cent moisture at field capacity and 8.5 % moisture at PWO. What would be the total moisture deficit in this soil in upper 30 cm soil ? **1** RPSC Pre-1995
(1)594 x 10-2 cm (2) 494 x 10-2 cm
(3) 59.4 x 10-2 cm (4) 49.4 x 10-2 cm

4. Addition of which increases the water holding capacity of sandy soil **A** AO SDAU-2015
A. Organic matter B. Fertilizer
C Pesticide D. Weedicide

5. Adsorption of water by hydrophilic surface is called **a** Agri Pre PG-2014
(a)Hydration (b) Solonet (c)Osmosis (d)Hygration

6. Among the following types of soil water which one is the most useful for the plants : **a** UPPSC Pre-1995
(a) Capillary water (b) Gravitational water
(c) Hygroscopic water (d) Combined water

7. An irrigation water contains 1280 mg per litre soluble salts. Calculate the electrical conductivity in milli siemens per meter (mSm-1) **1** Agri Pre PG-2015
(1) 200 (2) 819 (3) 50 (4) 20

8. An irrigation water is unsuitable with SAR value of – **4** TNPSC – TNPSC – Ag: 1999
(1) Less than 10 (2) Between 10-18
(3) Between 18-26 (4) Between 26-32

9. At field capacity the water is held at **A** IAS Pre-2002
(a) 0.033 MPa (b) 0.30 MPa (c) 3.00 MPa (d) 30.00 MPa

10. At what critical stage in wheat irrigation is required essentially in M.P ? **A** ADA MP-2015
(A) CRI stage (B) Tillering stage (C) Jointing stage (D) Flowering stage

11. At which crop stage of groundnut soil moisture stress is harmful the most ? **c** BHU PET-2016
(a)Early growth (b) Maturity (c)Pegging (d) Nut formation

12. At which of the following water potential, soil water is available to plants ? **c** UPPSC Pre-2009
(a) Above - 15 bars pressure (b) - 31 bars pressure
(c) Between - 0.3 bars pressure to - 15 bar pressure (d) None of the above

13. At wilting point moisture is retained at **a** Agri Pre PG-2014
(a) More than 15 bars (b) Less than 15 bars (c) 5 bars (d)1/3 bars

14. Atraction of moisture on the soil particle is known as : **c** UPPSC Pre-1998
(a) Plasticity (b) Adhesion (c) Cohesion (d) Stickiness

15. Availability of soil water to plants is maximum at – **c** MP PAT-2013

(A) Hygroscopic coefficient (B) Wilting point
(C) Field capacity (D) None of these

16. Available water (cm) in soil layer is expressed as – **a** Agri Pre PG-2017

(a) $\frac{\text{Soil Depth (cm)} \times \text{Bulk density} \times (\text{Field capacity \%} - \text{Permanent wilting point \%})}{100}$

(b) Soil Depth (cm) × Bulk density × (Field capacity % – Permanent wilting point %)

(c) $100 \times \frac{\text{Soil Depth (cm)} \times \text{Bulk density}}{(\text{Field capacity(\%)} - \text{Permanent wilting point \%})}$

(d) $\frac{(\text{Field capacity (\%)} - \text{Permanent wilting point \%}) \times 100}{\text{Bulk density} \times \text{Depth of SOil}}$

17. Available water holding capacity is maximum in : **3** UPPSC Pre-2003
(1) Clay loam (2) Sandy Clay loam (3) Silty Clay loam (4) Loam

18. Available water is between – **1** TN AO-2012
(1) FC and PWP (2) FC and Saturation
(3) PWP and Hygrosocopic coefficient (4) None of the above

19. Available water retention capacity of sandy loam soil is : **b** UPPSC Pre-2007
(a) 5.0% (approx) (b) 10.0% (approx) (c) 15.0% (approx) (d) 20.0% (approx)

20. Between field capacity and permanent wilting point the water in the soil – **a** Gujrat AO-2017
(a) Available water (b) Difficultly available water
(c) Unavailable water (d) Superfluous water

21. Calculate the total water presently contained in the top 30 cm soil if present water content is 15%, water content at field capacity is 20%, and PWP is 10% with bulk density of 0-30 cm depth surface soil is 0.5 g/cc :- **4** Agri Pre PG-2015
(1) 0.5 cm (2) 1.0 cm (3) 1.5 cm (4) 2.25 cm

22. Capillary movement of water in a soil an example of – **b** Gujrat AO-2017
(a) Saturated flow (b) Unsaturated flow
(c) Osmotic potential (d) Vapour flow

23. Capillary water will not be available to the plants. It is held at a tension of **C** ADA Guj-2013
(A) Less than 15 atmospheres
(B) 20 atmospheres
(C) More than 15 atmospheres
(D) Less than 5 atmospheres

24. Chemical precipitation in irrigation water occurs due to increase in – **1** TN AO-2012
(1) Fe and HCO_3 (2) HCO_3 (3) Ca (4) CO_3

25. Consider the following statements **c** IAS Pre-1996
According to cohesion theory for the ascent of sap water moves from the roots through the stems to the leaves in tall trees because of
1. forces of root pressure

2. the gradient in decreasing water potentials form the soil, through the plant to the leaves

3. forces of adhesion of water to cell walls, especially in the leaves

4. forces of cohesion between molecules

Of these statements

(a) 1,2, and 3 are correct (b) 2,3and 4 are correct

(c) 1,3and 4 are correct (d) 1,2and 4 are correct

26. Darcy's low in water management explains – **2** TN AO-2018

(1) Flow of water in dam (2) Flow of water in soil

(3) Flow of water in forest trees (4) Flow of water in hills

27. Denitrification is more in **A** ADA Guj-2013

(A) Waterlogged soils (B) Well drained soils

(C) Heavy soils (D) Light soils

28. Downward movement of water through gravity : **percolation** BOM AO-2021

29. Evaporation from a bare soil will be - **b** Gujrat AO-2017

(a) More than free water surface (b) Less than that from free water surface

(c) Same as that from free water surface (d) No relation

30. Field capacity generally comes after **D** ADA Guj-2013

(A) 10 -12 hrs. (B) 12 - 24 hrs. (C) 24 - 48 hrs. (D) 48 - 72 hrs.

31. Flow of water in saturated soil is described by : **1** UPPSC Pre-2003

(1) Poiseuille's law (2) Darcy's law (3) Fick's law (4) Stocke law

32. For measuring energy status of soils water, tensiometer works well within narrow moisture range upto :- **1** AARO Agro-2016

(1) 0.8 bars (2) 1.2 bars (3) 1.5 bars (4) 1.8 bars

33. Gravitational water also refers to – **2** TN PSC Ag-II: 2001

(1) Capillary water (2) Free water (3) Available water (4) Non available water

34. Height of rise of water in a capillary tube is directly proportion to : **1** UPPSC Pre-2003

(1) Surface tension of water (2) Radius of capillary tube

(3) Viscosity of water (4) as in (a) and (c) above

35. High sodium content in irrigation water causes _____ of soil – **2** TN AAO-2019

(1) Flocculation (2) Deflocculation (3) Cementation (4) Aggregation

36. Hydraulic conductivity of soils varies directly with **c** IAS Pre-1997

(a) capillary porosity (b) non-capillary porosity

(c) total porosity (d) water holding capacity

37. Hydraulic conductivity of soils varies directly with : **b** UPPSC Pre-2000

(a)Capillary porosity (b)Non-capillary porosity

(c)Total porosity (d)Water holding capacity

38. Hydraulic force is equivalent to **a** MP PAT-2014

(A) $\frac{\text{Area} \times \text{Height of water column}}{\text{Density of water}}$

(B) $\frac{\frac{1}{2}\text{Area} \times \text{Height of water column}}{\text{Density of water}}$

(C) $\frac{\text{2 Area} \times \text{Height of water column}}{\text{Density of water}}$

(D) None of the above

39. Hygroscopic water in soils is the moisture that is **B** TNPSC Ag-1998

(A) Fairly available to plant (B) Not available to plant

(C) Moderately available to plant (D) None of these

40. If 'A' stand for mineral matter, 'B' for organic matter, 'C' for soil water and 'D' for soil air, then the average volumetric composition of a mineral soil is : **4** RPSC Pre-1994

	A	B	C	D
(1)	35%	15%	28%	22%
(2)	45%	15%	20%	20%
(3)	40%	15%	15%	30%
(4)	45%	5%	25%	25%

41. If a soil contains 25% moisture, calculate the specific heat of the soil (Given : Sp. Heat of water and Sp. Heat of soil solid are 1.0 cal/g and 0.2 cal/g, respectively) – **4** Agri Pre PG-2018

(1) 0.18 Cal/g (2) 1.36 Cal/g (3) 3.6 Cal/g (4) 0.36 Cal/g

42. If an irrigation water source has the concentration of Na+, Ca++& Mg++ as 20, 10 & 8 milliequivalents per liter respectively, then sodium absorption ratio of this water? **b** IBS,AFO-2022

(a) 3.36 **(b) 6.67** (c) 4.87 (d) 2.91 (e) 5.28

43. If moisture content at field capacity is denoted by 'FC', actual soil moisture content at permanent wilting point by 'MC', the depth of effective root zone of the crop by 'D' and the bulk density of the soil by 'Bd', then total soil moisture deficit can be estimated by using one of the following formula : **1** RPSC Pre-1994

(1) FC - MC ÷ 100 × D xBd (2) FC-MC ÷ Bd × D ÷ 100

(3) (FC – MC) × Bd × D × 100 (4) FC - MC ÷ 100 × Bd + D

44. If moisture content on wet basis is 20%, then what would be the moisture content dry basis : **1** RPSC ACF AE -2018

(a) 25% (b) 18% (c) 20% (d) 22%

45. If only one irrigation is available, then the wheat crop should be irrigated at ………stage. **1** Agri Pre PG-2019

(1) CRI (2) Flowering (3) Milking (4) Dough

46. If the EC of irrigated water is 250 to 750 micro-mhos/cm, salinity class is – **3** TN PSC Ag-II: 2001

(1) Low (2) Moderate (3) Medium (4) High

47. If the field capacity is 18% and permanent wilting point is 6%. The 50% of the available soil moisture will be - **4** RPSC ARO Agro-2022

(1) 6% (2) 8% (3) 10% (4) 12%

48. If the gravimetric moisture content of soil is 15% and the bulk density is 1.4 g/cc, the volumetric moisture content is : **b** UPPSC Pre-2000

(a) 18.0% (b) 21.0% (c) 24.0% (d) 27.0%

49. If the total dissolved salts of irrigation water is 1664 mgL^{-1}, then the EC of water is ____dSm^{-1} **2** TN AAO-2019

(1) 2.0 (2) 2.6 (3) 1.6 (4) 3.0

50. In irrigation water, a number of ions are present. They have been arranged in the order of increasing harmfulness to soil health and crop production. Selectthe correct order of arrangement **A** TNPSC Ag-1998
(A) Potassium, Calcium, Carbonate, Sodium
(B) Sodium, Calcium, Potassium, Carbonate
(C) Sodium, Calcium, Carbonate, Potassium
(D) Carbonate, Potassium, Calcium and Sodium

51. In water logged soils, different compounds/ions undergo reduction from the oxidized state to the reduced state. The correct order of the given species (compounds/ions) in the sequence of first to be reduced to the last to be reduced in a water logged soil is **B** IAS Pre-2000
(a) NO_3^-, SO_4^{2-}, Fe^{3+}, MnO_2 (b) SO_4^{2-}, NO_3^-, MnO_2, Fe^{3+}
(c) Fe^{3+}, MnO_2, NO_3^-, SO_4^{2-} (d) NO_3^-, MnO_2, Fe^{3+}, SO_4^{2-}

52. In waterlogged lands **D** HPSC ADO-2022
(A) the soil pores are saturated within a depth of 1 m
(B) the soil pores are saturated within a depth of 60m
(C) the soil pores are saturated within a depth of 40m
(D) the soil pores are saturated up to the root zone of the crop

53. In which of the following structure the infiltration rate will be minimum – **b** Gujrat AO-2017
(a) Granular (b) Platy (c) Prismatic (d) Blocky

54. In which type of soil low permeability is present **a** ICAR Gen Agri-2007, 08
(A) Alkali (B) Saline (C) Acidic (D) None

55. Increase in surface tension in soil results in: **a** MP PAT-2016
1. Increase in capillary water 2. Decrease in capillary water
3. Increase in soil temperature 4. Decrease in Soil pH

56. Irrigation water having salt concentration of less than0.16 g/litre is: **a** NSC SR T-2019
(a) Safe for irrigation (b) Unsafe of irrigation
(c) Needs leaching before use (d) None of the above

57. Irrigation water is measured by **c** TNPSC Agri-1997
(A) SAR (B) EC (C) SAR and EC (D) None of these

58. Irrigation water with SAR values ranging between 18 and 26 is classified as – **3** TN PSC Ag-I:1999
(1) Low (2) Moderate (3) High (4) Very high

59. Match List I with List II and select the correct answer using the code given below the Lists : **b** IAS Pre-2009

List I (*Soil moisture constant*)	List II (*pF value*)
A. Capillary water	1. Tension free
B. Hygroscopic water	2. 0 to 2.5
C Ground water	3. 2.5 to 4.5
D. Gravitational water	4. 4.5 to 7.0

Code :

	A	B	C	D
(a)	3	4	1	2
(b)	3	1	4	2

(c) 2 4 1 3
(d) 2 1 4 3

60. Match ListI with List II and select the correct answer — **C** IAS Pre-2003

List I (Soil Moisture Constant)	List II (pF Value)
A. Field capacity	1. 6.0
B. Maximum water holding capacity	2. 7.0
C. Wilting point	3. 0.0
D. Oven dry	4. 2.5
	5. 4.2

	A	B	C	D		A	B	C	D
(a)	2	3	5	1	(b)	4	2	3	5
(c)	4	3	5	2	(d)	3	5	4	2

61. Method of using fertilizers with irrigation water is called ? — **c** Raj JET-2015
(a) Irrigation (b) Herbigation (c) Fertigation (d) Chemigation

62. Moisture at 'Field capacity' in soil is measured after the irrigation of – — **a** Raj JET-2014
(a) 48-72 hours (b) 12-14 hours
(c) Just after irrigation (d) Before irrigation

63. Moisture content of soil is measured by — **b** MP PAT-2016
(a) Potometer (b) Hygrometer (c)Barometer (d) Rain gauge

64. Most widely used method moisture determination is of soil — **A** AO GPSC-2013
(A) Gravimetric method
(B) Gypsum cube
(C) Tensiometer
(D) Neutron method

65. Negative potential at hygroscopic coefficient is approximately ….bar — **c** BHU PET-2016
(a) 15 (b) 20 (c) 31 (d) 41

66. Permanent wilting of sunflower is expressed earlier in — **c** TNPSC Ag-1996
(A) Black soil (B) Alluvial soil (C) Sandy soil (D) Red soil

67. Permeability of water is rapid in soil of the following textual class – — **2** TNPSC – Ag: 1999
(1) Loam (2) Sandy loam (3) Clay loam (4) Sandy clay loam

68. Plant die at stage of moisture content called : — **2** RPSC Pre-1994
(1) wilting coefficient (2) permanent wilting
(3) ultimate wilting (4) wilting range

69. Plants wilt when soil water content reaches the suction of – — **a** BHU PET-2011
(a) 15 bar (b) 5 bar (c) 1 bar (d) 1/3 bar

70. Plants wilt when water content goes below – — **d** BHU PET-2012
(a) 0.1 bar (b) 1/3 bar (c) 5 bar (d) 15 bar

71. Pore space (%) is equivalent to which of the following? — **a** MP PAT-2014
(A) $100 - \frac{\text{Bulk density}}{\text{Particle density}} \times 100$ (B) $100 + \frac{\text{Bulk density}}{\text{Particle density}} \times 100$
(C) $\frac{\text{Bulk density}}{\text{Particle density}} \times 100$ (D) $\frac{\text{Particle density}}{\text{Bulk density}} \times 100$

72. Primary source of water to the soil is – — **3** TN PSC Ag-II: 2001
(1) Dew (2) Ground water (3) Rainfall (4) Frost

73. Red soils has? **A** IBS,AFO-2014
(A) Poor drainage capacity (B) Phosphorus rich and potassium low (C) High drainage capacity (D) Very high drainage capacity (E)Medium drainage capacity

74. Resistance blocks give reasonably good moisture reading in the range of – **b** BHU PET-2017
(a) 0 to 0.8 bar potential (b) -1 to -15 bar potential
(c) 0 to -15 bar potential (d) -1 to 0.8 bar potential

75. Retention of water molecules on clay particles occurs due to the force of ……. **a** BHU PET-2016
(a) Adhesion (b) Cohesion
(c)Adhesion and cohesion (d) Centrifugation

76. Salt index of irrigation water is positive, it indicates – **1** Agri Pre PG-2019
(1) Water is harmful for irrigation
(2) Water is high quality for irrigation
(3) Water has low sodium hazards
(4) Water has low permeability hazards

77. Soil have highest water holding capacity – **b** Delhi PGT-2014
(a) Laterite soil (b) Black cotton soils
(c) Alluvial soil (d) Red soil

78. Soil moisture content can directly and accurately be estimated with – **3** TN PSC Ag-I:1999
(1) Tensiometer (2) Electrical resistance block
(3) Neutron moisture meter (4) None of these

79. Soil moisture could be measured by :- **d** ARO Agro-2016
(a) Picnometer (b) Moisture meter
(c) Gravimetry method
(d) Moisture meter & Gravimetry method Both

80. soil moisture tension at field capacity in a loam soil is : **a** UPPSC Pre-2008
(a)0.33 bar (b) 1.0 bar (c) 2.0 bar (d) 3.0 bar

81. Soil water is available between **1** RPSC Pre-2008
(1) 1/3 – 15 atm (2)15 – 30 atm (3) 2/3 - 15 atm (4) 10-30 atm

82. Soil water is available between : **1** RPSC ACF Agri -2011
(a) 1/3 -15 atm (b) 15 - 31 atm (c) 2/3 - 15 atm (d) 10 - 30 atm

83. Soil water measurement is done by **a** Agri Pre PG-2014
(a) Neutron scattering method (b) Lysimeter method
(c) Inflow – out flow method (d)Blaney-Criddle method

84. Soil Water potential at FC ranges from: **c** Agri Pre PG-2021
(a). -0.01 to -0.03 bars (b). -0.1 to -0.3 M Pa (c). -0.001 to -0.003 M Pa
(d). -0.0001 to -0.003 M Pa

85. Soil water potential is expressed in terms of **4** RPSC Pre-2010
(1) atmospheric pressure (kg/cm^2)
(2) 760 M.M. Hg of water column
(3) bar (4) All of these

86. Soils transported by running water is known as **c** MP PAT-2016
1. Colluvial 2. Eolian 3. Alluvial 4. Glacial

87. Tension with which water is held in a saturated soil at the air-water interface is : **a** UPPSC Pre-2008
(a) Zero bar (b) 1/3 bar (c) 15 bar (d) 31 bar

88. The adverse effect of poor quality of water will be more on- **1** TN PSC Ag-2003
(1) Clay soil (2) Loamy soil (3) Sandy soil (4) None of these

89. The adverse effect of poor quality water will be more on – **1** TN AO-2008
(1) Clayey soil (2) Loamy soil (3) Sandy soil (4) Sandy soil

90. The amount of heat energy absorbed to evaporate 1cm of water covering 1ha. ofland is about - **3** RPSC ARO Ag Chem - 2022
(1) 530×10^6kcal (2) 560×10^6 kcal (3) 580×10^6 kcal (4) 610×10^6 kcal

91. The available soil moisture is – **4** TN PSC Ag-I:1999
(1) Moisture content between field capacity and saturation capacity
(2) Moisture content between saturation and permanent wilting point
(3) moisture content between field capacity and maximum water holding capacity
(4) Moisture content between field capacity and permanent wilting point

92. The available water for plants present in soil is between : **2** UPPSC Pre-2003
(1) Saturation and field capacity (2) Field capacity wilting point
(3) Saturation and wilting point (4) None of the above

93. The contents of which of the following increase the water holding capacity of the soil – **d** Gujrat AO-2017
(a) Coarse sand and fine sand (b) Fine sand and silt
(c) Fine sand and clay (d) Silt and Clay

94. The continuous circulation of water between hydrosphere, atmosphere and lithosphere is called as - **2** RPSC ARO Agro-2022
(1) Geohydrological cycle (2) Hydrological cycle
(3) Rainfall cycle (4) None of the above

95. The downward entry of water into the soil termed as : **b** BHU PET-2013
(a) Percolation (b) Infiltration (c) Permeability (d) Seepage

96. The force with which the moisture is held by the soil at a point corresponding to 15-atmosphere is : **d** UPPSC Pre-1998
(a) Field capacity (b) Permanently absorbed water
(c) Ground water (d) permanent wilting point

97. The infiltration rate will be maximum in – **d** Gujrat AO-2017
(a) Clayey soil (b) Loam (c) Clay loam (d) Sandy soil

98. The irrigation water RSC value ____ is safe – **4** TN AAO-2019
(1) 1.25 – 2.5 meL-1 (2) >2.5 meL-1 (3) 1.5 meL-1 (4) < 1.25 meL-1

99. The moisture content at which the wilting is complete and the plant die is called the : **2** RPSC Pre-1993
(1) permanent wilting point (2) ultimate wilting
(3) wilting co-efficient (4) wilting range

100. The moisture content of the soil attained after the drainage of gravitational water is known as **A** AO KTPSC-2021
(A) Field capacity (B) Water holding capacity (C) Permanent wilting point
(D) Moisture equivalent (E) Answer not known

101. The moisture content of the vermibed for vermicomposting should be maintained around **C** AO KTPSC-2021
(A) 20% (B) 40% (C) 60% (D) 80% (E) Answer not known

102. The moisture retention curve obtained by gradual wetting of an initially dry soil is termed as :- **4** AARO Agro-2016
(1) Cohesion (2) Adhesion (3) Desorption (4) Sorption

103. The movement and filtration of water through soils and permeable rock is termed as? **B** IBS,AFO-2016
A. Osmosis B. Percolation C. Sedimentation
D. Neutralization E. Diffusion

104. The pF value of heavy soils at field capacity is - **2** RPSC ARO Ag Chem - 2022
(1) 1.0 (2) 2.5 (3) 4.2 (4) 4.5

105. The probe unit of neutron moisture meter consist a mixture of :- **1** AARO Agro-2016
(1) Americium & beryllium (2) Barium & americium
(3) Helium & beryllium (4) Radium & barium

106. The quality of irrigation water is determined by – **4** TN ACF-2012
(1) Total concentration of soluble salts (2) Relative proportion of sodium
(3) Concentration of boron (4) All of these

107. The rate of entry of water into the soil would be best described as – **b** Delhi PGT-2014
(a) Transpiration rate (b) Infiltration
(c) Permeability (d) Water holdina capacity

108. The ratio of carbonate to bicarbonate ions in ground water generally between **c** TNPSC Ag-1996
(A) 1:10 and 1:2 (B) 1:2 and 1:10 (C) 2:1 and 1:10 (D) 1:10 and 2:1

109. The ratio of percentage of irrigation water available for use of crops of that delivered to a field is known as : **d** UPPSC Pre-1998
(a)Field capacity (b) Field efficiency
(c) Field irrigation requirement of crops (d) field irrigation efficiency

110. The result of soil moisture stress due to imbalance between available soil moisture and evoporation of a crop is :- **1** AARO Agro-2016
(1) Agricultural drought (2) Meteorological drought
(3) Atmospheric drought (4) Hydrological drought

111. The soil moisture constant at-15bar tension is called **3** RPSC Pre-2007
(1) Field capacity (2) Permanent wilting point
(3) Hygroscopic coefficient (4) Gravitational constant

112. The soil moisture tension of Field capacity is – **1** TN PSC Ag-II: 2001
(1) 1/3 atm (2) 1/5 atm (3) 1/8 atm (4) 1/15 atm

113. The temporary hardness of irrigation water is due to the presence of **a** TNPSC Agri-1997
(A) Bicarbonate (B) Chloride and sulphate (C) Fluoride (D) Nitrates

114. The tension of soil water at permanent wilting point is **C** IAS Pre-2004
(a) 0.1 atm (b) 0.3 atm (c) 15 atm (d) 33 atm

115. The texture of soil influences the water retention capacity of soil. How much suction pressure will deplete 98% of the ? **Ans.: 5 Bar** RRB SO-2018

116. The total depth of water required by a crop is known as: **A** PPSC ADO-2017

a) Delta b) Duty of water c) Cusec d) Dead storage

117. The uppar limit of available water in soil is determined at : **(a)** UPPSC Pre-2001

(a) 1/3 bar (b)½ bar (c) 2/3 bar (d) 1 bar

118. The upper limit of available soil moisture is – **2** TN PSC Ag-2003

(1) Saturation (2) Field capacity (3) PWP (4) None of these

119. The upper limit of soil moisture availability for plant growth? **2** RPSC, AAO-2018

(A) Matric Suction (B) Field Capacity

(C) Hygroscopic coefficient (D) PWP

120. The upper limit of the soil moisture available for the plant growth is : **2** RPSC Pre-2003

(1) PWP (15 bars) (2) Field capacity (1/3 bar)

(3) Hygroscopic coefficient (4) Matric suction

121. The volume wetness of soil can be derived from which one of the following? **A** IAS Pre-2007

(a) Mass wetness and bulk density

(b) Bulk density and particle density

(c) Hydraulic conductivity maximum water-holding capacity

(d) Particle density and intrinsic permeability

122. The water is available to plant communities **B** AO SDAU-2015

A. Hygroscopic B. Capillary

C. Gravitational D. All of these

123. The water is not suitable for irrigation, when the electrical conductivity is more than – **4** TN AAO-2019

(1) 0.25 dSm^{-1} (2) 0.75 dSm^{-1} (3) 0.5 dSm^{-1} (4) 2.25 dSm^{-1}

124. The water-form easily available to crop plant is – **b** BHU PET-2012

(a) Gravitational water (b) Capillary water

(c) Hygroscopic water (d) None of the three

125. Total amount of water present in the soil is called - **2** MP PG PAT-2016

(1) Combined water (2) Holard

(3) Podsole (4) None of these

126. Total amount of water present in the soil is called: **a** MP PAT-2016

1. Holard 2. Combined water

3. Capillary water 4. None of the above

127. Total soil water potential is – **1** TN AO-2018

(1) Sum of Gravitational, Osmostic, Capillary and Pressure Potential

(2) Sum of Gravitational, Osmostic and Capillary Potential

(3) Sum of Gravitational and Osmotic Potential

(4) Equal to Gravitational Potential

128. Transport of water through soil column is known as **c** MP PAT-2016

1. Surface tension 2. Surface run off

3. Percolation 4. Permeability

129. Under high SALINE irrigation water we will Prefer to grow – **a** RPSC, AAO-2012

(a) Barley (b) Gram (c) Pea (d) Wheat

130. Under water logged condition which nutrient occurs in toxic condition ? **A** AO GPSC-2013

(A) Fe (B) Zn (C) Cu (D) P

131. Vertical Movement of water is known as – **3** TN AO-2008

(1) Transformation (2) Diffision (3) Percolation (4) Filtration

132. Water available between field capacity and permanent wilting point is called as **3** RPSC Pre-2010

(1) Gravitational water (2) Capillary water

(3) Available water (4) None of these

133. Water conservation study under which subject? **B** IBS,AFO-2015

(A) Pomology (B) Soil Science (C) Olericulture (D) Food science

(E)Horticulture

134. Water content of soil at saturation is : **a** UPPSC Pre-1999

(a) two times that of field capacity (b) Three times that of field capacity

(c) Four times that field capacity (d) Five time that of field capacity

135. Water held between 1/3 bar to 31 bars in the soil is classified as **b** ICAR Gen Agri-2007

(A) Gravitational water (B) Capillary water

(C) Hygroscopic water (D) Available water

136. Water held in the soil is not available to the plant, if it is held at tension…… **E** BOD AO-2008

(A) 1/3 atmosphere (B) below 1/3 atmosphere (C) 1-3 atmosphere

(D) 3-15 atmosphere (E) above 15 atmosphere

137. Water holding capacity of soils in decreasing order ? **a** IBS,AFO-2021

(a) Clay> silt> sand (b) Clay > sand > silt (c) Silt > Clay > sand (d) Sand > clay > silt (e) Sand silt Clay

138. Water infiltration in soil means :- **b** ARO Agro-2016

(a) Water movement in soil (b) Water enters in soil

(c) Percolation (d) Leaching

139. Water movement by capillary action will be more in – **c** Gujrat AO-2017

(a) Sandy soil (b) Loamy soil

(c) Clayey soil (d) Organic soil

140. Water that is available to the plants and readily absorbed is : **3** RPSC Pre-1993

(1) hygroscopic water (2) rain water

(3) capillary water (4) gravitational water

141. Water that occurs as thin film (4 to 5 milli mimicron)and held with a tension of 31 atmosphere of more and not available to plant is : **3** RPSC Pre-1993

(1) capillary water (2) gravitational water

(3) hygroscopic water (4) surface water

142. Water which lies between field capacity and wilting point is – **1** TN PSC Ag-II: 2001

(1) Available water (2) Capillary water (3) Free water (4) Saturated water

143. What is meant by Moisture quivalent? **C** HPSC ADO-2022

(A) Percent of water a soil can retain in opposition to a centrifugal force 10 times that of gravity

(B) Percent of water a soil can retain in opposition to a centrifugal force 100 times that of gravity

(C) Percent of water a soil can retain in opposition to a centrifugal force 1000 times that of gravity

(D) Percent of water a soil can retain in opposition to a centrifugal force 10000 times that of gravity

144. What will be the moisture content of soil at 50% A.S.M. if it has field capacity and permanent wilting point values of 20% and 8% respectively. **b** UPPSC Pre-1997

(a) 18% (b) 12% (c) 14% (d) 10%

145. When a soil holds all the water it can, but no gravitational water,it is said to be it's **b** MP PAT-2016

1. Soil water potential 2. Field capacity

3. Moisture equivalent 4. None of the above

146. When ammonia reacts with water, what is the result? **C** IAS Pre-2007

(a) Increased nitrate content and decreased pH

(b) Decreased nitrate content and increased pH

(c) Increased ammonium content and decreased pH

(d) Increased ammonium content and increased pH

147. When soil is heated at 105 degree C to remove moisture and then come in 100% humidity is called? **Ans.: Saturation point** PSB AO-2019

148. When soil moisture decreased below wilting point and water hold by soil particle firmly as a state of water vapour this condition known as ? **(c)** IBS,AFO-2020

(a) Parmanent wilting point (b) Gravitational water (c) Hygroscopic coefficient (d) Capillary water (e) Superfluous water

149. When the contact of soil moisture still decreased below the wilting point in a way that the water is held very tightly and may be state of vapour around soil colloids that stage is called? **Ans.: Hygroscopic coefficient** RRB SO-2021

150. Which form of nitorgen is absorbed by paddy under waterlogged condition : **b** UPPSC Pre-2002

(a) N_2 (h) NH_4 ion (c) NO, ion (d) Nitrate ion

151. which of the following fact is not true? **2** RPSC, AAO-2018

(1) when the intensity of rain is more than infiltration rate, it causes runoff and soil loss.

(2) coarse soils are more susceptible to erosion than fine soils.

(3) deep lateritic soils have lower rate of runoff.

(4) alluvial soils have high rate of runoff.

152. Which of the following soil water types is the most important for crop growth ? **c** Delhi PGT-2014

(a) Chemically bound water (b) Hygroscopic water

(c) Capillary water (d) Gravitational water

153. Which of the following soil will have highest water holding capacity: **d** NSC SR T-2019

(a) Sandy soil (b) Sandy loam (c) Loam (d) Clay loam

154. Which of the following soils has the highest water holding capacity- **4** Raj JET-2020

(1) Sandy loam (2) Silt loam (3) Loamy sand (4) Clay

155. Which of the following statements explain the true relationship between soil water potential and moisture content of loam, sandy and clay soils? **d** IAS Pre-1998

1. Clay soils hold much more water at a given potential than loamy soils

2. Loamy soils hold much more water at a given potential than clayey soils

3. Loamy soils hold much more water at a given potential than clayey soils

3. Loamy soils hold much more water at a given potential than sandy soils
4. Clay soils hold much less water at a given potential than loamy soils.
(a) 1and 2 (b) 2and 3 (c) 3 and 4 (d) 1 and 3

156. Which of the method is considered to be best for quantitative estimation of change in soil moisture? **1** RPSC Pre-2008
(1) Tensiometer (2) Neutron probe
(3) Electrical resistance (4) Pressure plate and pressure membrane apparatus

157. Which of the soil has higher buffering capacity – **b** RPSC, AAO-2012
(a) Sandy soils (b) Clay soils (c) Loamy sand soils (d) Loamy soils

158. Which one of the following crops is sensitive to salt as well as boron in soil and water? **C** BOD AO-2008
(A) Grape (B) Sugar beet (C) Carrot (D) Cotton (E) None of these

159. Which one of the following is NOT a component of the moisture potential in soils? **b** IAS Pre-1995
(a) Matric potential (b) Turgor potential (c) Gravity potential (d) Osmotic potential

160. Which one of the following soils retains maximum water at field capacity (-33kpa)? **B** IAS Pre-2004
(a) Sandy soil (b) Clay soil (c) Loamy soil (d) Silty soil

161. Which one of the following type of soil water is available to the plants? **1** RPSC ACF Agri -2011
(a) Capillary water (b) Gravitational water
(c) Hygroscopic water (d) Run-off water

162. Which Soil has high water holding capacity but poor drainage? **A** BOM AO-2021
a. Black soil b. Redsoil c. Laterite soil d. Alluvial soil

163. With the increase in soil moisture content it's thermal conductivity **b** MP PAT-2016
1. Increases 2. Decreases 3. No change 4. None of these

CHAPTER- 153: SOIL AIR PYQ'S

1. Soil aeration status is best measured by ? — 1 — Agri Pre PG-2018
(1) ODR measurement (2) Percent Microposity
(3) Percent Porosity (4) WHC measurement

2. Area of Alluvial soil in Uttar Pradesh is – — c — BHU UET-2013
(a) 10.85 % (b) 51.22 % (c) 61.78% (d) 20.95 %

3. Area wise which of the following problems of soil degradation is most prominent in India — 2 — RPSC Pre-1999
(1) Floods (2) Draught (3) Salinity (4) Alkalinity

4. Highest area of saline alkaline soil is in State of – — a — BHU UET-2011
(a) Uttar Pradesh (b) Bihar (c) Gujarat (d) Madhya Pradesh

5. Highest pyrites is found in which State ? — b — BHU UET-2011
(a) Uttar Pradesh (b) Bihar (c) Andhra Pradesh (d) Tamil Nadu

6. In India, laterite soils are found commonly in the state of – — b — BHU PET-2010
(a) Uttar Pradesh (b) Karnataka
(c) Himachal Pradesh (d) Madhya Pradesh

7. Maximum area of black soil in India is in : — 1 — RPSC Pre-1998
(1Maharashtra (2)M.P. (3)U.P (4) Rajasthan

8. Top growth of plant is normally satisfactory as long as the oxygen diffusion rate remains above – — b — BHU PET-2017
(a) 20×10^{-8} g/cm^2/minute (b) $30\text{-}40\times10^{-8}$ g/cm^2/minute
(c) $10\text{-}20\times10^{-8}$ g/cm^2/minute (d) $20\text{-}80\times10^{-8}$ g/cm^2/minute

9. The dominant gas in atmosphere is — A — AO SDAU-2015
A. Nitrogen B. CO_2 C. O_2, D. None of these

10. Nitrogen per cent in atmosphere is — A — AO SDAU-2015
A 78% B. 0.037 % C 21% D. 0.09 %

11. Which gas is present in anaerobic condition ? — B — AO SDAU-2015
A. CO_2 B. Methane C. O_2 D. Ozone

12. In comparison to atmosphere soil air is rich in : — c — UPPSC Pre-1998
(a) Nitrogen (b) Oxygen (c) Carbon dioxide (d) Ozone

13. Carbon dioxide content in soil air is : — c — UPPSC Pre-2001
(a) 0.03% (b) 0.003% (c) 0.25% (d) 0.50%

14. Concentration of nitrogen in soil air is : — c — UPPSC Pre-2002
(a) 70% (b) 74% (c) 78% (d) 82%

15. Soil aeration units plants present in soil is between : — 4 — UPPSC Pre-2003
(1) 50-60% (2) 60-70% (3) 70-80% (4) 80-90%

16. Soil aeration limits plant growth when percent saturation by water is more than : — d — UPPSC Pre-2004
(a) 50-60 (b) 60-70 (c) 70-80 (d) 80-90

17. CO_2 content of soil air is : — b — UPPSC Pre-2008
(a) 0.03 % (b) 0.25 % (c) 2.50 % (d) 3.00 %

18. The best method for characterization of aeration status of the soil is – — 4 — TN AO-2018
(1) Air filled porosity (2) Redox potential

(3) Diffusion coefficient of gases (4) Oxygen diffusion rate

19. The average biogas production estimated per kg of dry matter is – 1 TN ACF-2012

(1) 160 lts (2) 100 lts (3) 50 lts (4) 20 lts

20. Carbon dioxide content of soil air will be highest in - 2 RPSC ARO Ag Chem -2022

(1) Bare soil (2) Manured soil (3) Well aggregated soil (4) Cultivated soil

21. The resistance time of N_2O in atmosphere is approximately – 4 RPSC ARO Ag Chem -2022

(1) 120 days (2) 120 weeks (3) 120 months (4) 120 years

22. Which of the following is not a source of greenhouse gases? 1 RPSC ARO Ag Chem -2022

(1) A wind turbine (2) Fertilizer industry

(3) A coal fired power plant (4) A sport utility vehicle

23. By entrapping one tonne of carbon into soil, how much carbon dioxide will be reduced in the atmosphere? 3 RPSC ARO Agro-2022

(1) 1.67 tonnes (2) 2.67 tonnes (3) 3.67 tonnes (4) None of the above

CHAPTER-154: SOIL BIOLOGY/ SOIL MICRORGANISM PYQ'S

1. 'PGPR' is concerned with – **a** BHU UET-2017
(a) beneficial bacteria in plants (b) harmful bacteria in plants
(c) beneficial fungus in plants (d) harmful fungus in plants

2. ……….. is considered as a free living bacteria, for nitrogen (N_2) fixing is soil. ***** Agri Pre PG-2019
(1) Rhizobia (2) Anabaeana (3) Beijerinckia (4) Acetbacter

3. An organism, which converts nitrite to nitrate is. **2** RPSC Pre-1995
(1) Azotobactor (2)Nitrobactor (3) Nitrosomonas (4)Nitrogenase

4. Atmospheric Nitrogen fixation in legumes is done by which bacteria **b** Raj JET-2014
(a) Actinomycetes (b) Rhizobium bacteria
(c) Bacillus bacteria (d) Mycorrhiza

5. Azatobactor is a **b** Agri Pre PG-2014
(a) Phosphorus solubilizing bacteria (b) Nitrogen fixing bacteria
(c) VAM fungi (d)Soil binding agent

6. *Azorhizobium* produces stem nodules on :- **1** AARO Agro-2016
(1) Sesbania rostrata (2) Sesbania grandiflora
(3) Sesbania aculeate (4) Sesbania quadrata

7. Bacteria responsible for N-fixation in berseem is – **c** Raj JET-2017
(a) Rhizobium phaseoli (b) Rhizobium japonicum
(c) Rhizobium trifoli (d) Rhizobium meliloti

8. Bacteria responsible for N-fixation in soyabean is : **3** RPSC Pre-2003
(1)Rhizobium phaseoli (2) Rhizobium glycicum
(3) Rhizobium japonicum (4) Rhizobium leguminoserum

9. Bacteria responsible for the reduction of sulphate and sulphur -] **4** Agri Pre PG-2019
(1) Thiobacillus (2) Nitrosomonas
(3) Nitrobacter (4) Desulfovibrio

10. Biofertilizers are : **c** School Lect. 2019
(a) Organic manure (b) Mineral fertilizer
(c) Microbial culture (d) All of the above

11. Biofertilizers are – **b** BHU PET-2017
(a) organic manure (b) culture of the microorganisms
(c) green manures (d) mineral fertilizers

12. Biological activity in soil profile will be maximum in – **a** Gujrat AO-2017
(a) Horizon A (b) Horizon C (c) Horizon B (d) Parent material

13. 'cfu' is a unit for measuring **4** Agri Pre PG-2015
(1) soil pollution (2) metal contamination
(3) soil quality (4) microbial population

14. Due to bacterial action the dead leaves change into : **4** RPSC Pre-1993
(1) humus (2) algae (3) fungi (4) organic matter

15. Free living N-fixers are :- ***** ARO Agro-2016
(a) *Rhizobia* (b) *Azotobacter*
(c) *Azospirillum* (d) *Azotobactor & Azospirillum* Both

16. Fungi are active is soil at pH ? — **b** — BHU UET-2014

(a) 5.0 (b) 7.0 (c) 8.0 (d) 9.0

17. Lichen is an association of: — **1** — RPSC Pre-2007

(1) Algae and fungus (2)Bacterium and fungus

(3) Fungus and virus (4) Fungus and nematode

18. Lichens are sensitive to which of the air contaminant ? — **2** — Raj JET-2020

(1) N_2O (2) SO_2 (3) CO_2 (4) CO

19. Match list-1 (Rhizobium species) with list-2 (Legumes included) and selected the correct answer using the codes given below the lists : — **2** — RPSC Pre-1994

List-1	List-2
A. *Rhizobium japonicum*	1. Beans
B. *Rhizobium leguminosarum*	2. Clover
C. *Rhizobium melilotii*	3. Fenugreek
D. *Rhizobium trifolii*	4. Lentil
	5. peas
	6. soybean

Codes :

	A	B	C	D
(1)	6	5	3	2
(2)	6	4	2	3
(3)	3	1	5	2
(4)	2	3	4	1

20. Microoranisms which grow at temperature below 10^0 C are known as — **3** — Agri Pre PG-2016

(1) Mesophiles (2) Thermophiles (3) Psychrophiles (4) All are correct

21. Mycorrhiza is associated with – — **c** — BHU PET-2015

(a) Stem (b) Leaf (c) Root (d) Flower

22. Non-Symbiotic anarobic N- fixing bacteria is – — **b** — BHU PET-2012

(a) Azotobacter *(b) Clostridium*

(c) Rhizobium Sps. *(d) Rhodospoirillium*

23. Nutrient that play a key role in biological nitrogen fixation is — **b** — MP PAT-2016

1. Chlorine 2. Molybdenum 3. Potassium 4. Cobalt

24. Organism have a significant effect on soil formation by controlling the .... — **3** — Agri Pre PG-2015

(1) time of soil formation (2) development of C horizon

(3) decomposition and transformation of organic matter

(4) rate of soil formation

25. Phosphorus solubilizing Micro-organism — **1** — Agri Pre PG-2016

(1) VAM *(2) Mucor* *(3) Rhizopus* *(4) E. coli*

26. Rhizobium inoculation is effective only when an active and efficient strain is used under optimum : — **4** — RPSC Pre-1998

(1)EC (2)N (3) Zn (4) pH

27. *Rhizobium* strain suitable for inoculation of berseem seeds is – — **a** — BHU PET-2014

(a) R. trifolii (b) R. Japonicum (c) R. meliloti *(d) R. leguminosarum*

28. Soil enzyme that has been widely used as a measure of soil quality is – **b** BHU PET-2012
(a) Deaminases (b) Dehydrogenases (c) Proteases (d) Amylase

29. Soil organisms responsible for conversion of NH_4^+ to NO^-_{2} is **a** Agri Pre PG-2013
(a) *Nitrosomonas* (b) *Nitrobacter* (c) *Rhizobium* (d)*Azotobacter*

30. Symbiotic –N – fixing bacteria is **c** BHU PET-2016
(a)Closteridium *(b)Azotobacter* *(c) Rhizobium spp.* *(d) Bacillus*

31. The Bacteria responsible for nitrogen fixation in nodules of legumes is – **c** Delhi PGT-2014
(a) *Nitro-bacter* (b) *Streptococcus* (c) *Rhizobium* (d) *Sporangium*

32. The biofertilizer that can neither be cultured in the absence of living roots nor isolated on agar plate by standard microbiological technique is – **a** RPSC, AO-2012
(a) VAM (b) *Azospirillum* (c) *Azotobacter* (d) *Rhizobium*

33. The correct combinations are : **2** RPSC Pre-1994
A. Nitrifying organisms – *nitrobacteria*
B. Convert ammonia into nitrites – *nitrosomonas*
C. Oxidizes nitrites to nitrates – nitro-*bactor*
D. Wide spread type of voltalization – denitrification
(1) A, B and C (2) A, B, C and D (3) B and C (4) A and D

34. The group of organisms which convert ammonia into nitrite and nitrate , respectively :- **1** RPSC, AAO-2009
(1) Nitrosomonas , Nitrobacter *(2) Pseudomonas, Azotobactor*
(3) Agrobacterium, Bacillus *(4) Streptomyces, Nocardia*

35. The microbial fertilizer needed for nodulation in gram is – **c** Gujrat AO-2017
(a) *Azatobactor* (b) *Azospirillum* (c) *Rhizobium* (d) *Phosphobacterin*

36. The microorganism responsible for the conversion fo ammonium ion to nitrite nitrogen in soil is – **c** BHU PET-2011
(a) Rhizobium *(b) Nitrobacter* *(c) Nitrosomonas* *(d) Algae*

37. The most abundant microorganisms in soils are – **d** BHU PET-2011
(a) Protozoa *(b) Nitrobacter* *(c) Nitrosomonas* *(d) Algae*

38. The organism responsible for conversion of NO_2 to NO_3 is – **a** Gujrat AO-2017
(a) Nitrobacter *(b) Nitrosomonas* *(c) Azospirillum* *(d) Azotobacter*

39. the process of formation of nitrogen and nitous oxide gases from ammonical fertilizers in soil is known as? **3** RPSC, AAO-2018
(1) nitrification (2) ammonification (3) denitrification (4) mineralization

40. the transformation of elemental nitrogen to an organic form by micro-organisms is called as - **1** RPSC, AAO-2018
(1) nitrogen fixation (2) nitrogen synthesis
(3) nitrogen metabolism (4) ammonification

41. VAM increase the uptake of which nutrient ? **2** RPSC Pre-2008
(1) Nitrogen (2)Phosphorus (3) Iron (4) All of the above

42. Which bacteria converts NO_2 to NO_3 ? **2** RPSC Pre-2008
(1) Nitrosomonas (2)Nitrobacter *(3) Nitrospira* *(4) Nitrogela*

43. Which is not a free living nitrogen fixing microbe ? **2** Raj JET-2020
(1) *Azotobactor* (2) *Rhizobium* (3) *Nostoc* (4) *Beijerinckia*

44. Which nitrifying bacteria oxidizes Nitrite (NO_2^-) to Nitrate (NO^{3-}) is soils – b BHU PET-2014

(a) Nitrosomonas (b) Nitrobacter (c) Nitrospira (d) Nitroglea

45. which of the following is a bio-fertilizer? 2 RPSC Pre-1993

(1)compost (2)green algae (3)green manure (4) farm yard manure

46. Which of these elements can partially substitute molybdenum in nitrogen fixation by *Rhizobium* ? c RPSC, AO-2012

(a) Sodium (b) Silicon (c) Vanadium (d) Cobalt

47. Which of the following bacteria are responsible for the conversion of nitrogen from nitrite to nitrate form? 2 RPSC Pre-1999

(1) Nitrosomonas (2) Nitrobactor (3) Clostridium (4) Bacillus

48. Which of the following belong to the association of 'lichens' ? 2 RPSC Pre-1994

(1) algae and bacteria (2) algae and fungi

(3) bacteria and virus (4) bacteria and fungi

49. Which of the following is the denitrification bacteria ? 1 RPSC Pre-2007

(1) *Pseudomonas* (2) *Nitrosomonas*

(3) *Nitrobactor* (4) None of the above

50. Which of the following nutrients is supplied by mycorhiza to the plant ? 2 RPSC Pre-1999

(1) Nitrogen (2)Phosphorus (3)Sulphur (4) Iron

51. Which of the following Rhizobium bacteria is responsible for nodule formation in soybean 4 RPSC Pre-1999

(1) Rhizobium legumenosarum (2) Rhizobium trifolii

(3) Rhizobium meliloti (4) Rhizobium japonicum

52. Which of these orgamisms involved in denitrification process in soil is not a heterotroph ? 4 AARO Agro-2016

(1) Pseudomonas (2) Bacillus (3) Achromobacter 4) Thiobacillus

53. Which of these species of *Rhizobium* is classified under slow growing type – a RPSC, AO-2012

(a) *R.mililodi* (b) *R.trifolli* (c) *R.lupini* (d) *R. leguminosarum*

54. Which one is a microorganism in a soil – c BHU PET-2012

(a) Protozoa (b) Termites (c) Fungi (d) Nematodes

55. Which one of the following is used as biofertilizer ? d BHU UET-2017

(a) Rhizobium culture (b) Trichoderma (c) Azola (d) All of these

56. Which organism fixes atmospheric nitrogen a Agri Pre PG-2013

(a) *Azotobacter* (b) *Nitrobacter* (c) *Nitrosomonas* (d)*Nitrosococcus*

57. Which organism fixes atmospheric nitrogen non symbiotically ? a Delhi PGT-2014

(a) Azotobacter (b) Nitrobacter (c) Nitrosomonas (d) *Nitrosococcus*

58. Which autotroph microorganism derives its energy from the oxidation of inorganic compounds? 2 RPSC AAO-2022

(1) Photoautotrophs (2) Chemoautotrophs

(3) Thermoautotrophs (4) None of the above

59. Minimum population of the bacteria Azotobacter per gram dry carrier should be – 1 Ag Sup JAU 2017

(1) 10^6 (2) 10^7 (3) 10^4 (4) 10^8

60. Biofertilizer is a c IAS Pre-1994

(a) Mixtures of organic manure and micro organism

(b) mixture of inorganic fertilizer and micro organisms

(c) Mixture having the desire strain of micro organisms

(d) decomposed compost enriched with mineral solubilising bacteria

61. Match List first (Soil bacteria with List second (Microbiological reactions) and select the correct answer: a IAS Pre-1995

List first	List second
A. Nitrobactor	1. Symbiotic fixation of atmospheric nitrogen
B. Azotobacter	2. Non symbiotic fixation of atmospheric nitrogen
C. Nitrosomonas	3. Conversion of ammonia into nitrite in soil
D. Rhizobium	4. Oxidation of nitrite to nitrate

	A	B	C	D		A	B	C	D
a)	4	2	3	1	b)	2	4	1	3
c)	4	2	1	3	d)	2	4	3	1

62. Which of the following pairs of rhizobium spp. And the host genera on which the rhozobium spp. Subsists, are correctly matched? a IAS Pre-1995

1. R. leguminosrum ……*Pisum*
2. R. japonicum…….*Glycine*
3. R. meliloti ......*Medicageo*

(a) 1,2 and3 (b) 1,2 (c) 1,3 (d) 2,3

63. Match List first (Microbial reaction) with List second (Soil organisms) and select the correct answer: b IAS Pre-1996

List first	*List second*
A. Sulphate reduction	1. Thiobacillus
B. Sulphite oxidation	2. Desulfotomaculum
C. Nitrate oxidation	3. Rhodospirillum
D. Nitrogen fixation	4. Nitrobactor

	A	B	C	D		A	B	C	D
a)	1	2	3	4	b)	2	1	4	3
c)	2	1	3	4	d)	1	2	4	3

64. Match List 1 (Biofertilizers) with List 2 (Properties) and select th correct answer c IAS Pre-1997

List I	*List II*
A. *Azosptrillum*	1.Helps in phosphorus uptake
B. *Azotobacter*	2. Floating aquatic fern
C. VAM	3.Grows on and inside the roots of graminaceous crops
D. *Azolla*	4. Free-living nitrogen fixing bacterium

	A	B	C	D		A	B	C	D
(a)	4	3	2	1	(b)	3	4	2	1
(c)	3	4	1	2	(d)	4	3	1	2

65. Match List I (Technique) with List II (organism) and select the correct answer c IAS Pre-1998

List I	*List II*
A. Colwell technique for B deficidency	1. Aspergillus niger
B.Sackett and stewart method for P deficiency	2. Cunnighamela sp.
C. Mulder method for Cu and Mg	3. Sunflower

D. Mehlich plaque method 4. Azotobacter

	A	B	C	D		A	B	C	D
(a)	4	3	2	1	(b)	3	4	2	1
(c)	3	4	1	2	(d)	4	3	1	2

66. Match List I (Bacteria) List II (Function) and select the correct answer using the codes given below the lists c IAS Pre-1999

Lists I	*Lists II*
A. *Nitrobacter spp.*	1. Fixation of atmospheric
B. *Ammonifying bacteria*	2. Formation of NH_4^+
C. *Denitrifying bacteria*	3. Formation of NO^-_3 nitrogen
D. *Rhizobium spp.*	4. Formation of N_2 nitrogen

	A	B	C	D		A	B	C	D
(a)	3	2	1	4	(b)	2	3	1	4
(c)	3	2	4	1	(d)	2	3	4	1

67. Which one of the biofertilizers is used both for nitrogen fixation and as an organic manure? A IAS Pre-2000

(a) Blue green algae (b) *Rhizobium* (c) Azolla (d) *Azotobacter*

68. Match List I with List II and select the correct answer B IAS Pre-2001

List I (Organism)	List II (Associated function)
A. *Pseudomonas*	1. Photosynthetic N_2 fixation
B. *Trichoderma*	2. phosphorus solubilisation
C. *Azospirillum*	3. Composting
D. *Azolla- Anabanea*	4. N2 fixation

	A	B	C	D		A	B	C	D
(a)	3	1	4	2	(b)	2	3	4	1
(c)	2	3	1	4	(d)	4	2	3	1

69. Which one fo the following paris is NOT correctly matched? D IAS Pre-2002

(a) Cyanobacterial culture : Nitrogen nutrition
(b) VAM culture : Phosphorus nutrition
(c) Rhizobial culture : Nitrogne nutrition
(d) Azospirillum culture : Phosphurs nutrition

70. Which one of the following elements is oxidized by thiobacillus thiooxidans? A IAS Pre-2002

(a) Sulphur (b) Nitrogen (c) copper (d) Iron

71. Bio-fertilizers are C IAS Pre-2004

(a) dead organisms mixed with essential nutrients in fairly large amounts
(b) living organisms mixed with large amount of essential nutrients
(c) living organisms containing no essential nutrients but they either fix or mobilize nutrients
(d) inorganic fertilizers mixed with organic manures

72. Which one of the following anaerobic micro organisms fixes atmospheric nitrogen non-symbiotically? C IAS Pre-2004

(a) *Rhizobium* (b) *Azatobacter* (c) *Clostridium* (d) *Rhodospirillum*

73. Which one of the following organisms is involved in the formation of N_2O? B IAS Pre-2005

(a) *Thiobacillus ferroxidans* (b) *Paracoccus denitrificans*
(c) *Nitrosomonas europaea* (d) *Desulfovibrio desulfuricans*

74. Ammonium fixation in the soil is due to — D IAS Pre-2005
(a) Microbial assimilation (b) Microbial fixation
(c) Microbial immobilization (d) Soil exchange reaction

75. Match List I with List II select the correct answer using the code given below the lists — B IAS Pre-2006

List I (Microbial process)	List II (Micro organism)
A. Nitrification	1. *Nitrosomonas*
B. Denitrification	2. *Rhizobium*
C. symbotic nitrogen fixation	3. *Bacillus*
D. non symbiotic nitrogen fixation	4. *Clostridium*

	A	B	C	D		A	B	C	D
(a)	1	2	3	4	(b)	1	3	2	4
(c)	4	2	3	1	(d)	4	3	2	1

76. The biological nitrogen fixation in nodulating plants converts the molecular dinitrogen in air into several compounds in — D IAS Pre-2006
Which one fo the following sequences?
(a) Dinitrogen – ammonia – hydrazine – amino acid – polypeptide – protein
(b) Dinitrogen – imino compounds – ammonia – hydrazine – amino acid – polypeptide – protein
(c) Dinitogen – hydrazine – ammonia – amino acid – polypeptide – protein
(d) Dinitrogne – hydrazine – ammonia – amino acid – polypeptide – protein

77. Consider the following bacteria : — A IAS Pre-2006
1. *Azotobacter* 2. *Bacillus* 3. *Klebsiella*
Which of the above is/are facultatively anaerobic bacteria?
(a) 1and 2 (b) 2only (c) 2and 3 (d) 1and 3

78. Consider the following: — C IAS Pre-2007
1. *Angiococcus* 2. *Clostrdium* 3. *Polyangium*
Which of the above decompose/decomposes cellulose in soil?
(a) 1and 2only (b) 2 only (c) 1and 3 only (d) 1,2 and 3

79. Match List I with List II and select the correct answer using the code given below the lists — C IAS Pre-2008

List I (Microorganisms)	List II (Functions)
A. Nitrobacter	1. Conversion of NH_4N to NO_2N
B. Nitrosomonas	2. Hydrolysis of Urea
C. Clostridium	3. Oxidation of sulphur
D. Thiobacillus	4. Conversion of NO_2N to No_3N
	5. Asymbiotic fixation of Nitrogne

	A	B	C	D		A	B	C	D
(a)	5	3	2	1	(b)	4	3	5	1
(c)	4	1	5	3	(d)	5	1	2	3

80. Consider the following : — a IAS Pre-2009

1. Bacteria 2. Grain straw 3. Clover residues 4. Soil humus

What is the ascending order of C : N ratio in the above materials ?

(a) 1 – 2 – 3 – 4 (b) 4 – 3 – 1 – 2

(c) 1 – 4 – 3 – 2 (d) 4 – 1 – 3 – 2

81. In which nutrients, microbial process are more important to make it available? a Agri Pre PG-2021

(a) N ad P (b) N and K (c) N and S (d) N and Ca

82. A symbiotic association of a fungus with the roots of a higher plant is called? d Agri Pre PG-2021

(a) Nitrification (b) Lichen (c) Nodulation (d) Mycorrhiza

83. Rhizobium helps in fixation of which nutrient? Ans.: N PSB AO-2019

84. Which one of the following is a symbiotic nitrogen fixing bacteria ? a IBS,AFO-2020

(a)*Rhizobium* (b)*Beijerinckia* (c)*Azotobacter* (d) *Cyanobacteria* (e) *Clostridium*

85. Which among the following biofertilizer do not provide nitrogen a IBS,AFO-2019

(a) Trichoderma viride *(b) Rhizobium* *(c) Azotobactar*

(d) Acetobacter *(e) Aspergillum*

86. A simple technique has been developed in India by using which of the following organism as bio fertilizers? A IBS,AFO-2017

A. *Azotobacter and Rhizobium* B. *Azolla and Azotobacter*

C. *Azolla and Rhizobium* D. *Azotobacter and Nostoc* E. None of these

87. _______ convert nitrite (NO_2) compounds into nitrates (NO_3): A IBPS SO-2017

A. Nitrobacter *B. Nitrosomonas* *C. Rhizobium* *D. Azotobacter*

88. _______ converts ammonia into nitrite: B IBPS SO-2017

A. *Nitrobacter* B. *Nitrosomonas* C. *Rhizobium* D. *Azotobacter*

89. Which one of the following statement is correct? A IBPS SO-2017

A.Blue green algae fix 20-30 kg N/ha in a rice field

B. Blue green algae fix 40-50 kg N/ha in a rice field

C.Blue green algae fix 8-10 kg N/ha in a rice field

D. Blue green algae fix 60-70 kg N/ha in a rice field

90. Which of the following microorganism is as associated with ammonifiction? B IBPS SO-2017

A.Rhizobium leguminosarum B.Bacillus mycoides C.Clostridium D.Nitrosomonas

91. Which nitrogen fixation is symbiosis? C IBS,AFO-2014

(A) *PSB* (B) *VAM* (C) *Rhizobium* (D) *Actinomycetes* (E)All of these

92. A simple technique has been developed in India by the using of which biofertilizer? B IBS,AFO-2012

(A) *Azotobacter* and *Nostoc* (B) *Azotobacter* and *Rhizobium*

(C) *Azolla* and *Rhizobium* (D) *Azolla* and *Azotobacter* (E) None of these

93. Obligate anaerobic bacteria grow? A IBS,AFO-2012

(A) Without oxygen and produce high energy

(B) Have a fermentative metabolism and respiratory chain

(C) Grow with or without oxygen and produce medium energy

(D) Without oxygen and produce low energy (E) None of these

94. This 'Biofertilizer' is a nitrogen fixing micro-organism, beneficial for non-leguminous as well as for vegetable crops— B PNB AO-2009

(A) *Rhizobium* (RHZ) (B) *Azotobacter* (AZT) (C) *Azospirillum* (AZS)

(D) Blue Green Algae (BGA) (E) Phosphate Solubilising (PSB) mobilizing bacteria

95. Which of the following organic material has lowest C: N ratio? RRB SO-2020

Ans.: Soil microbes

96. Symbiotic bio fertilizer for cereal grains and grasses ? RRB SO-2019

Ans.: *Azosprillium*

97. Azotobacter and Rhizobium bacteria are B ADA Guj-2013

(A) Antibiotic producers (B) Nitrogen fixers

(C) Plant pathogens (D) Animal pathogens

98. Which of the following organism fix nitrogen under anaerobic condition ? D AO GPSC-2013

(A) *Rhizobium* (B) Blue green alga (C) *Azotobacier* (D) *Azospirillum*

99. The element fixed by Mycorrhiza is C AO SDAU-2013

A. Nitrogen B. Sulphur C. Phosphorus D. None of these

100. Azatobactor is unseful in flxing of nitrogen from air in : a UPPSC Pre-1994

(a) Non-leguminous crops like rice and wheat (b) Leguminous crops

(c) None of the above (d) Soabean

101. The group of organisms which Convert ammonia into nitrites and nitrites are Nitrate respectively : a UPPSC Pre-1994

(a) *Nitrosomonas*, *nitrobactor* (b) *Pseudomonas*, *Azatobactor*

(c) *Streptomyces*, *Bacillus anthracis* (d) *Micromonospore*, *Nocardia*

102. Berseem seeds are inoculated with : b UPPSC Pre-1995

(a)*Azola* culture (b)*Rhyzobium* culture (c)*Azotobacter* culture (d) None of these

103. Which micro-organism is present in large quantities in soil : c UPPSC Pre-1995

(a) Algae (b) Fungi (c) Bacteria (d) Protozoa

104. Decomposition of organic matter in submerged soil is carried out by : b UPPSC Pre-1996

(a) Bacteria (b) Fungi (c) Actinomycetes (d) Earthworm

105. *'Azolla'* (a nitrogen fixing organism) is symbiotic association with : a UPPSC Pre-1997

(a) Fern and blue green algae (b) Bryophyta and blue green algae

(c) Fungi and blue green algae (d) Nostoc and blue green algae

106. Which group of microbes increases phosphate solubility : c UPPSC Pre-1997

(a) *Azatobactor* (b)*Clastridium* (c) *Pseudomonas* (d) *Rhizobium*

107. Ammonia is converted into nitrate by : d UPPSC Pre-1997

(a) Fungus (b) Earthworms (c) Algae (d) bacteria

108. Azotobacter fixes atmospheric nitrogen : b UPPSC Pre-1997

(a) Symbiotically (b) Non-symbiotically

(c) Both symbiotically and non-symbiotically (d) None of the above is correct

109. Which one of the following micro-organisms is involved in nitrification in the soil : d UPPSC Pre-1997

(a) *Pseudomonas* (b) *Thio-bacillus* (c) Micro-*coccus* (d) *Nitrosomonas*

110. Match list I with List II and select the correct answer using the code given below the list : c UPPSC Pre-1998

List IList II

(Bacteria)(Function)

A. Nitrobactor 1. Fixation of atmoshpheric nitrogen

B. Ammonifying Bacteria 2. Formation of NH_4^+ nitrogen

C. Denitrifying Bacteria 3. Formation of NO_3^- nitrogen

D. Rhizobium spp. 4. Formation of N_2 nitrogen

	A	B	C	D
(a)	3	4	1	2
(b)	1	2	4	3
(c)	3	2	4	1
(d)	4	1	2	3

111. Which one of the following is a phosphate solubilizing micro-organism : a UPPSC Pre-1998

(a) Pseudomonas straita (b) Rhizoboium phaseoli (c) Azotobacter paspali (d) None

112. Solubility of rock phosphate can he improved by d UPPSC Pre-2001

(a) Nitrosomonas (b) Nitrobacter (c) Azotobacter (d) Bacillus Polytnexa

113. V A micorrhiza promotes mainly the plant uptake of : b UPPSC Pre-2001

(a) Nitrogen (b) Phosphorus (c) Potassium (d) Molybdenum

114. Which one of the following increases phosphate solubility: b UPPSC Pre-2002

(a) Rhizobium (b) Pseudomonas (c) Azotobacter (d) Nitrosomonas

115. VAM is a : b UPPSC Pre-2002

(a) Bacteria (b) Fungi (c) Virus (d) Algae

116. Match list I and II and select the correct answer using the code given below : a UPPSC Pre-2002

List I (Bacteria)	List II (Function)
A. Nitrobacter	1. Formation of NH4+-N
B. Ammonifying bacteria	2. Atmospheric N fixation
C. Denitrifying bacteria	3. Formation of nitrate nitrogen
D. Rhizobium bacteria	4. Formation of N2

Answer code:

	A	B	C	D
(a)	3	1	4	2
(b)	1	2	3	4
(c)	2	3	4	1
(d)	4	3	2	1

117. Soil micro-organisms are most active at : b UPPSC Pre-2002

(a) 18-20°C (b) 34-36°C (c) 30-32°C (d) 26-28°C

118. Nitrogen Fixation in soil by Rhizobium is increase by – 1 UPPSC Pre-2003

(1) P (2) Ca (3) Mg (4) K

119. Nitrogen is fixed in leguminous crops by : 2 UPPSC Pre-2003

(1) *Azotobecter* (2) *Rhizobium* (3) *Nitrobecter* (4) Blue- green-algae

120. Which one is not a biofertilizer – 4 UPPSC Pre-2003

(1) Vermi Culture (2) PSB (3) NA DEP (4) Multe Pl

121. Which one of the following biofertilizers is a symbiotic N. fixer ? d UPPSC Pre-2005

(a) *Azotobacter* (b) *Azospirillum* (c) Blue green algae (d) *Rhizobium*

122. Phosphate solubilization in the soil is carried out by : d UPPSC Pre-2007

(a) Aspergillus awamori (b) Penicillium (c) Mucor (d) Trichoderma

123. Azolla is a : a UPPSC Pre-

(a)Fern (b)Bacteria (c)Algae (d)Fungi 2008

124. Biofertilizers are : b UPPSC Pre-
(a) Organic manures (b) Culture of micro-organisms 2008
(c) Green manures (d) None of the above

125. Organism present abundantly in soil is : c UPPSC Pre-
(a) Virus (b) Fungi (c) Bacteria (d) Earthworm 2008

126. Bacteria responsible for nitrogen fixationin soyabean is : a UPPSC Pre-
(a) Rhizobium japonicum *(b) Rhizobium meliloti* 2008
(c) Rhizobium trifoli *(d) Rhizobium leguminoserum*

127. The amount of Nitrogen fixed by blue green algae is estimated to be : a UPPSC Pre-
(a) 15 - 45 kg/ha (b) 50-75 kg/ha (c) 60 - 80 kg/ha (d) 100 - 120 kg/hi 2009

128. The bacteria responsible for fixation of nitrogen in soyabean is : d UPPSC Pre-
(a) Rhizobium leguminosarum *(b) Rhizobium haseoli* 2009
(c) Rhizobium meliloti *(d) Rhizohium japonicum*

129. Which one of the following biofertilizers is not bacterial biofertilizer ? d UPPSC Pre-
(a) Rhizobium *(b) Azospirillum* *(c) Azotobactor* *(d) Azolla* 2009

130. Sugarcane frash can be easily composted by adding ------ A AO KTPSC-
(A) Fungi (B) Bacteria (C) Yeast (D) Actinomycetes (E) Answer not known 2021

131. Free floating fresh water fern is ? b NSC MT P-
(a) Anabaena (b)Azolla (c)Azospirillum (d) None of these 2019

132. Depression in efficiency of Rhizobium is due to ? d NSC MT P-
(a) Iron application (b) Phosphorus application 2019
(c) Potash application (d) Excessive nitrogen use

133. Symbiotic bacteria is: d NSC S T-
(a) *Azotobactor* (b) Algae (c) Fungi (d) *Rhizobium* 2019

134. The nitrogen fixing bacterium is: c NSC S T-
(a) *Escherichia* (b) *Diplococcus* (c) *Azotobacter* (d) *Hemophilus* 2019

135. *Azospirillum lipoferum* is reported to be associated with the roots of D HPSC ADO-
(A)Rice (B)Potato (C) Pigeon pea (D)Maize 2022

136. For determination of soil microbial biomass, carbon extracting agent used is C HPSC ADO-
(A) silver sulphate (B) sodium sulphate 2022
(C) potassium sulphate (D) ammonium sulphate

137. Chemicals that have been implicated in attraction of rhizobia are C HPSC ADO-
(A) peptides (B) organic acids (C) flavonoids (D) sugars 2022

138. ___ bacteria present in the root nodules and fix the atmospheric nitrogen. 2 TN AAO-
(1) Blue green (2) Rhizobium (3) Azospirillum (4) Phosphobacteria 2019

139. Vesicular Arbuscular Mycorrhiza (VAM) which have symbiotic association with 1 TN AAO-
plant roots are ______ type of fungi . 2019
(1) Endomycorrhiza (2) Ectomycorrhiza (3) Aspergillus (4) Penicillium

140. Consider the following statements : 3 TN AAO-
Assertion (A) : The phosphobacteria increase the P availability for plants 2019
Reason (R) : The organic acids produced by this bacteria dissolve mineral
phosphates and make it available to crop plants

(1) A alone is true (2) R alone is true

(3) Both A and R are true (4) Both A and R are false

141. VAM refers to – 2 TN AO-2018

(1) Very Attractive Microorgansim (2) Vesicular Arbuscular Mycorrihzae

(3) Virtual Azolla Microbes (4) Visual Azolla Medium

142. The optimum temperature for activities of the most of the micro organisms is – 3 TN AO-2018

(1) 15-20°C (2) 20-25°C (3) 25-35°C (4) 35-45°C

143. Symbiotic association of fungal hyphae with plant root is known as – 1 TN AO-2012

(1) Mycorrhiza (2) Mutual infection (3) Parasitism (4) Lichen

144. Micro organism responsible for the solubilisation of fixed P is – 4 TN AO-2012

(1) Blue green algae (2) Azolla (3) Azospirillum (4) Phosphobacteria

145. The association between plant root system and certain group of soil fungi is – 1 TN AO-2008

(1) Vesicular Arbuscular Mycorrhiza *(2) Vesicular Arbuscular Mucosa*

(3) Vehicular Arbuscular Mycorrhiza *(4) Vehicular Arbuscular Mucosa*

146. The name of P mobilizing biofertilizer is – 1 TN AO-2008

(1) Arbuscular mycorrhiza *(2) Azospirrillum* *(3) Azotobacter* *(4) Azolla*

147. Ammonia is transformed into nitrate by – 2 TN ACF-2012

(1) Algae (2) Bacteria (3) Actinomycetes (4) Fungi

148. Which one of the following is correctly matched ? 2 TN ACF-2012

(1) Rhizobium - Apple

(2) Azospirillum - Sorghum

(3) BGA - Coffee

(4) VAM - Paddy

149. Which one of the following increases 'P' uptake in soil ? 4 TN ACF-2012

(1) Frankia *(2) Nostoc* *(3) Herbaspirillum* *(4) Arbuscular mycorrhiza*

150. The autrophic bacteria involved in Nitrification are – 3 TN PSC Ag-I:1999

(1) *Nitrosomonas* (2) *Nitrobacter*

(3) Both *Nitrosomonas* and *Nitrobacter* (4) *Rhizobium*

151. The Cyanobacteria, that is symbiotically associated with Azolla is – 2 TN PSC Ag-I:1999

(1) Anobaena cylindrical (2) Anabaena azolla

(3) Both 1 and 2 (4) None of these

152. Which one of the following is correctly matched - 1 TN PSC Ag-2003

(1) Azospirillum - Nitrogen

(2) Phosphobacteria - Nitrogen

(3) Acetobacter - Pottash

(4) Rhizobia - Phosphorus

153. Symbiotic nitrogen fixing bacterium is - 3 TN PSC Ag-2003

(1) Azotobacter (2) Azospirillum (3) Rhizobium (4) Clostridium

154. Which one of the following micro organisms is responsible for maximum nutrient cycling in soil – 1 TN PSC Ag-II: 2001

(1) *Actinomycetes* (2) Bacteria (3) Fungi (4) Alge

155. Nitrification is carried out by – 3 TN PSC Ag-II: 2001

(1) *Nitrosomonas* (2) *Nitrobacter* (3) Both (1) and (2) (4) None of these

156. Which one of the following statement is correct ? 4 TN PSC Ag-II: 2001

(1) Rhizobia fix nitrogen in soil symbiotically

(2) Azotobacters fix nitrogen in soil symbiotically

(3) BGA fix nitrogen in paddy fields under aerated condition

(4) None of the above

157. Match List I correctly with List II and select your answer using the codes given below. 3 TN PSC Ag-II: 2001

List I	List II
(A) Nitrifying bacteria	I. Fixes atmospheric nitrogen
(B) Ammonifying bacteria	II. Releases free nitrogen
(C) Symbiotic bacteria and nitrites	III. Oxidises ammonia into nitrates
(D) Denitrifying bacteria	IV. Converts proteins into ammonia

codes :

(1) A-II, B-IV, C-III, D-I (2) A-II, B-III, C-IV, D-I

(3) A-III, B-IV, C-I, D-II (4) A-IV, B-III, C-I, D-II

158. Biofertilizer recommended for sunflower is – 4 TN PSC Ag-II: 2001

(1) *Rhizobium* (2) *BGA* (3) *Azotobacter* (4) *Azospillum*

159. Consider the following statements 3 TN PSC Ag-II: 2001

Assertion (A) : Earthworms are useful to man

Reason (R) : Earthworms help in nitrogen fixation in plants

Now select your answer according to the coding scheme given below.

(1) Both (A) and (R) are true is the correct explanation of (A)

(2) Both (A) and (R) are true but (R) is not the correct explanation of (A)

(3) (A) is true but (R) is false

(4) (A) is false but (R) is true

160. Mycorrhizae belong to the following group - 3 TNPSC – Ag: 1999

(1) Bacteria (2) Actinomycetes (3) Fungi (4) Algae

161. The pH of a biofertilizer product should be – 2 TNPSC – Ag: 1999

(1) 5.0 to 6.0 (2) Around 7.0 (3) Above 7.0 (4) Any level of pH

162. The process that converts gaseous nitrogen to compounds that can be used by the biological community is called – 2 TNPSC – Ag: 1999

(1) Mineralization (2) Nitrogen fixation

(3) Nitrogen mobilization (4) Ammonification

163. Activities of earthworms in soil B TNPSC Ag-1998

(A) Reduce soil fertility (B) Increase soil fertility

(C) Harm plants (D) Cause plant disease

164. Match the List I correctly with List II and select your answer using the codesgiven below C TNPSC Ag-1998

List I		List II
a. Eishcherichia		1. Symbiotic bacteria
b. Chlorobium	-	2. Aerobic bacteria
c. Azotobactor	-	3. Anaerobic bacteria
d. Rizhobium	-	4. Facultative anaerobes

Codes

	a	b	c	d
(A)	1	2	3	4
(B)	2	3	4	1
(C)	4	3	2	1
(D)	3	4	1	2

165. The mainly reason why Vascular Arbuscular Mycorrihiza (VAM) are not widely used by farmers is — B — TNPSC Ag-1998

I. It has not been produced on a commercial scale

II. The Micro-organism cannot be grown on laboratory culture media

III. It cannot be used for agricultural crops

IV. It is antagonist to other beneficial soil microorganism

Of the statements

(A) I & II are correct (B) II alone is correct

(C) II & III are correct (D) II &IV are incorrect

166. Coir pith composting is done with the organism — b — TNPSC Agri-1997

(A) Azotobactor (B) Pleurotus sp. (C) Trichoderma (C) Azospirillum

167. The micro organism associated with root nodules of *casuarinas* is — a — TNPSC Agri-1997

(A) Frankia (B) *Azospirillum* (C) *Rmzbbium* (D) *Agrobacterium*

168. The dominant group of micro organisms in soils is — b — TNPSC Agri-1997

(A) Fungi (B) Bacteria (C) Viruses (D) Algae

169. The carrier material used in mass production of bacterial fertilizers is — a — TNPSC Agri-1997

(A) Lignite (B) Coir (C) Soil (D) Culture medium

170. Mycorrhiza refers to the association of plant roots with — d — TNPSC Agri-1997

(A) Bacteria (B) Actinomycetes (C) Nematodes (D) Fungi

171. Symbiotic nitrogen fixation carried out by — b — TNPSC Agri-1997

(A) Azotobacter (B) Rhizobium (C) Bacillus (D) Psedomonas

172. *Rhizobium japonicum* fixes atmospheric nitrogen symbiotically In association with — d — TNPSC Agri-1997

(A) Cowpea (B) Peas (C) Clover (D) Soyabean

173. The Bacteria involved in the decomposition process of Biogas production is — b — TNPSC Agri-1997

(A) *Humicola sp* (B) *Methanococcus sp* (C) *Phoma sp* (D) *Aerobacter sp*

174. Which of the following bio fertilizer is recommended for black gram? — a — TNPSC Agri-1997

(A) *Rhizobium* (B) *Azotobacter* (C) *Azospirillum* (D) *Acetobacter*

175. Name the enzyme invoed in biological nitrogen fixation — c — TNPSC Ag-1996

(A) Phosphoralase (B) Ribonuclease

(C) Nitrogenase (D) Phosphodiesterase

176. Match list I correctly with list II and select your answer using the codes given below- — c — TNPSC Ag-

List-I List-II 1996

(A) Phosphate solubilizing bacteria – Nitrobactor species

(B)Vesicular arbuscular mycorriza – Azospirillum spp.

© Associative symbiotic - Bacillus circulans

(D) Nitrifying bacteria - Endogone spp.

codes

	a	b	c	d
(A)	1	2	3	4
(B)	2	1	4	3
(C)	3	4	2	1
(D)	4	3	1	2

177. Choose the correct sequence in soil taxonomical classification. a TNPSC Ag-1996

(A) Order - Sub order - Great group - Sub group - Family – series - Type - phase

(B) Order - Great group - Sub order - Sub group - Series - Family - Type - Phase

(C) Order - Sub order - Great group - Sub group - Phase - Type -Series - Family

(D) Order - Sub order - Sub group - Great Group - Serial - Family - Phase - Type

178. The Largest density micro organisms per gram of soil is c TNPSC Ag-1995

(A) Earthworms and nematodes (B) Protozoa (C) Soil bacteria (D) Soil algae

179. Regarding Rhizobium d TNPSC Ag-1995

(1) Rhizobium is recommended for seed treatment in pulses

(2) Rhizobium is recommended for seedling dipping in pulses

(3) Rhizobium is recommended for soil application in pulses

(4) All the three applications are recommended for pulses

of these statements

(A) 1 and 2 are correct (B) 2 and 3 are correct

(C) 1 and 3 are correct (D) 4 alone is correct

180. Consider the following statements a TNPSC Ag-1995

Assertion (A): Phosphobacteria is mixed with seed and sown to increase the availability of phosphorus

Reason (B): It solubilizes P in soil

Select your answer

(a) A and R are true and (R) is the correct explanation of (A)

(b) (A) and (R) are true but (R) is not the correct explanation of (A)

(c) (A) is true and (R) is false (d) (A) is false but (R) is true

181. Which one of the following is correctly matched? a TNPSC Ag-1995

(A) *Azolla anabacha* - Heterocyst

(B) *Bdellovibro* – Bacteroides

(C) *Helminthosporium* oryzae --- Hartigs net

(D) *Aspergillus* sp. --- Arbuscules

182. Match List-I correctly with List-II and select your answer using the codes given below c TNPSC Ag-1995

List-I List-II

(A) Rhizobium (1) Potted plat

(B) Blue green algae (2) Makes P available

(C) Phospho bacterium (3) Leguminous crops

(D) Vermiculture (4) Rice

Codes

	a	b	c	d
A	2	3	1	4
B	1	2	4	3
C	3	4	2	1
D	4	1	3	2

183. Which one is the class of soil blue green algae ? 1 RPSC ACF Agri -2018

(1) Cyanophyta (2) Chlorophyta (3) Xanthophyta(4) Bacillariophyta

184. Root Fungi which help in incrersingthe availability of phosphorus in higher plants. 1 RPSC ACF Agri -2018

(1) Mycorrhizae *(2) Fusarium* *(3) Trichoderma* *(4) Aspergillus*

185. The non-symbiotic nitrogen fixing bacteria is : 3 RPSC ACF AF -2018

(1) Rhizobium *(2) Frankia* *(3) Clostridium* *(4) Nostoc*

186. Organism most tolerant to soil moisture stress is - 4 RPSC ARO Ag Chem - 2022

(1) Fungi (2) Bacteria (3) BGA (4) Actinomycetes

187. For normal growth of soil micro-organisms the OD1Z values (gmlcm2/min) should be at least – 3 RPSC ARO Ag Chem - 2022

(1) 20×10^{-8} (2) 30×10^{-8} (3) 40×10^{-8} (4) 50×10^{-8}

188. Which one of the following micro-organisms is responsible for maximum nutrient cycling in the soil? 3 RPSC ARO Ag Chem - 2022

(1) Fungi (2) Algae (3) Bacteria (4) Actinomycetes

189. 'Hartig net' is present in - RPSC ARO Ag Chem - 2022

(1) Ectotrophic mycorrhizae (2) Endomycorrhizae (3) BGA (4) Rhizobium

190. Which autotroph microorganism derives its energy from the oxidation of inorganic compounds? 2 RPSC AAO Ag -2022

(1) Photoautotrophs (2) Chemoautotrophs

(3) Thermoautotrophs (4) None of the above

191. Which is a P solubilizing bacterium? a ICAR Gen Agri-2007, 08

(A) PSB (B) VAM (C) Clostridium (D) Azotobacter

192. Which is natural genetic engineer? b ICAR Gen Agri-2007, 08

(A) *Xanthomonas citri* (B) *Agrobacterium tumifacience*

(C) *Azotobactor* (D) *Clostridium*

193. Which nutrient helps in Biological Nitrogen Fixation? c ICAR Gen Agri-2009

(A) N (B) P (C) Mo (D) B

194. The microorganism, constituting the largest share in the total microbial population in soil is - 3 RPSC ARO Agro-2022

(1) Nematodes (2) Fungi (3) Bacteria (4) Actinomycetes

CHAPTER- 155 : ORGANIC MATTER/ ORGANINC FARMING PYQ'S

1. 'Indore Process' is related to: B PPSC ADO-2017
a) Green manuring b) Composting c) Poultry feeding d) Irrigation scheduling

2. 'POUDRETE' is a useful organic manure derived out of – 2 TN ACF-2012
(1) Farmyard manure (2) Night soil (3) Poultry manure (4) Sewage and sludge

3. "Organic farming policy" of Madhya Pradesh was adapted in the year: a MP PAT-2016
1. 2011 2. 2001 3. 2003 4. 1999

4. A carbon rich porous product obtained after the partial combustion of rice straw at low temperature in presence of little or no oxygen is B PPSC ADO-2020
a) Press mud b) Prali char c) Parli compost d) Prali wonder

5. A given soil sample contans b IAS Pre-1998
Organic carbon = 0.6% Phosphorous = 0.1%
Potassium = 1% the percent organic matter P2 O5 and K2O contents of the soil is

Organic matter	P_2O_5	K_2O
(A) 1.02	0.29	1.2
(B) 1.02	0.229	1.2
(C) 1.12	2.29	0.83
(D) 1.7	0.86	0.43

6. A soil having the organic carbon content of 0.55% then how much organic matter (%) would be: A PPSC ADO-2017
a) 0.96 b) 0.97 c) 0.98 d) 0.99

7. Alkali soluble and acid soluble fraction of humus is B IAS Pre-2004
(a) Humic acid (b) Fulvic acid (c) Humin (d) Acetic acid

8. Among the following four common constituents of organic manures, the slowest rate of decomposition is seen with which of the following? C IAS Pre-2007
(a) Cellulose (b) Sugar (c) Lignin (d) Hemicellulose

9. Among the following the correct sequence of biotic biopolymer dgradation pathway is C IAS Pre-2003
(a) Recalcitrant biopolymers → Humin → Humic acid → Fulvic acid
(b) Fluvic acid → Humic acid → Recalcitrant biopolymers → Humin
(c) Humin → Humic acid → Fulvic acid → Recalcitrant biopolymers
(d) Humic acid→ Fulvic acid → Recalcitrant biopolymers → Humin

10. Amongst oil cakes , the highest nitrogen content is in : 3 RPSC Pre-2003
(1)Castor cake (2) Neem cake (3) Ground nut cake (4) Coconut cake

11. Amongst oil cakes the highest nitrogen content is in ……..cake. 2 RPSC Pre-1995
(1) Neem (2) Groundnut (3) Coconut (4) Castor

12. Average composition of humus includes – 4 TN AO-2012
(1) Carbon (2) Oxygen (3) Nitrogen (4) All the above

13. Blue-green algae is also known as:- 4 RPSC, AO-2016
(1) Chlorophyta (2) Xanthophyta (3) Diatoms (4) Cyanophyta

14. Brown manuring is recommended in – c BHU PET-2015

(a) Sorghum (b) Pigeonpea (c) Rice (d) Mustard

15. Carbon content in humus? **B** IBS,AFO-2014
(A) 40% (B) 58% (C) 70% (D) 75% (E)80%

16. Carbon content in organic matter is **d** TNPSC Ag-1995
(A) 28% (B) 38% (C) 48% (D) 58%

17. Charcoal consist ____ % of carbon – **3** TN AAO-2019
(1) 55 to 65 (2) 65 to 75 (3) 75 to 85 (4) 85 to 100

18. Composting method suitable for rainy season is **1** RPSC Pre-2010
(1) Heap method (2) Pit method (3) Both (1)and(2) (4) None of these

19. Consider the following : **b** IAS Pre-2010
Organic matter in soil influences
1. Soil moisture2. Soil strength 3. Soil structure
4. Soil texture5. Soil temperature
Select the correct answer using the code given below :
Code :
(a) 1, 2, 3 and 4 only (b) 1, 3, 4 and 5 only
(c) 1, 2, 3 and 4 only (d) 1, 2, 3, 4 and 5 only

20. Consider the following components: **D** IAS Pre-2000
1. Cellulose 2. Crude proteins 3. Hemicellulose
4. Oils, fats, lignin, waxes 5. Sugars, starch
These components in the raw organic matter undergo decomposition in the soil due to the activity of soil micro-organisms under favourable conditions. The correct sequence of these components in terms of the most easily decomposed to least easily decomposed
(a)1,3,2,5,4 (b) 5,3,2,4,1 (c) 4,5,3,1,2 (d) 5,2,3,1,4

21. Consider the following organic manures **a** IAS Pre-1999
1. Bat's guano 2. Goat manure 3. Pig manure 4. FYM
The correct sequence in descending order in terms of nitrogen content of these manures is
(a) 1,3,2,4 (b) 3,2,1,4 (c) 3,1,4,2 (d) 1,3,4,2

22. Consider the following statements **a** IAS Pre-1996
Vermicompost is consider to be better because
1.itdoes not require turning of compost material
2.it needs less composting time
3. it takes place at a comparatively low temperature
4. it has higher enzymatic activity
Of these statements
(a) 1,2,3and 4 are correct (b) 1and 2 are correct
(c) 2,3and 4 are correct (d) 1,3and 4 are correct

23. Consider the following statements **A** IAS Pre-2000
1. Manures contain all the nutrients essential for the growth of plants
2. Manures exert desirable effects on the physical conditions of the soil
3. Manures cause detrimental effects on the activities of soil micro organisms

Which of the above statements are correct?

(a) 1and 2 (b) 2and 3 (c) 1 and 3 (d) 1,2 and 3

24. Consider the following statements **D** IAS Pre-2006

Green manuring with dhaincha *(Sesbania aculate)* improves soil fertility by

1. lowering the pH of soil
2. atmospheric nitrogen fixation through root nodules
3. contributing large quantity of biomass to the soil

Which of the statements given above is/are correct?

(a) 1and 2only (b) 2and 3 only (c) 3only (d) 1,2 and 3

25. Consider the following statements : **d** IAS Pre-2009

The application of bulky organic manure to soil is advantageous because it

1. Increases C/N ratio of soil and thus favours mineralization of organic nutrient pools.
2. Reduces phosphate fixation by soil.
3. Favours rapid release of nutrients from the incorporated organic pool.

Which of the statements given above is/are correct ?

(a) 1 only (b) 2 and 3 only (c) 1, 2 and 3 (d) 2 only

26. Consider the following statements regarding the dung slurry coming out a biogas plant **c** IAS Pre-1998

1. The slurry contains nitrogen both in the ammoniacal and non-ammoniacal form
2. The nitrogen percentage of the slurry is much higher than that of dung used in the gas plant
3. The carbon-nitrogne ratio of the slurry form the gas plant is 10:1

Of these statements

(a) 1 and 2 are correct (b) 1and 3 are correct

(c) 2and 3 are correct (d) 1,2 and 3 are correct

27. Consider the following: **D** IAS Pre-2007

1. *Crotalaria juncea* 2. *Cyamopsis tetragonoloba*

3. *Phaseolus trilobus* 4. *Melilotus parviflora*

Which of the above are commonly sued for green-manuring in India?

(a) 1and 3 only (b) 1,2 and 4 only (c) 2and 4 only (d) 1,2,3 and 4

28. Consider the statement **b** TNPSC Ag-1995

Assertion (A) : Organic matter in the soil is considered as the key for soil fertility and productivity

Reason (R): Organic matter supplies large amounts of nutrients to crop

Select your answer

(a) (A) is wrong and (R) is correct (b) (A) is correct and (R) is wrong

(c) Both (A) and (R) are wrong (d) Both (A) and (R) are correct

29. Conversion factor for conversation of organic carbon to organic matter is usually taken as? **D** IBS,AFO-2016

A. 0.45 B. 0.91 C. 1.36 D. 1.72 E. 2.04

30. Effect on organic matter : **3** RPSC Pre-1994

(1) aerobic condition to bacteria (2) nitrogen availability

(3) fertility maintenance (4) complete nutrient

31. Farm yard manure contains ____% ____% and ____% N, P2 O5 and K2) respectively : — **2** — RPSC, AAO-2009

(1) 1.5, 1.1, 0.5 (2) 0.5, 0.2, 0.5 (3) 0.5, 1.5, 2.3 (4) 0.6, 0.4, 0.5

32. Fresh organic residue as addition to a standing crop leads to — **D** — IAS Pre-2006

(a) Denitrification loss of soil nitrogen (b) Volatilization loss of nitrogen
(c) Decomposition of ammonia in soil
(d) Immobilisaton of available nitrogen in soil

33. Fulvic acid is soluble in — **A** — IAS Pre-2010

(a) both acid and alkali (b) acid only
(c) alkali only (d) organic solvents only

34. Gas is generated due to anaerobic fermentation of organic material — **C** — AO SDAU-2015

A. CO_2 B. Oxygen C. Methane D. None of these

35. Generally U.P. soils have organic matter percentage – — **a** — BHU UET-2014

(a) 0.1 to 0.3 % (b) 0.3 to 0.5% (c) 0.5 to 0.7 % (d) 0.7 to 0.9%

36. Groundnut seed normally contains percent protein and oil — **A** — ADA Guj-2013

(A) 25 and 45 (B) 22 and 43 (C) 45 and 26 (D) 43 and 22

37. Highest certified area in organic farming lies in the state of — **b** — Agri Pre PG-2014

(a) Maharashtra (b) Madhya Pradesh (c)Uttar Pradesh (d)Rajasthan

38. How much carbon content in organic matter? — **a** — Agri Pre PG-2021

(a) 58% (b) 92% (c) 49% (d) 5%

39. Humic acid is a fraction of humus, which is — **B** — IAS Pre-2001

(a) soluble in alkali and acid (b) soluble in alkali and insoluble in acid
(c) insoluble in alkali and soluble in acid (d) insoluble both in alkali and acid

40. Humic acid isolated from soils is — **A** — IAS Pre-2002

(a) aromatic with high molecular weight (b) aromatic with low molecular weight
(c) aliphatic with high molecular weight (d) aliphatic with low molecular weight

41. Identify from following manures, which is not a bulky organic manure – — **2** — TN AAO-2019

(1) FYM (2) Oil cakes (3) Poultry manure (4) Compost manure

42. Immobilization of sulphur takes place when the 'S' content of organic matter is less than : — **a** — UPPSC Pre-2000

(a) 0.45% (b) 0.60% (c) 0.30% d) 0.15%

43. In a compost pit, the heat of combustion fo organic matter raises the temperature when decay is occurring rapidly. During decay, the temperature rises by — **a** — IAS Pre-1995

(a) 75 to 90°C (b) 60 to 80°C (c) 50 to 72°C (d) 40 to 60°C

44. In an average well decomposed FYM(Farmyard manure) contains/ — **4** — MP PG PAT-2016

(1) N_2 (2) 0.2% P_2O_5 (3) 0.5% K_2O (4) All of these

45. In which one of the following states, more than 2,000 'Vermicomposting units' started by individuals and/or organization in rural and urban centres ? — **B** — BOB AO-2008

(A) Maharashtra (B)Andhra Pradesh (C)Punjab (D)Himachal Pradesh (E) Karnataka

46. Lignin is found mainly in : — **b** — UPPSC Pre-2000

(a) Leaf Lamina (b) Middle lamella (c) Pedicle (d) Leaf veins

47. Material used to control acidity in decomposition of compost is: — **d** — NSC S T-2019

(a) Urea (b) Ammonium sulphate (c) Potassium sulphate (d) Lime

48. Mineralization of soil sulphur occurs when C:S ratio of organic matter is - **2** RPSC ARO Ag Chem -2022

(1) > 200: 1 (2) < 200: 1 (3) > 300: 1 (4) < 300: 1

49. Modern Charcoal retorts operating at about 600C produces around ___ % of the dry matter biomass as charcoal . **3** TN AAO-2019

(1) 15 to 20 (2) 20 to 25 (3) 25 to 35 (4) 35 to 45

50. Neem cake acts as : **b** UPPSC Pre-2009

(a) Nitrification promoter (b) Nitrification inhibitor

(c) Urea hydrolysis promoter (d) Urea hydrolysis inhibitor

51. Neem cake contains **B** TO MPUAT-2014

(A) Saponin (B) Azadirachtin

(C) Dhurrin (D) None of the above

52. Neem cake is used to increase the efficiency of urea by: **a** UPPSC Pre-2001

(a) Reducing leaching and denitrification losses

(b) Reducing leaching losses only

(c) Reducing den i tri fication losses only

(a) Reducing ammonia volatilization

53. Nitrification is inhibitedby : **c** UPPSC Pre-2008

(a)Mustard cake (b)Linseed cake (c) Neem cake (d)Groundnut cake

54. Nitrogen content in vermin compost? **A** IBS,AFO-2014

(A) 3% (B) 5% (C) 7% (D) 10% (E)15%

55. On an average, humus contains ………. % carbon. **b** MP PAT-2013

(A) 52 (B) 58 (C) 62 (D) 68

56. Organic acids developed from organic matter decomposition act as chelating agent may be **D** HPSC ADO-2022

(A) abscisic acids (B) gibberellic acids (C) mercuric acids (D) amino acids

57. Organic carbon in organic soil is **B** AO SDAU-2013

A. > 1 % B. < 1 % C Both A & B D. None of these

58. Organic carbon is a measure of : **a** UPPSC Pre-2000

(a)available nitrogen in soil (b)available phosphorus in soil

(c)available potassium in soil (d)Available magnesium in soil

59. Organic matter content in organic soils is the range of : **c** UPPSC Pre-1999

(a) 10-15% (b) 16-20% (c) 20-25% (d) Above 25%

60. Organic matter content is most Indian soils range between – **a** BHU PET-2014

(a) 0.5-2 (b) 3 -4 (c) 0.2-0.4 (d) 5-6

61. Organic matter content of "histosols" and Hydromorphic soils is **a** IAS Pre-1995

(a) 30-40% (b) 50-57% (c) 60-70% (d) 12-18%

62. Organic matter content of most of Indian soil varies between – **d** BHU PET-2012

(a) 3-4 (b) 0.2-05 (c) 5-6 (d) 0.5-2.0 percent on dry soil basis

63. Organic matter content of out Indian soils is less, because – **4** TN PSC Ag-II: 2001

I. Indian is with tropical climate

II. The life period of organic matter is less than a year

III. Crop residues and cow dung are used as fuel

IV. It acts as a source of food to micro organisms

of these

(1) I, II and III are correct (2) II, III and IV are correct

(3) I and III are correct (4) All these are correct

64. Organic matter in soil is an index of : **a** UPPSC Pre-2005

(a) Available Nitrogen (b) Available Phosphorus

(c) Available Potassium (d) Available Zinc

65. Organic matter is abundantly available in - **2** TN AO-2012

(1) Sandy loam (2) Clay loam (3) Silt (4) None of the above

66. Percentage of nitrogen in castor cake is **D** ADA Guj-2013

(A) 2.0 (B) 3.0 (C) 4.0 (D) 5.0

67. Percentage of nitrogen present in dry farmyard manure is – **2** TN PSC Ag-2003

(1) 0.3 – 1.0 (2) 0.4 – 1.5 (3) 0.5 – 2.0 (4) 0.6 – 2.5

68. Percentage of organic matter in mineral soils is- **1** RPSC Sch Lect.2022

(1) less than 20% (2) less than 28% (3) less than 32% (4) less than 40%

69. Poor nitrification rate of non-edible *mahua* (*Madhuca latifolia*) cake is due to **c** IAS Pre-1995

(a) the presence of oil (b) wide C:N ratio

(c) low nitrogen content (d) the presence of certain alkaloids

70. Practice of turning under of green succulent part of herbs, shrubs and trees collected from elsewhere is denoted as **4** RPSC Pre-2008

(1) Composing (2) Crop residue management

(3) Green manuring (4) Green leaf manuring

71. Pre-incubation plant residue and cow dung helps in vermicomposting through – **d** Agri Pre PG-2017

(a) Softening and Heat-release

(b) Heat release and initiation of m.o. activity

(c) Softening and Initiation of microbial activity

(d) Softening, heat-release and initiation of microbial activity

72. Preparation of farm yard manure by trench method was given by **2** RPSC Pre-2007

(1) N S Subbarao (2) C N Acharya (3) T S Bishwas (4) B.Bear

73. Raw Bone Meal Contains P_2O_5 Content to the extent of - **3** RPSC, AAO-2018

(1) 5-10 % (2) 10-15 % (3) 20-25 % (4) 30-35 %

74. Read the following statements and mark your ansawer according to the code given below : **a** UPPSC Pre-2001

I. Organic matter improves the structure of clayey soil.

II. Organic matter improves the structure of sandy soil.

III. Sandy soils are heavy in texture.

IV. Clayey soils are lighter in texture.

Answer code :

(a) I and II are correct (b) I and III are correct

(c) I and IV are correct. (d) III and IV are correct.

75. Recommended seed rate per hectare of Dhaincha for green manuring in sodic soil is : **b** UPPSC Pre-1997

(a) 20 kg (b) 60 kg (c) 40 kg (d) 80 kg

76. State of India which has highest area under certified organic agriculture **2** RPSC AO Ag -

(1) Rajasthan (2) Madhya Pradesh (3) Gujarat (4) Uttar Pradesh 2021

77. Synthesis of new compounds through degradation of plant and animal residues is known as – **1** Ag Sup JAU 2017

(1) Humification (2) Podzolyzation (3) Glygesan (4) Salinization

78. The average percentage of nitrogen in vermicompost is - **1** TN AO-2018

(1) 3 (2) 30 (3) 10 (4) 15

79. The broader objectives of organic recycling are **d** TNPSC Ag-1995

(1)Waste disposal and environment pollution check

(2) Plant nutrients generation

(3) Fuel energy generation

(4) Integrated nutrients supply system

Of this statement

(A) 1 alone is correct (B) 1 and 2 are correct

(C) 1,2 and 3 are correct (D) All are correct

80. The conversion of inorganic nitrogen to organic nitrogen is termed as : **c** UPPSC Pre-2009

(a) Mineralization (b) Mobilization (c) immobilization (d) Nitrification

81. The green manure crop should be turned in to the soil at stage **A** AO SDAU-2015

A. Flowering B. Vegetative C Maturity D. None of these

82. The highest nitrogen content is found in : **b** UPPSC Pre-1996

(a) farmyard manure (b) Poultry manure (c) Vermi compost (d) Biogas slurry

83. The infrared spectrum of fulvic acid shows weak medium strong and strong bands at **c** IAS Pre-1999

(a) 2980 to 2920 , 1720 and 3400 cm^{-1} respectively

(b) 1720, 2980 to 2920 and 3400 cm^{-1} respectively

(c) 3400, 1720 and 2980 to 2920 cm^{-1} respectively

(d) 2980 to 2920,3400 and 1720 cm^{-1} respectively

84. The main aim of organic farming is : **a** UPPSC Pre-2006

(a) To reduce the dependance on chemical fertilizers

(b) To reduce the cost of production of crops

(c) To increase the crop production

(d) To improve the quality of crop produce

85. The major organic cementing agent in soil-aggregate formation is **D** IAS Pre-2001

(a) lipids (b) proteins and protein derivatives

(c) polysaccharides (d) organic acids

86. The most commonly used inorganic amendment is **D** AO SDAU-2015

A FYM B. Compost C .Urea D. Gypsum

87. The most commonly used organic amendment is **B** AO SDAU-2015

A. Gypsum B. FYM C. Lime D. None of these

88. The most important potential contaminant of food produced on sewage sludge amended soils is **D** IAS Pre-2003

(a) chromium (b) lead (c) zinc (d) cadmium

89. The nitrogen percentage in humus is about – **b** RPSC, AO-2012

(a) 4 – 4.5% (b) 5 – 5.5% (c) 6 – 6.5% (d) 7 -7.5%

90. The organic matter content of soil varies with – **4** TN ACF-2012

(1) Vegetation (2) Climate (3) Biological activities (4) All of these

91. The percent nitrogen content in poultry manure ranges from : **2** RPSC Pre-1999

(1) 1-2 (2) 2-5 (3)5-7 (4) 14-15

92. The ratio of 'organic carbon' to organic matter in soils is **a** IAS Pre-1998

(a) 1.0: 1.7 (b) 1.0 : 2.0 (c) 1.7 : 1.0 (d) 20.0 : 1.0

93. The system of composting is- **4** MP PG PAT-2016

(1) Activated compost process (2) Indoor method

(3) Bangalore method (4) All of these

94. To obtain percent organic matter from percent organic carbon, 1.724 is a multiplying factor, is called as - **3** RPSC ARO Ag Chem -2022

(1) Bray factor (2) Van-half factor (3) Van-Bemmelen factor (4) Wilkinson factor

95. Trench method of FYM preparation is also known as - **2** MP PG PAT-2016

(1) Pit method (2) Dr. C. N. Acharya method

(3) Heap method (4) None of these

96. Vermi compost contains – **3** TN ACF-2012

(1) 2.5%N, 7.01% P_2O_5, 0.5% K_2O (2) 1.5%N, 3% P_2O_5, 0.2% K_2O

(3) 1.6% N, 5.04% P_2O_5, 0.8 % K_2O (4) 2% N, 3% P_2O_5, 0.3% K_2O

97. Vermicast is also known as – **c** BHU PET-2015

(a) Green gold (b) Brown gold (c) Black gold (d) Red gold

98. Vermicompost is made by use of – **a** RPSC, AAO-2012

(a) Earthworms (b) House fly (c) Termites (d) Birds

99. Vermicompost is prepared by : **c** UPPSC Pre-2000

(a) Fungi (b) bacteria (c) Earthworm (d) Chemical treatment

100 Vermicompost is prepared with the help of following...... **B** BOD AO-2008

(A) Bacteria (B) Earthworms (C) Ants (D) Virus (E) Fungus

101. Vermiculture is associated with : **3** RPSC Pre-2003

(1)Prawn (2) Honey bee (3) Earth worm (4) None of these

102 Vermiculture is related to rearing of - **3** TN PSC Ag-I:2001

(1) Honeybee (2) Soil insects (3) Earthworm (4) Silkworm

103. Waste materials are used in the production of : **4** RPSC Pre-1993

(1) starch (2)biogas (3) alcohol (4) humus

104. well rotted FYM contain N – **a** RPSC, AAO-2012

(a) 0.5 % (b) 1.0 % (c) 1.5 % (d) 2.0 %

105 Well rotten FYM contains 40-50 % moisture and one ton of such FYM supplies N, P and K equivalent to **B** PPSC ADO-2020

a) 4 kg Urea, 5 kg Superphosphate and 3 kg muriate of Potash

b) 4 kg Urea, 10 kg Superphosphate and 6 kg muriate of Potash

c) 2 kg Urea, 10 kg Superphosphate and 6 kg muriate of Potash

d) 4 kg Urea, 6 kg Superphosphate and 4 kg muriate of Potash

106 What is the process of making manure of decomposable waste is known as ? **3** TN AAO-2019

(1) Pulverization (2) Neutralization (3) Composting (4) Disposal

107. What amount of energy is released during the decomposition of one gram of dried organic matter added to soil ? **b** BHU PET-2015

(a) 4-5 kilocalories (b) 8-10 kilocalories
(c) 16-20 kilocalories (d) 20-24 kilocalories

108. What is optimum time of application of farmyard manure — 3 — RPSC Pre-2010
(1) Six months before sowing of crop (2) At the time of sowing
(3) One month before sowing of crop (4) One week after sowing

109 What is the content of organic matter in alluvial soil ; — b — UPPSC Pre-1994
(a)0.86 – 6.53 (b) 0.28 – 1.10 (c) 0.34 – 0.77 (d) 5.9 – 8.7

110. What is the drawback of poultry manure? — 1 — MP PG PAT-2016
(1) It ferments very quickly (2) It has less nutrient content
(3) It smells badly (4) None of these

111 What is the fraction of soil organic matter which is soluble both in alkali and acid? — B — IAS Pre-2006
(a) Humic acid (b) Fulvic acid (c) Hymatomeloinc acid (d) Humin

112 When organic matter is added to the soil : — b — UPPSC Pre-1997
(a) Bulk density is increased (b) bulk density is decreased
(c) Bulk density does not change (d) None of these

113. Which among the following is an organic fertilizer ? — 1 — AARO Agro-2016
(1) Calcium cyanamide (2) Ammonium chloride
(3) Calcium ammonium nitrate (4) Ammonium sulphate

114. Which fraction of humus is soluble both in alkali and alcohol..? — 4 — RPSC Pre-1998
(1)Humin (2)Fulvic acid (water)
(3) Humic acid (4) Hymatomelanic acid

115. Which is the most important green manure crop? — 4 — MP PG PAT-2016
(1) Sunhemp (2) Dhaincha (3) Pillipesara (4) All of these

116 Which is the most useful earthworm used for — 1 — RPSC Sch Lect.2022
(A) Eisenia (2) Endogeic (3) Epigeic (4) None of the above

117. Which is the organic Mn fertilizer ? — 1 — Agri Pre PG-2019
(1) Manganese lignosulfonate (2) Manganese sulphate
(3) Manganese oxysulfate (4) Manganese frits

118. Which of the following is a non edible oil cake ? — 2 — RPSC, AAO-2019
(1) Mustard cake (2) Mahua cake (3) Linseed cake (4) Sesame cake

119. Which of the following is caused by fermentation, decomposition of organic matter, resulting in simple compounds — 3 — RPSC Pre-1993
(1) algae (2) fungi (3) micro organism (4) bacteria

120. Which of the following is concentrated organic manure ? — d — School Lect. 2019
(a) Compost (b) Sewage and sludge
(c) Vermicompost (d) Neem cake

121. Which of the following is not a fraction of humid substance — 3 — Agri Pre PG-2015
(1) humic acid (2) fulvic acid (3) fumeric acid (4) humin

122. Which of the following is not a function of humus in soil – — b — Gujrat AO-2017
(a) Adds nutrients to the soil (b) Increases pH
(c) Improves soil physical codition
(d) Improves aeration especially in heavy soil

123. Which of the following is not a principle of organic farming — 2 — Agri Pre PG-

(1) Principle of ecology (2) Principle of maximization 2015
(3) Principle of health (4) Principle of fareness

124 Which of the following is organic in nature? **Ans.: Cow dung** NABARD-2021

125. Which of the following is suitable method for application of FYM? **3** MP PG PAT-2016
(1) Foliar (2) To Mix with seeds
(3) To spread uniformly on the surface of soil (4) None of these

126 Which of the following materials do not fit into the list of the raw materials used for feeding the earthworms in the scientific management of Vermiculture? **B** BOD AO-2008
(A) Grass Clippings (B) Curd (C) Carrot tops (D) Lettuce leaves (E) All are useful

127 Which of the following organic manures has the NARROWEST C/N ratio? **d** IAS Pre-1994
(a) Biogas slurry (b) Farm-yard manure (c) Compost (d) Groundnut cake

128 Which of the following pairs are correctly matched? **c** IAS Pre-1994
1. Hum us ……Ligno-protein complexes
2. Hum in …….Insoluble in dilute alkali
3. Fulvic acid….High molecular weight
4. Humic acid…Insoluble in dilute acid
Select the correct answer using the codes given below:
(a) 2,3,4 (b)1,2,3 (c) 1,2,4, (d) 1,3,4

129 Which one among the following components of soil organic matter is most resistant to decomposition ? **D** IAS Pre-2005
(a) Cellulsoe (b) Hemicellulose (c) Starch (d) Lignin

130. Which one is non-edible oil cake? **1** RPSC AAO-2022
(1) Castor cake (2) Rapeseed and mustard cake
(3) Groundnut cake (4) Coconut cake

131 Which one of the following be concentrated organic manures has maximum phosphorus content? **d** IAS Pre-1993
(a) Fish meal (b) Stera meal (c) Poultry manure (d) Guano

132. Which one of the following concentrated organic manures has maximum phosphorus – **a** BHU UET-2013
(a) Fishmeal (b) Neem cake (c) Poultry manure (d) Guano

133. Which one of the following is a "Concentrated Organic Manure" – **b** Agri Pre PG-2017
(a) Farmyard Manure (b) Castor Cake
(c) Compost Manure (d) Green-leaf Manure

134. Which one of the following is an organic fertilizer **4** RPSC Pre-2010
(1) Anhydrous ammonia (2) Diammonium phosphate
(3) Single super phosphate (4) Urea

135. Which one of the following is biofertilizer ? **d** BHU UET-2010
(a) Urea (b) FYM (c) Compost (d) Green algae

136. Which one of the following is known as Amide and Organic fertilizer – **c** Raj JET-2014
(a) Sodium nitrate (b) Ammonium (c) Urea (d) Calcium sulphate

137 Which one of the following is the correct sequence of the organic acids in the krebs' cycle in mitochondria? **A** IAS Pre-2007
(a) Citrate → Isocitrat → α-ketoglutart →succinate

(b) Citrat →α-ketoglutarate →Isocitrate → Succinate

(c) Isocitrate → succineate → α-Ketoglutarate → Citrate

(d) α-Ketoglutarate → Isocitrate → succinate → citrate

138 Which one of the following is the correct stage through which the protein in the soil organic matte breaks down to release ammonia? **A** **IAS Pre-2001**

(a) Proteins → Proteoses → Peptones → Amino acids → Ammonia

(b) proteins → proteoses → Amino acids → Peptones

(c) proteins → peptones → proteoses → Amino acids

(d) Proteins → Amino acids → Protesoes → Peptones → Ammonia

139. Which one of the following manure making method is not related to FYM making **b** **Agri Pre PG-2013**

(a)Pit Method (b)Indore Method (c) Heap Method (d)Trench method

140 Which one of the following oil-cakes, in addition to its manurial value, acts also as a nitrification inhibitor? **c** **IAS Pre-1994**

(a) Mustard (b) Groundnut (c) Neem (d) Sesamum (til)

141 Which one of the following sequences of manures is correct in terms of the nitrogen content, expressed as percent on oven dry basis, in descending order? **B** **IAS Pre-2007**

(a) Groundnut cake – poultry litter – Meat meal – farmyard manure

(b) Meat meal – groundnut cake – poultry litter – farmyard manure

(c) Groundnut cake – poultry litter- farmyard manure – meat meal

(d) Meat meal – poultry litter – farmyard manure – groundnut cake

CHAPTER- 156: GREEN MANURE PYQ'S

1.	A stem nodulating green manure crop is - (1) Daincha (2) Sunhemp (3) *Sesbania rostrata* (4) All of these	3	TN PSC Ag-2003
2.	Any crop or plant grown and ploughed in situ is called – (1) Farmyard manure (2) Green manure (3) Green leaf manure (4) Organic matter	2	TN AO-2008
3.	Besides Rhizobium, the stem nodulating microbes are – (1) *Azospirillum* (2) *Frankia* (3) *Azolla* (4) All of these	2	TN PSC Ag-2003
4.	Consider the following statements **Assertion (A)**: Azolla fixes atmospheric N_2 **Reason (B):** Anabaena azolla , present in leaf cavity alone fixes atmospheric N_2 (a) (A) is true and (R) is false (b) (A) is false but (R) is true (c) A and R are true and (R) is the correct explanation of (A) (d) (A) and (R) are true but (R) is not the correct explanation of (A)	c	TNPSC Ag-1995
5.	Green manure crop providing maximum nitrogen is: (a) Moong (b) Guar (c) Sanai (d) Lobia	c	NSC S T-2019
6.	Green manure increase the availability of nutrients through its favourable effects on – (1) Chemical properties of soil (2) Physical properties of soil (3) Biological properties of soil (4) All of these	4	TN ACF-2012
7.	Nitrogen contribution to the succeeding crop whom green gram is grown earlier – (1) 15 to 20 kg N/ha (2) 15 to 120 kg N/ha (3) 40 to 120 kg N/ha (4) 20 to 30 kg N/ha	1	TN AO-2018
8.	The common shrub used for green manuring is? (a) Dhaincha (b) Cluster bean (c) Sunhemp (d) Glyricidia	c	Agri Pre PG-2021
9.	The slow growing species of legume root nodule bacteria are included in bacterial genus : (a) *Rhizobium* (b) *Brady-Rhizobium* (c) *Sino-Rhizobium* (d) *Azo-Rhizobiurn*	d	UPPSC Pre-2002
10.	Which crop of the following has the double symbiotic relationship with nitrogen fixing bacteria : (a) *Phaseolus vulgaris (b) Cajanuscajan (c) Sesbaniarostrata (d) Glycine max*	c	UPPSC Pre-2000
11.	Which one is the stem nodulating green manure crop ? (a) *Sesbania aculeate* (b) *Crotoleria juncea* (c) *Sesbania rostrata* (d) Cowpea	c	UPPSC Pre-2009
12.	Which one of the following is a popular green leaf manure ? (1) Dhaincha (2) Glyricidia (3) Sesbania (4) Sunhemp	2	TN AO-2008

CHAPTER-157 : C:N RATIO PYQ'S

1. C/N ratio of a normal cultivated soil ranged between – c BHU PET-2017
   (a) 6 to 8 (b) 14 to 16 (c) 10 to 12 (d) 18 to 20
2. C/N ratio of stable O/M is about – c BHU PET-2014
   (a) 30 : 1 (b) 20 : 1 (c) 10 : 1 (d) 25 : 1
3. C: N ratio in FYM is- b MP PAT-2016
   (a) 1: 1 (b) 20 : 1 (c) 30 : 1 (d) 60 : 1
4. Immobilization bf nitrogen occurs when C:N ratio of organic matter is – c BHU PET-2015
   (a) <20 : 1 (b) 20-30: 1 (c) > 30 : 1 (d) > 300 : 1
5. Normally C : N : S ratio of soil is 2 RPSC Pre-2003
   (1) 100:20:1 (2)100:10:1 (3) 200:10:1 (4) 100:10:2
6. The C : N ration of humus is – a BHU UET-2016
   (a) 10 : 1 (b) 12 : 1 (c) 15 : 1 (d) 20 : 1
7. The carbon-nitrogen ratio in cultivated soil of humid temperate regions usually stabilizes in neighborhood of : 1 RPSC Pre-1993
   (1) 10 : 1 to 12 : 1 (2) 8 : 1 to 1 : 8 (3) 4 : 1 to 9 : 1 (4) 20 : 1 to 30 : 1
8. What is C:N ratio of a normal soil 1 RPSC Pre-2010
   (1) 10:1 (2) 16:1 (3) 5:1 (4) 20:1
9. What is optimum C/N ratio of compost for application as manure to soil – a BHU PET-2011
   (a) 10 (b) 15 (c) 20 (d) 25
10. Which one of the following organic manures has the narrowest C : N ratio ? c BHU UET-2013
    (a) Biogas slurry (b) FYM (c) Compost (d) Groundnut cake
11. When organic matter with wide C:N ratio (70:1) is added to the soil, the net effect is the disappearance of mineral nitrogen due to b IAS Pre-1993
    (a) mineralization (b) immobilization
    (c) nitrogen transformation (d) nitrogen reduction
12. There is a net increase in the mineralisation of organic nitrogen in soil when c IAS Pre-1997
    (a) C:N ratio is 20 to 30:1 (b) C:N ratio is below 20:1
    (c) C:N ratio is above 30: 1 (d) nitrogen is taken up by the crops
13. Which one of the following nitrogen factors would bring down wide C:N rato material of 100:1 to the desirable C:N ratio of 40:1 for compost making? d IAS Pre-1998
    (a) 1.0 (b) 105 (c) 2.0 (d) 2.5
14. The organic residues with wider C:N ratios as compared to narrow C:N ratios are decomposed at B IAS Pre-2002
    (a) faster rate (b) slow rate
    (c) equal rate (d) faster rate followed by slow rate
15. Due to a wide C:N ratio, application of bulky organic manures like paddy straw will lead to C IAS Pre-2006
    (a) Greater supply of available N due to quick decomposition
    (b) Gaseous loss of N by increased microbial activity in the soil
    (c) Hymatomeloic acid (d) Humin
16. C:N ratio of normal soils? A IBS,AFO-2013

(A) 10-12:1 (B) 5:01 (C) 10:02 (D) 15:05 (E)15:01

17. The average carbon/nitrogen ratio of soils is generally…… D BOD AO-2008
(A) 25 : 1 (B) 5 : 1 (C) 30 : 1 (D) 14 : 1 (E) None of these

18. In a good quality manure C/N ratio should not be more than : (d) UPPSC Pre-2000
(a) 10 (b) 20 (c) 30 (d) 40

19. In comparison of the surface soil the C : N ratio of sub-soft is : (a) UPPSC Pre-2004
(a) Narrow (b) Wide (c) Very wide (d) Equal

20. Among the following which organic manure has the narrowest C/N ratio ? (d) UPPSC Pre-2006
(a) Biogas slurry (b) FYM (c) Compost (d) Groundnut cake

21. C : N ratio of mineral soils is : (b) UPPSC Pre-2006
(a) 5 to 6 (b) 10 to 12 (c) 13 to 15 (d) 18 to 20

22. As compared to surface soil, the C : N ratio of subsoil is : (b) UPPSC Pre-2010
(a) Narrow (b) Wide (c) Very wide (d) Equal (similar)

23. C/ N ratio of paddy straw, in general, is: C PPSC ADO-2017
a) 60:1 b) 70:1 c) 80:1 d) 90:1

24. C:N ratio of Farm Yard Manure (FYM) is – 2 TN AO-2012
(1) 20 : 1 (2) 40 : 1 (3) 50 : 1 (4) 80 : 1

25. C : N ratio of normal soil is – 1 TN PSC Ag-II: 2001
(1) 10 :1 (2) 20 : 1 (3) 30 : 1 (4) 50 : 1

26. Mobilization of soil nitrogen occur when CN ratio of added organic matter is – 4 TNPSC – Ag: 1999
(1) <10:1 (2) < 20:1 (3) > 30: 1 (4) 10 : 1 to 30 : 1

27. What is C: N ratio of a normal soil ? 2 RPSC ACF Agri -2011
(a) 5:1 (b) 10:1 (c) 16:1 (d) 20:1

28. The C : N ratio of soil microorganisms is nearly - 2 RPSC ARO Agro-2022
(I) 5:1 (2) 8:1 (3) 10:1 (4) 18:1

29. The interaction processes of minerals withorganic compounds are called as - 3 RPSC ARO Ag Chem -2022
(1) Adsorption (2) Desorption (3) Chelation (4) Retention

CHAPTER- 158: FERTILIZERS PYQ'S

1. % K_{20} = % K × ………. **a** RPSC, AO-2012
(a) 1.2 (b) 2.2 (c) 3.2 (d) 4.2

2. 'Kisan Khad' is Know as – **d** BHU UET-2014
(a) Ammonium sulphate (b) Ammonium Nitrate
(c) Urea (d) Calcium Ammonium Nitrate

3. 'Rose mix' is a **1** RPSC Pre-2008
(1) Fertilizer (2)Insecticide (3) Sweet dish (4) Fungicide

4. "Biosuper" is a combination of – **3** TNPSC – Ag: 1999
(1) Rock phosphate + Phosphobacteria + Rhizobium
(2) Super Phosphate + Phosphobacteria + Thiobacillus
(3) Rock Phosphate + Phosphobacteria + Thiobacillus
(4) Rock Phosphate + Phpsphobacteria + Azospirillum

5. A compound containing a single primary nutrient is called …. **C** AO KTPSC-2021
(A)Compund (B) Complex (C) Straight (D) Mixed (E) Answer not known

6. A fertilizer containing at least two or more of the primary essential nutrients is called as – **b** MP PAT-2013
(A) Straight fertilizer (B) Complex fertilizer
(C) Mixed fertilizer (D) Soluble fertilizer

7. A fertilizer containing more than one primary nutrient is called : **1** RPSC Pre-1994
(1) compound fertilizer (2) straight fertilizer
(3) complex fertilizer (4) mixed fertilizer

8. A fertilizer which is present in the form of granules instead of vapour form?Ans: **Granulated fertilizer** BOM AO-2021

9. A fertilizers which supplies three essential plant nutrients is **C** IAS Pre-2003
(a) diammonium phosphate (DAP)
(b) muriate of potash (MOP)
(c) single superphosphate (SSP)
(d) sulphate of potash (SOP)

10. A plant fertilizer which is used in dry form and are in tiny pellets is known as? PSB AO-2019
Ans.: Granular fertilizer

11. A synthetic nitrification inhibitor is – **4** TN PSC Ag-I:1999
(1) Urea form (UF) (2) Thiourea (3) Neem cake (4) Both (1) and (2)

12. According to the fertilizer (Control) Under, rock phosphate Marketd for direct application should contain a minimum P_2O_5 of ***** RPSC, AAO-2018
(1) 12% (2) 18% (3) 35% (4) 24%

13. After application of fertilizers "Salt Index" is the measurement of : **d** UPPSC Pre-1998
(a) salt concentration of plant roots (b) Salt cconcentration in palnt cell
(c) salt concentration in leaves (d) Salt concentration of soil solution

14. After China and USA which among the following is the largest producer of fertilizers ? IAS Pre-2010

(a) Brazil (b) India (c) Indonesia (d) Russia

15. Agricultural grade gypsum contains – **1** TN AO-2018

(1) 70% purity (2) 90% purity (3) 30% purity (4) 35% purity

16. Ammonia anhydrous contains: **1** RPSC Pre-2008

(1) 81% Nitrogen (2)70% Nitrogen (3) 46% Nitrogen (4) 20% Nitrogen

17. Ammonium sulphate contain approximately – **2** TN AO-2008

(1) 10% nitrogen (2) 20% nitrogen (3) 39% nitrogen (4) 46% nitrogen

18. Ammonium sulphate contains: **b** NSC SR T-2019

(a) 15% nitrogen (b) 20% nitrogen (c) 25% nitrogen (d) 30% nitrogen

19. Ammonium sulphate fertilizer is ....in nature. **a** MP PAT-2013

(A) Acidic (B) Basic (C) Neutral (D) None of these.

20. Among these which one is not a slow release fertilizer: **Ans.: Ammonium sulphate** RRB SO-2019

21. An example of concentrated Organic manure is – **3** TN AO-2012

(1) FYM (2) Goat manure (3) Oil cakes (4) Poultry manure

22. Application of which of the following fertilizer can add sulfur also to the soil – **c** Gujrat AO-2017

(a) DAP (b) Urea

(c) Single Super phosphate (d) Muriate of Potash

23. Availability of rural compost is maximum in – **2** TN PSC Ag-2003

(1) Tamil Nadu (2) Uttar Pradesh (3) Andhra Pradesh (4) Orissa

24. Available phosphorus in fertilizer is the fraction – **b** BHU PET-2012

(a) Water soluble P (b) Water soluble + Citrate soluble P

(c) Na HCO_3 extractable P (d) NH_4F extractable P

25. Basic Slag is a: **a** MP PAT-2016

1. Citrate soluble fertilizer 2. Water soluble fertilizer

3. Alcohol soluble fertilizer 4. Water Insoluble fertilizer

26. Better response of phosphatic fertilize in acid soil lowland ecosyster takes place when applied in the form of **D** IAS Pre-2004

1. water soluble phosphate 2. rock phosphate

3. any p– containing fertilizer 4. citrate soluble phosphate

Select the correct answer using the codes given below

(a) 1and 2 (b) 1and 4 (c) 2and 3 (d) 2and 4

27. Bio-super is made up of : **(c)** UPPSC Pre-1999

(a) Bio-fertilizer and superphosphate (b) rock phosphate and sulphur

(c) Bio-fertilizer and podultry manure (d) Rock phosphate and powdered zinc

28. Biurate content in urea is permissible only to an extent of – **a** BHU PET-2014

(a) 1.5 % (b) 2.0 % (c) 3.0 % (d) 4.0 %

29. Biuret content in urea fertilizer is permitted upto (by FCO) – **1** TN PSC Ag-I:1999

(1) Less than 2.5% (2) Maximum upto 1.0%

(3) Between 2 and 3% (4) Zero

30. Biuret content in urea should be less than – **2** TN AO-2012

(1) 2 (2) 1.5 (3) 10 (4) 3

31. Biuret content in urea should not exceed in foliar spray on wheat more than the **b** UPPSC Pre-

following one : 2001

(a) 0.5% (b) 1.0% (c) 1.5% (d) 2.0%

32. Biuret content in urea should notexceed: **1** RPSC Pre-2003

(1) 1.0% (2) 2.0% (3) 3.0% (4) 4.0%

33. Bone meal should contain total minimum P_2O_5 : **3** RPSC ACF Agri -2011

(a) 5% (b) 10% (c) 20% (d) 30%

34. Calcium ammonium nitrate is a mixture of - **b** MP PAT-2013

(A) Calcium nitrate and Ammonium carbonate

(B) Calcium carbonate and Ammonium nitrate

(C) Calcium sulphate and Ammonium nitrate

(D) Calcium nitrate and Ammonium sulphate

35. Calcium favours the soil fertility status by – **2** TN PSC Ag-I:1999

(1) Encouraging aggregation (2) Displacing Na ion from soil exchange complex

(3) Supporting soil microflora (4) Making available other soil complex

36. Calculate the amount of urea for applying 50 kg N_2 **a** ICAR gen Agri-2010

(A) 100 kg (B) 109 kg (C) 50 kg (D) 119 kg

37. chemical formula of gypsum is? **4** RPSC, AAO-2018

(1) $CaSO_4$ (2) $CaSO_4.1/2H_2O$ (3) $CaSO_4.5H_2O$ (4) $CaSO_4.2H_2O$

38. Chemical formula of pyrite is – **c** Gujrat AO-2017

(a) H_2S (b) $CaSO_4$ (c) FeS_2 (d) FeS

39. Chemical formula of single superphosphate is : **d** UPPSC Pre-2001

(a) $Ca(H_2PO_4)_2$ (b) $CaHPO_4$ (c) $Ca_3(PO_4)_2$ (d) $Ca(H_2PO_4)_2.CaSO_4.2H_2O$

40. Chemical formulae of Gypsum is- **c** MP PAT-2016

(a) $CaOCl_2$ (b) $CaCO_3$ (c) $CaSO_4 . 2H_2O$ (d) $Ca(OH)_2$

41. Citrate Soluble fertilizer but water insoluble fertilizer is ? **Ans.: DCP** RRB SO-2019

42. Composition of humus with different ration is – **1** TN PSC Ag-I:1999

	C	O	N	H	Ash
(1)	50	35	5	5	5
(2)	40	30	10	15	5
(3)	30	50	5	5	5
(4)	20	55	10	10	5

43. Consider the following : **C** IAS Pre-2009

1. Zinc sulphate monohydrate 2. Zinc Phosphate

3. Zinc Oxide 4. Zn-EDTA

Based on the content of Zn, what is the sequence of the above materials in descending order ?

(a) 3 – 1 – 4 – 2 (b) 3 – 2 – 1 – 4

(c) 2 – 1 – 3 – 4 (d) 2 – 4 – 3 – 1

44. Consider the following : **C** IAS Pre-2009

1. Ammonium Nitrate 2. Potassium Nitrate

3. Sodium Nitrate 4. Urea

What is the correct sequence of the above fertilizer in ascending order based on their salt index per unit of Nitrogen content ?

(a) 4 – 1 – 2 – 3 (b) 4 – 2 – 1 – 3

(c) 3 – 2 – 4 – 1 (d) 3 – 2 – 1 – 4

45. Consider the following phosphatic fertilizers **B** IAS Pre-2003

1. Single superphosphate 2. Dicalcium phosphate

3. Monoammonium phosphate 4. Calcium metaphosphate

Which of these contain water soluble?

(a) 1and 2 (b) 1and 3 (c) 2and 3 (d) 2and 4

46. Consider the following statements **B** IAS Pre-2005

1. Muriate of potash is nto suitable for sugarcane

2. Saltpetre contains 65% K_2O

3. Single superphosphate contains gypsum

4. Ammonium phosphates are completely water soluble

Which of the statements given above are correct?

(a) 1and 2 (b) 1,3 and 4 (c) 3and 4 (d) 1,2,3 and 4

47. Consider the following statements **B** IAS Pre-2008

1. On percentage basis, muriate of potash contains less potash as compared to sulphate of potash.

2. Sulphate of potash is considered better than muriate of potash for tobacco, chillies and potato.

Which of the statements given above is/are correct?

(a) 1only (b) 2only (c) Both 1and 2 (d) Neither 1nor2

48. Consider the following statements: **c** IAS Pre-1997

1. Foliar application of ammonium sulphate reduces loss of nitrogen

2. Band application of single superphosphate at low rate reduces phosphorus fixation in an acid laterite soil.

3.Application of ammonium sulphate at high rate on the surface of calcareous soil reduces loss of nitrogen.

4. Band application of muriate of potash at high rate in a soil of pH4.5 induces toxicity in plants:

Of these statements

(a) 1and 2 are correct (b) 2and 3 are correct

(c) 1,3 and 4are correct (d) 2and 4 are correct

49. Consider the following statements: **B**

The response of phosphatic fertilizer in acidic soil under lowland ecosystem is better when applied in the form of

1. water soluble phosphate 2. rock phosphate

3. any P-containing fertilizer 4. citrate soluble phosphate

Which of the above statements are correct?

(a) 1and 3 (b) 2and 4 (c) 3and 4 (d) 1and 2

50. Consider the following States/UT: **d** IAS Pre-1994

1. Pondicherry 2. Punjab 3. Andhra pradesh 4. Haryana As per the 1991-92 data, the correct sequence of the DECREAS-ING order in

respect of the consumption of $N+P_2O_5+K_2O$ fertilizer nutrients (in kg/ha/year) is

(a) 1,2,4,3 (b) 2,1,3,4 (c) 1,2,3,4 (d) 2,1,4,3

51. Consider the following: **D** IAS Pre-2008

1. Zinc sulphate monohydrate 2. Zinc chelates 3. Zinc oxide

What is th correct sequence of the above in terms of the increasing oreder of zinc content in them?c

(a) 1,2,3 (b) 2,3,1 (c) 2,1,3 (d) 3,1,2

52. Continues use of ammonium sulphate makes the soil – **2** TNPSC – Ag: 1999

(1) Alkaline (2) Acidic (3) Neural (4) None of these

53. Conversion factor for phosphorus (P) to P_2O_5 : **2** RPSC, AAO-2009

(1) 1.20 (2) 2.29 (3) 1.40 (4) 1.63

54. Conversion of ammonia into nitrate by bacteria is known as **2** RPSC Pre-2010

(1) Ammonification (2) Nitrification

(3) Denitrification (4) Loss of nitrogen

55. Conversion of calcium sulphate to gypsum is a process of - **2** RPSC ARO Ag Chem -2022

(1) Hydrolysis (2) Hydration (3) Oxidation (4) Solution

56. Crop innocuous biuret content (%) of urea for foliar sprays is : **b** BHU PET-2013

(a) < 1.0 (b) < 2.0 (c) < 3.0 (d) < 4.0

57. Current rate of fertilizer consumption in India is **d** ICAR gen Agri-2010

(A) 128 kg/ha (B) 148 kg/ha (C) 138 kg/ha (D) 158 kg/ha

58. DAP is a - **4** TN PSC Ag-I:1999

(1) Straight fertilizer (2) Mixed fertilizer

(3) Compound fertilizer (4) None of these

59. Diammonium phosphate requirement for supplying 45 kg N and 115 kg P_2O_5 to one hectare groundnut crop is — **4** RPSC ARO Ag Chem -2022

(1) 100 kg (Z) 150 kg (3) 200 kg (4) 250 kg

60. Direct application of rock phosphate as phosphorous for crops is recommended in : **a** UPPSC Pre-1999

(a) Acid soils (b) Netural soils (c) Alkaline soils (d) Saline soils

61. Dominium phosphate requirement for supplying 45kg N and 115kg P2 O5to one hectare peanut crop is **d** IAS Pre-1993

(a) 100kg (b) 150kg (c) 200kg (d) 250kg

62. During the process of manufacture of urea, an organic compound may be formed which restricts the use of urea as nitrogen source, the compound is – **b** Agri Pre PG-2017

(a) Hydrocyanide (b) Biuret

(c) Amino acid glycine (d) Acetic acid

63. EDTA is a – **1** TN PSC Ag-I:1999

(1) Chelate (2) N-Serve (3) Slow release fertilizer (4) Micronutrient

64. Enriched FYM contains FYM and SSP in the ratio of – **3** TN AO-2012

(1) 5 : 2 (2) 5 : 3 (3) 5 : 1 (4) 4 : 1

65. Equivalent acidity of Ammonium sulphate Fertilizers is – **3** Ag sup 2018

(1) 93 (2) 128 (3) 110 (4) 80

66. Fertiliser is defined as **A** HPSC ADO-2022

(A) inorganic material with a definite chemical composition and high analytical value that supplies one or more plant nutrients in plant available form (B) organic material with a definite chemical composition and high analytical value that supplies one or more plant nutrients in plant available form

(C) inorganic material with no definite chemical composition and high analytical value that supplies one or more plant nutrients in plant available form

(D) inorganic material with a definite chemical composition and low analytical value that supplies one or more plant nutrients in plant available form

67. Fertilizer consumption ($N+P_2O_5+K_2O$) in M.T. by the end of Ninth Five year plan was: **2** RPSC Pre-2003

(1)15 (2) 20 (3) 25 (4) 30

68. Fertilizer control order was implemented by Government of Tamil Nadu during 1985 mainly to **3** TN ACF-2012

(1) Reduce the fertilizer application (2) Avoid wastage of fertilizers

(3) Assure standard quality parameters (4) Control the distribution of fertilizers

69. Fertilizer which incurred the acidity in soil is **3** RPSC Pre-2010

(1) Ammonium sulphate (2) Ammonium nitrate

(3) Both (1) and (2) (4) None of these

70. Fertilizers containing Cl^- ions are not suitablefor which crops? **2** RPSC ARO Ag Chem -2022

(1) Wheat (2) Potato (3) Soybean (4) Sugarcane

71. Fertilizers containing two or more nutrients are called as **2** RPSC Pre-2010

(1) Double fertilizer (2) Complex fertilizer

(3) Mixed fertilizer (4) Organic fetilizer

72. Following fertilizers are available for preparing a fertilizer mixture] **c** IAS Pre-1998

1. Ammonium sulphate 2. Urea 3. single superphosphate

4. Basic slag 5. Muriate of potash

A combination of the above mentioned fertilizers which can be mixed and kept for three months or more is

(a) 1,4and 5 (b) 2,3 and 4 (c) 2,4 and 5 (d) 1,3 and 5

73. For application of phosphorus at the rate of 50 kg P_2O_5 ha^{-1} to cotton crop, the quantity in kg of single super-phosphate ($P_2O5 = 16\%$) required for 1½ acres is **C** IAS Pre-2007

(a) 80 (b) 108 (c) 188 (d) 216

74. For applying 100 kg nitrogen how much urea is required – **b** Gujrat AO-2017

(a) 122 (b) 222 (c) 45 (d) 67

75. For applying 40 kg nitrogen, D.A.P. required – **b** Raj JET-2015

(a) 200 kg (b) 222 kg (c) 230 kg (d) 240 kg

76. For applying 92 kg of nitrogen, how much urea would one use ? **b** Raj JET-2013

(a) 20 kg (b) 200 kg (c) 300 kg (d) 400 kg

77. For balanced fertilizer use the optimum N : P : K ratio should be – **b** BHU PET-2011

(a) 6 : 2 : 1 (b) 4 : 2 : 1 (c) 6 : 4 : 2 (d) 5 : 3 : 1

78. For foliar spray of urea, the biurate content in urea should be **D** TO MPUAT-2014

(A) 1.0 - 1.5 percent (B) 1.5 - 2.0 per cent

(C) 2.0 - 2.5 per *cent* (D) < 0.5 per cent

79. For preparing a mixed fertilizer, 100kg of ammonium sulphate and 125kg of single superphosphate were mixed. 25kg of filler was added to this mixture. In terms. of N- P_2-O_5 K_2O, there fertilizer grade of this mixture will be **a** IAS Pre-1997
(a) 5-5-0 (b) 5-10-0 (c) 8-8-0 (d) 10-10-0

80. For which type of fertilizer India is fully dependent on imports ? **3** RPSC Pre-2003
(1)N-fertilizers (2) P-fertilizers (3) K-fertilizers (4) None of these

81. General recommendations of N, P and K fertilizer doses for Chickpea in Rajasthan are : **2** RPSC ACF Agri -2011
(a) 15-50-90 (b) 20- 40-0 (c) 30-20-20 (d) 20-40-20

82. Gypsum is used to amend – **2** TN PSC Ag-2003
(1) Acidic soil (2) Alkaline soil (3) Saline soil (4) Laterite soil

83. Heavy applications of potassium fertilizers often lead to reduced absorption of **A** IAS Pre-2003
(a) Mg and Ca (b) B and Mn (c) N and P (d) Zn and Cu

84. Highest Ca% in which manure-**Poultry** **B** IBS,AFO-2018
(A) Cow (B) Poultry (C) Human (D) Earthworm (E) None of these

85. Highest use of potassic fertilizer is in the state of – **a** BHU UET-2016
(a) Maharashtra (b) Andhara Pradesh (c) Tamil Nadu (d) Punjab

86. How many days it generally takes to convert urea into nitrate form **2** AARO Agro-2016
(1) About 3 days (2) About 7 days (3) About 15 days (4) About 20 days

87. How much % P_2O_5 is contained in triple super phosphate ? **B** ADA MP-2015
(A) 25% (B) 48% (C) 40% (D) 15%

88. How much muriate of potash will be required to supply 45 kg K_2O/ha : **b** UPPSC Pre-2000
(a) 50 kg (b) 75 kg (c) 100 kg (d) 125 kg

89. How much nitrogen is obtained from urea? **b** MP PAT-2014
(A) 42% (B) 46% (C) 25% (D) 60%

90. How much percentage of nitrogen is present in ammonium chloride ? **1** TN AO-2008
(1) 25 (2) 18 (3) 15 (4) 10

91. How much percentage of Nitrogen is present in ammonium chloride ? **1** TNPSC – Ag: 1999
(1) 25 (2) 28 (3) 14 (4) 15

92. How much quantity of urea is required for 80 kg nitrogen in a crop ? **A** TO MPUAT-2014
(A) 174 kg (B) 154 kg (C) 164 kg (D) 144 kg

93. How much Urea (kg) will be required for 10 hectares area at the rate of 150 kg Nitrogen per hectare application ? **2** RPSC ACF Agri -2018
(1) 690 (2) 3255 (3) 32.5 (4) 306

94. Hydrolysis of urea in soils results in : **b** UPPSC Pre-1999
(a) Uric acid (b) Ammonium carbonate (c) Ammonium carbomate (d) Amides

95. In ammonium sulphate nitrate fertilizer, the ratio of ammonical-N and nitrate-N is: **B** PPSC ADO-2017
a) 50:50 b) 75:25 c) 25:75 d) 40:60

96. In CAN, nitrogen is present in the **C** ADA Guj-2013
(A) Nitrate form (B) Ammonical form
(C) Both of the above (D) None of the above

97. In compost making, different materials are added for specificpurpose. Which among the following is correctly matched? **C** TNPSC Ag-1998

(A) Bone meal - To supply k

(B) Powdered rock - Added for P enrichment

(C) Basic slag - To control Acidity

(D) Saw dust - To control Basicity

98. In Haber's process for the manufacture of ammonia, the catalyst used is: **b** NSC S T-2019

(a) Finely divided Ni (b) Finely divided Fe

(c) Finely divided Platinum (d) Finely divided calcium

99. In natural soil most of the urea is converted to ammonium form after : **c** UPPSC Pre-2002

(a) 6 hours (b) 12 hours (c) 24 hours (d) 48 hours

100. In respect of s sugarcane crop to be grown in an acidic soil high P-fixing capacity the fertilizer of choice would be **b** IAS Pre-1997

(a) triple superphosphate (b) finely ground rock phosphate

(c) coarse rock phosphate (d) superphosphate

101. In the pulse crops, which fertilizer is advised to basal application? **a** ICAR Gen Agri-2005, 08

(A) SSP (B) Urea (C) DAP (D) CAN

102. In which agro-climatic zone of India "The soils are mostly alluvial and are prone to floods" ? **1** RPSC AO Ag - 2021

(1) Lower Gangetic plains zone (2) Middle Gangetic plains zone

(3) Upper Gangetic plains zone (4) Trans-Gangetic plains zone

103. Indicate nitrogen content in Calcium Ammonium Nitrate (CAN) **3** RPSC Pre-2010

(1) 16% (2) 20% (3) 26% (4) 32%

104. Indicate nitrogen content in Calcium Ammonium Nitrate (CAN) ? **3** RPSC ACF Agri -2011

(a) 16% (b) 20% (c) 26% (d) 32%

105. Indicate P_2O_5 content in Diammonium phosphate **3** RPSC Pre-2010

(1) 16% (2) 32% (3) 46% (4) 60%

106. Indicate P_2O_5 content in Diammonium phosphate : **3** RPSC ACF Agri -2011

(a) 16% (b) 32% (c) 46% (d) 60%

107. Indicate the percentage of nitrogen in D. A. P.: **b** NSC MT M-2019

(a) 15% (b) 18% (c) 32% (d) 46%

108. Lac dye contains ______ and used as manures – **4** TN AO-2018

(1) Phosphorous (2) Potash (3) Ammonium sulphate (4) Nitrogen

109. Legume crop is recommended NPK dose of **c** ICAR gen Agri-2010

(A) 4:2:1 (B) 1:2:2 (C) 4:2:2 (D) 1:2:4

110. Lime content in single superphosphate is : **a** UPPSC Pre-1998

(a) 15-20% (b) 20-25% (c) 25-30% (d) 30-35%

111. Loweset N is in which fertilizer **C** BOM AO-2021

a. Urea b. CAN c. Amonium sulphate d. Ammonium nitrate

112. Magnesium content (%) in calcium ammonium nitrate fertilizer as mentioned in F.C.O., 1985 is **3** RPSC AO Ag - 2021

(1) 2.5% (2) 3.5% (3) 4.5% (4) 5.5%

113. Manufacture of SSP is – **1** Agri Pre PG-

(1) Acidulation of rock phosphate with sulphuric acid 2018

(2) Acidulation of rock phosphate with nitric acid

(3) Acidulation of rock phosphate with phosphoric acid

(4) Acidulation of rock phosphate with oxalic acid

114. Match List 1 (Reactants sued for the preparation of fertilizers) with List 2 (Fertilizer produced) and select the correct answer **b** IAS Pre-1996

List I	*List II*
A. Rock phosphate, phosphoric	1.Urea
B. Rock phosphate, phosphoric	2. Ammonium sulphate
C. Ammonia, gypsum CO_2	3. Nitro phosphate
D. Ammonia Co_2	4. Concentrated super phosphate

	A	B	C	D		A	B	C	D
a)	4	3	1	2	(b)	4	3	2	1
c)	3	4	2	1	(d)	3	4	1	2

115. Match List 1 (fertilizer) with List ll 9equivalent acidity) and select the correct answer: **b** IAS Pre-1994

List l	List ll
A. Urea	1. 148
B. Ammonium sulphate	2. 128
C. Ammonium chloride	3. 110
D. Anhydrous ammonia	4. 84
	5. 64

	A	B	C	D		A	B	C	D
(a)	5	2	3	4	(b)	4	3	2	1
(c)	2	5	4	3	(d)	4	1	2	3

116. Match List l with List ll and select the correct answer: **c** IAS Pre-1994

List l (Name of fertilizer)	List ll (Type of fertilizer)
A. Ammonium sulphate	1. Biofertilizer
B. Dominium phosphate	2. Straight fertilizer
C. Algae	3. Organic manure
D. F.Y.M	4. Complex fertilizer

	A	B	C	D		A	B	C	D
(a)	2	4	3	1	(b)	3	2	4	1
(c)	2	4	1	3	(d)	4	2	3	1

117. Match List with List second and select the correct answer. **b** IAS Pre-1993

List first (Classes of fertilizer)	List second (Example of different classes)
A. organic fertilizer	1. Urea
B. Inorganic fertilizer	2. Isobutylidene diurea
C. Biofefrtiliser	3. Ammonium soleplates
Disallow release fertilizer	4. Azolla
	5. 2-chloro-6-pyridene

	A	B	C	D		A	B	C	D
(a)	1	2	3	5	(b)	1	3	4	2
(c)	2	1	5	4	(d)	5	1	4	3

118. Match List1 with List 2and select the correct answer **b** IAS Pre-1996

List I	*List II*
A. Gypsum	1. Magnesium fertilizer
B. 17:17:17	2. Micronutrient fertilizer
C. Serpentine	3. Calcium fertilizer
D. Chelates	4. Compound/complex fertilizer

	A	B	C	D		A	B	C	D
a)	3	2	1	4	b)	3	4	1	2
c)	1	2	3	4	d)	1	4	3	2

119. Match the list I with list II and select the correct answer using code given below : **a** UPPSC Pre-2000

List I (Acid forming fertilizers)	List II (Acid equivalent)
A. Ammonium Chloride	1.110
B. Urea	2. 93
C. Ammonium Sulphate Nitrate	3. 128
D. Ammonium Sulphate	4.8O

Code:

	A	B	C	D
(a)	3	4	2	1
(b)	2	3	1	4
(c)	1	2	3	4
(d)	3	1	2	4

120. Material added in fertilizer mixture to reduce hygroscopicity and improve the physical condition is known as : **d** UPPSC Pre-2010

(a) Filler (b) Neutralizer (c) Aggregator (d) Conditioner

121. Maximum amount of fertilizer is used in – **4** TN PSC Ag-2003

(1) Wheat (2) Rice (3) Cotton (4) Potato

122. Maximum amount of nitrogen is present in- **4** TN PSC Ag-2003

(1) Compost (2) Night soil (3) Poultry manure (4) Groundnut cake

123. Minimum percentage of K_2O in fertilizer grade potassium sulphate is **3** RPSC Pre-2007

(1) 30% (2)60% (3) 50% (4) None of these

124. Minimum percentage of K_2O in fertilizer grade Potassium Sulphate is : **2** RPSC ACF Agri -2011

(a) 30% (b) 50% (c) 60% (d) 80%

125. Mono ammonium phosphate contains .... % N. **2** Agri Pre PG-2015

(1) 18.0 (2) 11.0 (3) 28.0 (4) 21.0

126. Most commonly used nitrogenous fertilizer in India ? **c** Delhi PGT-2014

(a) CAN (b) Ammonium Sulphates

(c) Urea (d) Diammponium Phosphate

127. Most Effective phosphatic fertilizer for crops in acidic soil is : **b** UPPSC Pre-

(a) DAP (b) SSP (c) Rock Phosphate (d) None of these 1994

128. Most idealy used N fertilizer is **1** RPSC Pre-2010
(1) Urea (2) NH_4Cl
(3) Anhydrous ammonia (4) Ammonium sulphate

129. Murate of Potash is also known as **a** ICAR gen Agri-2010
(A) HCl (B) NaCl (C) KCL (D) NH4Cl

130. Muriate of potash contains **D** ADA Guj-2013
(A) 40% K_2O (B) 36% K_2O (C) 50% K_2O (D) None of the above

131. Muriate of potash contains **A** TO MPUAT-2014
(A) 60% K_2O (B) 50% K_2O (C) 48% K_2O (D) 52% K_2O

132. Muriate of potash is - **1** MP PG PAT-2016
(1) KCl (2) (K_2SO_4. $MgSO_4$) $6H_2O$
(3) KNO_3 (4) All of these

133. Muriate of potash is also called : **3** RPSC ACF Agri-2018
(1) Potassium sulphate (2) Potassium nitrate
(3) Potassium chloride (4) Sulphate of potash

134. Muriate of potash is also known as: **c** MP PAT-2013
(A) Potassium sulphate (B) Potassium nitrate
(C) Potassium chloride (D) None of these

135. N use efficiency of fertilizers can be enhanced by – **4** TN AO-2012
(1) Coating (2) Split application (3) Placement (4) All the above

136. N,P_2O_5 and K_2O contents of DAP are : **2** RPSC Pre-2003
(1) 46-18-0 (2)18-46-0 (3)0-18-46 (4)0-46-18

137. Night soil manure is prepared from : **3** RPSC ACF Agri-2011
(a) City waste (b) Cattle excreta (c) Human excreta (d) Legume crops

138. Nitrate nitrogen content in calcium ammonium nitrate is : **3** RPSC Pre-2003
(1) 8.5% (2) 10.5% (3) 12.5% (4) 15.5%

139. Nitrogen and Phosphorus containing commercial fertilizer is – **2** TN PSC Ag-I:1999
(1) CAN (2) Ammophos (3) Ammonium sulphate (4) Rock phosphate

140. Nitrogen content in groundnut cake is : **c** UPPSC Pre-2008
(a) 2 - 3 % (b) 4 - 5 % (c) 7 - 8 % (d) 9-10%

141. Nitrogen content is cow dung is **a** TNPSC Agri-1997
(A) 0.4% (B) 1.0% (C) 5% (D) 10%

142. Nitrogen content is urea is – **b** BHU UET-2016
(a) 42 % (b) 46 % (c) 48 % (d) 50%

143. Nitrogen content of Sulphur coated urea ranges between :- **b** ARO Agro-2016
(a) 26% - 28% (b) 36% - 37% (c) 40% - 42% (d) 46% - 48%

144. Nitrogen fertilizer use efficiency in rice can be increased by suing **d** IAS Pre-1998
(a) suphur-coated urea (b) blue green algae
(c) urea super granules (d) sulphur coated urea and urea super granules

145. Nitrogen in DAP is : **2** RPSC Pre-1995
(1) 9% (2) 18% (3) 36% (4) 46%

146. Nitrogen in groundnut cake is : **c** UPPSC Pre-

(a) 2.0-3.0% (b) 4.0-5.0% (c) 7.0-8.0% (d) 9.0-10.0% — 2007

147. Nitrogen is present in Urea as – **a** BHU UET-2014

(a) Amide (b) Ammonia (c) Nitrate (d) Nitrate

148. Nitrogen present in urea is in the form of – **c** BHU UET-2013

(a) nitrate (b) ammonia (c) amide (d) nitrite

149. Nitrogenous fertilizer use efficient in normal soils ranges from – **2** TN PSC Ag-I:1999

(1) 8-15% (2) 25 – 40% (3) 50 – 60% (4) 60 – 70 %

150. NPK Composition of standard fertilizer mixture for potato and Paddy is **3** MP PG PAT-2016

(1) 4,4,4 (2) 6,24,6 (3) 6,12,6 (4) None of these

151. One of the Soil-phosphorus fertilizer reaction product in acidic soils is – **3** RPSC ARO Ag Chem -2022

(1) Hydroxyapatite (2) Flour apatite

(3) Strengite (4) Magnesium Hydrogen Phosphate

152. Optimum fertilizer schedule per plant of three years age of grapevine is : **1** RPSC Pre-1993

	Urea (kg.)	superphosphate (kg.)	muriate of potash (kg.)
1)	0.40	0.50	0.20
2)	0.60	1.00	0.20
3)	0.80	1.50	0.40
4)	1.00	2.00	0.40

153. P content in DAP is : **a** UPPSC Pre-2001

(a) 20% (b) 36% (c) 46% (d) 50%

154. Per cent sulphur content in ordinary super phosphate is :- **1** AARO Agro-2016

(1) 12 (2) 21 (3) 09 (4) 15

155. Percent content of sulphur in single superphosphate is : **b** UPPSC Pre-2000

(a) 8 (b) 12 (c) 16 (d) 20

156. Percent content of Sulphur is SSP is – **d** Raj JET-2017

(a) 20 (b) 16 (c) 8 (d) 12

157. Percent of P_2O5 in single super phosphate is? **b** Agri Pre PG-2021

(a) 18 (b) 16 (c) 46 (d) 48

158. Percent P_2O_5 in DAP is – **b** BHU PET-2011

(a) 45 (b) 48 (c) 35 (d) 38

159. Percent sulphur content in single super-phosphate is : **b** UPPSC Pre-2004

(a) 9 (b) 12 (c) 19 (d) 24

160. Percent sulphur in ordinary Super phosphate is – **2** Ag sup 2018

(1) 24 (2) 12 (3) 18 (4) 21

161. Percentage of P_2O_5 in FYM is – **a** BHU UET-2011

(a) 0.25 (b) 0.50 (c) 0.75 (d) 1.00

162. Percentage of nitrogen in calcium ammonium nitrate is – **b** BHU UET-2013

(a) 21 (b) 25 (c) 31 (d) 44

163. Percentage of nitrogen in calcium ammonium nitrate is – **b** BHU UET-2014

(a) 18% (b) 25% (c) 30% (d) 35%

164. Percentage of sulphur in gypsum is – **b** BHU UET-2011

(a) 15 (b) 18 (c) 25 (d) 30

165. Percentage of sulphur in pyrites is – **b** BHU UET-2011

(a) 10-12 (b) 14-22 (c) 30-32 (d) 40-42

166. Percentage of zinc in zinc sulphate (monohydrate) is – **c** BHU UET-2011

(a) 25 (b) 30 (c) 33 (d) 35

167. Phosphorus is present in DAP in the form of – **a** BHU UET-2017

(a) phosphate (b) phosphoric acid (c) phosphaide (d) All of these

168. Potassic fertilizer containing maximum quantity of potash is : **a** UPPSC Pre-1995

(a) Muriate of potash (b) Potassium nitrate

(c) Sulphate of potash (d) Potassium ammonium nitrate

169. Potassic fertilizer containing maximum quantity of potash is : **2** RPSC, AAO-2009

(1) Potassium Nitrate (2) Muriate Potash

(3) Potassium sulphate (4) Potassium Ammonium Nitrate

170. Reaction of rock phosphate with phosphoric acid results in – **c** Agri Pre PG-2020

(a) Single super phosphate (b) phosphorus rich organic manure

(c) Triple super phosphate (d) Rhenania phosphate

171. Recommended urea concentration for the foliar spray is – **1** Ag Sup JAU 2017

(1) 2.5 – 3.0% (2) 3.0 – 5.0% (3) 5.0 – 5.7% (4) 7.5 – 10.0%

172. Relatively more hygroscopic fertilizer is – **d** BHU PET-2013

(a) SSP (b) DAP (c) MOP (d) Urea

173. Residual effect of applying nitrate nitrogenous fertilizers on the soil is **4** RPSC Pre-2008

(1) Neutral (2) Acidic (3) Neutral to acidic (4) Basic

174. Richest source of Nitrogen is : **a** UPPSC Pre-1995

(a) Dried blood (b) Fish manure (c) Raw bone meal (d) Dry activated sludge

175. Rock phosphate deposits are abundantly found in ______ district of Rajasthan :- **d** ARO Agro-2016

(a) Nagaur (b) Bikaner (c) Barmer (d) Udaipur

176. Rock phosphate is a **d** Agri Pre PG-2013

(a) Citric acid insoluble P fertilizer (b) Water insoluble P fertilizer

(c) Citric acid and water soluble P fertilizer

(d) Citric acid and water insoluble P fertilizer

177. Rock phosphate is used for the reclamation of - **b** MP PAT-2014

(A) alkaline soil (B) acidic soil (C) rocky land (D) sandy soil

178. Rock phosphate is used in : **c** UPPSC Pre-1997

(a) neutral soil (b) Alkaline soil (c) Acidic soil (d) Saline soil

179. S.S.P. is the source of mainly **D** ADA Guj-2013

(A) S (B) Ca (C) P_2O_5 (D) All of these

180. Select a fertilizer which is highly soluble in water. **2** TN PSC Ag-2003

(1) Rock phosphate (2) DAP (3) Urea (4) Potash

181. select incorrect match from the following :- **d** ARO Agro-2016

(a) For good crop growth - apply N Fertilizer

(b) For correcting "top sickness" of tabacco - apply B Fertilizer

(c) For quality produce - apply K Fartilizer

(d) For correcting yellowing in groudnut - apply Zn Fertilizer

182. Single super phosphate contains ....% sulphur. **c** MP PAT-2013

(A) 8.5 (B) 10.5 (C) 12.5 (D) 14·5

183. Single Superphosphate contains percent water soluble phosphorus **B** TO MPUAT-2014

(A) 20 (B) 16 (C) 12 (D) 8

184. Single superphosphate is preferred for P application in groundnut because it also supplies other nutrients like **3** RPSC Pre-2007

(1) sulphur (2) calcium

(3) sulphur & calcium (4) sulphur, calcium and nitrogen

185. Single superphosphate is produced by the reaction of rock phosphate with – **3** Agri Pre PG-2019

(1) HNO_3 (2) H_3PO_4 (3) H_2SO_4 (4) HCl

186. Soil fertility resulted by use of manures, fertilizers, ploughing and irrigation is known as – **b** Raj JET-2015

(a) Natural fertility (b) Acquried fertility

(c) Fertility (d) Soil productivity

187. Split application of fertilizer is very effective in enhancing fertilizer use efficiency of – **a** Delhi PGT-2014

(a) Nitrogen (b) Phosphorus (c) Potassium (d) Micronutrient

188. Sugar-digested compost is called so because **c** IAS Pre-1994

(a) it is prepared by allowing it to decompose beyond the normal process of decomposition

(b) it contains plant nutrients more than that present in ordinary compost

(c) superphosphate is added to the compost during its preparation

(d) its P_2O_5 content is more than that present in the ordinary compost

189. Sulphate of potash is preferable to Muriate of Potash (MOP) for tobacco because **a** IAS Pre-1996

(a) the chlorine in the MOP affects the burning quality of tobacco

(b) the chlorine in the MOP increases the nicotine content of tobacco

(c) the application of MOP results in the luxury consumption of potassium

(d) the sulphate iron helps to increase the availability of other nutrients

190. Sulphate of potash is preferable to muriate of potash (MOP) for tobacco because **A** AO GPSC-2013

(A) The chlorine in murite of potash (MOP) affect burning quality of tobacco

(B) The chlorine in murite of potash (MOP) increase the nicotine

(C) The sulphate ions helps to increase the availability of other nutrients

(D) None of these

191. Sulphur coated urea contains nitrogen : **a** UPPSC Pre-1997

(a) 36% (b) 40% (c) 25% (d) 46%

192. Sulphur content (%) in ammonium sulphate is – **b** Gujrat AO-2017

(a) 32 (b) 24 (c) 28 (d) 21

193. Sulphur content in ammonium sulphate is **3** RPSC Pre-2010

(1) 15% (2) 20% (3) 24% (4) 35%

194. Sulphur content in ammonium sulphate is : **c** UPPSC Pre-2002
(a) 12% (b) 20% (c) 24% (d) 30%

195. Sulphur content in Ammonium Sulphate is : **b** UPPSC Pre-2010
(a) 30% (b) 24% (c) 18% (d) 12%

196. Sulphur content in gypsum is : **b** UPPSC Pre-2006
(a) 20.0% (b) 18.6% (c) 16.8% (d) 12.0%

197. Sulphur content in gypsum is : **b** UPPSC Pre-2007
(a) 20.0% (b) 18.6% (c) 16.8% (d) 12.0%

198. The "equivalent basicity" of the fertilizer Sodium nitrate is : **b** BHU PET-2013
(a) 21 (b) 29 (c) 33 (d) 63

199. The actual K content (%) of a fertilizer sample having 1% K_2O will be - **3** RPSC ARO Agro-2022
(1) 0.63 (2) 0.73 (3) 0.83 (4) 0.93

200. the addition of excess soluble phosphatic fertilizers to solids may affect plant growth by **c** IAS Pre-1993
(a) inhibiting the growth of microorganisms
(b) precipitating iron and aluminium
(c) reducing the availability of zinc
(d) reducing the availability of calcium

201. The amount of Ammonium Chloride required for providing one Kg. nitrogen **D** PPSC ADO-2020
a) 2.2 kg b) 6.2 kg c) 1.7 kg d) 4 kg

202. The amount of NPK required to produce 50% of the maximum possible yield is one Baule unit One Baule is equal to (in lb/acre) **a** IAS Pre-1998

	Nitrogen	P_2O_5	K_2O
(a)	223	45	76
(b)	223	40	76
(c)	250	45	60
(d)	250	40	60

203. The average N,P,K composition of night soil is about :- **2** RPSC, AO-2016
(1) 3.5, 2.0, 1.0 % (2) 5.5, 4.0, 2.0 %
(3) 3.5, 4.0, 2.0 % (4) 5.5, 2.0, 1.0 %

204. The average nitrogen content of vermin-compost is of the order **b** BHU PET-2012
(a) 0.2-0.6% (b) 0.6-1.2% (c) 1.2-1.8% (d) 1.8-2.4 %

205. The basic fertilizer is – **2** TNPSC – Ag: 1999
(1) Urea (2) $NaNO_3$ (3) $(NH_4)_2SO_4$ (4) NH_4CL

206. The best estimate of the available pin phosphatic fertilizers is obtained from the **a** IAS Pre-1996
(a) water soluble fraction (b) citrate-insoluble fraction
(c) citrate soluble fraction (d) water soluble and citrate soluble fractions

207. The biuret percent limit of urea for foliar application is **1** RPSC Pre-2007
(1) 0.25 (2) 0.75 (3) 1.25 (4) 1.75

208. The blanket fertilizer recommendation for rainfed rice is – **1** TN ACF-2012
(1) 50: 25 : 25 Kg N: P_2O_5 : K_2O/ha
(2) 100 : 50 : 50 Kg N: P_2O_5 : K_2O/ha
(3) 200 : 100 : 100 kg N: P_2O_5 : K_2O/ha

(4) 80 : 40 : 40 Kg N: P_2O_5 : K_2O/ha

209. The calcium and sulphur content (%) in single superphosphate is – **2** RPSC ARO Agro-2022
(1) 11 and 20 (2) 20 and 11 (3) 16 and 20 (4) 20 and 16

210. The conversion factor to conversion P to % P_2O_5 is **C** ADA MP-2015
(A) 1.29 (B) 2.90 (C) 2.29 (D) 0.40

211. The correct group of slow release N fertilizers is **1** RPSC ACF Agri -2018
(1) Urea formaldehyde, Oxamide, CDU
(2) Oxamide, Diammonium Phosphate, IBDU
(3) IBDU, Rock Phosphate, Thiourea
(4) CDU, Oxamide, Ammonium nitrate

212. The example of organic fertilizer is : **3** RPSC Pre-2003
(1) Sodium nitrate (2) Ammonium sulphate
(3) Urea (4) Ammonium chloride

213. The example of Organic fertilizer is. **c** Raj JET-2016
(a)Sodium nitrate (b) Ammonium sulphate
(c) Urea (d) Ammonium chloride

214. The Fe-chelate suitable for application to crops grown on acid soils is **A** IAS Pre-2003
(a) Fe-EDTA (b) Fe- EDDHA (c) Fe- DTPA (d) Fe- HEDTA

215. The fertilizer containing nitrogen in amide form is : **a** UPPSC Pre-1994
(a) Urea (b) Ammonium Sulphate (c) C.A.N (d) Ammonium Phosphate

216. The form of nitrogen in urea is – **b** Gujrat AO-2017
(a) Nitrate (b) Amide (c) Nitrite (d) Ammoniacal

217. The formula of gypsum is: **b** NSC S T-2019
(a) $MgSO_4.2H_2O$ (b) $CaSO_4.2H_2O$ (c) $2CaSO_4$ (d) $CaSO_4.3H_2O$

218. The kind of chemical fertilizer which is consumed most in India is - **3** TN PSC Ag-II: 2001
(1) Potassic (2) Phosphatic
(3) Nitrogenous (4) Sometimes potassic and sometimes phosphatic

219. The most concentrated fertilizer used for nutrient supply is : **c** UPPSC Pre-2001
(a) Urea (b) DAP (c) Anhydrous Ammonia (d) SSP

220. The N, P_2O_5 and K_2O contents farmyard manure are respectively – **3** TN PSC Ag-II: 2001
(1) 0.5 – 1.5, 0.4-0.8, 0.5 – 1.9 (2) 0.5 – 1.5, 0.5 – 1.0, 0.4 – 0.8
(3) 0.5 – 1.0, 0.4 – 0.8, 0.4 – 0.8 (4) 0.5 – 2.0, 0.3 – 0.6, 1.5 – 1.9

221. The N-fertilizer use efficiency in rice can be increased by using : **4** RPSC Pre-2003
(1) S-coated urea (2)Urea super granules
(3)BGA (4) Both (1) and (2)

222. The nitrogen content in D.A.P. is: **a** NSC SR T-2019
(a) 17% (b) 15% (c) 13% (d) 11%

223. The nitrogen content in the nano urea (liquid) commercialized by IFFCO in India is - **4** RPSC ARO Agro-2022
(1) 46% (2) 4.6% (3) 40% (4) 4%

224. The nitrogenous fertilizer manufactured in India which occupies the first place in production to-day is **c** IAS Pre-1993
(a) Ammonium sulphate (b) Ammonium phosphate

(c) Urea (d) Calcium ammonium nitrate

225. The nitrogenous fertilizer of choice for tea is **b** IAS Pre-1995
(a) calcium ammonium nitrate (b) urea
(c) ammonium sulphate (d) ammonium nitrate

226. The optimum dose of phosphorus for pulses in arid zone is : **2** RPSC Pre-1998
(1) 40 kg./h. (2) 30 kg./h. (3) 20 kg./h. (4) 10 kg./h.

227. The P_2O_5 percentage in DAP is : **a** UPPSC Pre-1996
(a) 46 (b) 36 (c) 40 (d) 30

228. The percentage of Nitrogen (N) in DAP is…… **C** BOD AO-2008
(A) 46 (B) 26 (C) 18 (D) 80 (E) 30

229. The percentage of P_2O_5 in superphosphate is : **c** UPPSC Pre-1996
(a) 10% (b) 26% (c) 16% (d) 32%

230. The Phosphorus content of DAP is – **2** Raj JET-2018
(1) 18 per cent (2) 46 per cent (3) 16 per cent (4) 42 per cent

231. The quantity of single superphosphate (16% P2 O5) required for application to one acre of rice-field at a dose of 60 kg P2 O5 ha^{-1} is **C** IAS Pre-2003
(a) 250 kg (b) 200 kg (c) 150 kg (d) 100 kg

232. The quantity of urea required to supply 100 kgs of Nitrogen will be- **1** Raj JET-2019
(1) 217.39 kg (2) 92.00 kgs (3) 100.00 kgs (4) 200.00 kgs

233. The S content (%) in Single Super phosphate is – **c** BHU PET-2010
(a) 6 (b) 9 (c) 12 (d) 15

234. The soil more suitable for application of rock phosphate and basic slag is **a** TNPSC Agri-1997
(A) Acid soil (B) Saline soil (c) Neutral soil (D) Alkali soil

235. The sulphur coated urea contains generally - **4** RPSC ARO Agro-2022
(1) 20-25% N and 8-10% S (2) 20-25% N and 12-22% S
(3) 32-38% N and 8-10%, S (4) 32-38% N and 12-22% S

236. The terms 'citrate soluble' and water soluble' are associated with which of the following ? **C** IAS Pre-2010
(a) Nitrogenous fertilizers (b) Potassic fertilizers
(c) Phosphatic fertilizers (d) None of the above

237. The zinc content (%) of Zn-EDTA is – **a** BHU PET-2013
(a) 12 (b) 21 (c) 33 (d) 55

238. To get corresponding quantities of Muriate of potash – **1** TN PSC Ag-II: 2001
(1) Multiply K_2 O by 1.67 (2) Multiply K_2O by 2.00
(3) Multiply K2 O by 6.25 (4) None of these

239. To which group does urea belongs: **b** MP PAT-2016
1. Aldehyde 2. Amide 3. Alcohol 4. Nitrate

240. Universal antidote is mixture of – **4** TN AO-2012
(1) Charcoal and Lime (2) MgO and Charcoal
(3) Activated Charcoal and talc (4) Activated Charcoal, tannic acid and MgO

241. Urea contains nitrogen in the form of : **d** UPPSC Pre-2009
(a) Ammonium (b) Nitrite (c) Nitrate (d) Amide

242. Urea contains: **b** NSC MT P-

(a) 40%N (b)46%N (c)50%N (d)52%N 2018

243. Urea has highest content of……… With……… **Ans.: Nitrogen, 46%** NABARD-2021

244. Urea hydrolysis in soil is influenced by : **a** UPPSC Pre-2008

(a) Ni (b) Co (c) Fe (d) Mn

245. Urea hydrolysis in the soil produces : **b** UPPSC Pre-1997

(a) uric acid (b) ammonium carbonate (c) ammonium carbomate (d) amides

246. Urea hydrolysis in the soil produces : **b** UPPSC Pre-1998

(a) Uric acid (b) Ammonium carbonate (c) Ammonium carbomate (d) Amides

247. Urea is made of? **B** BOM AO-2021

a. $NH_3 + CO_2$ + NITRIC ACID b. Anhydrus ammonia + CO_2

248. Urea supergranule is efficient source of nitrogen for waterlogged paddy because **a** UPPSC Pre-2001

(a) its leaching losses are minimum

(b) its ammonia volatilization losses are low (c) its fixation in soil is low

(d) Denitrification losses from it are minimum

249. Use of high analysis fertilizers which minimize inadvertent addition of micronutrients **C** IAS Pre-2000

(a) causes toxicities of micronutreitns in soils and plants

(b) increases availability of micronutrients in soils and plans

(c) leads to deficiencies of micronutrients in soils and plants

(d) immobilizes micronutrients in soils and plants

250. Use of materials like sulphur. Polyform UF isobutyl idene diurea etc. improves fertilizer use efficiency. When such additives are used, the N-fertilizers are termed as **c** IAS Pre-1997

(a) prilled urea (b) controlled release nitrogenous fertilizers

(c) slow nitrifying N-fertilizers (d) complex fertilizers

251. Use of neem coated urea in paddy fields prevents : **c** UPPSC Pre-2008

(a) Leaching loss of nitrogen (b) Volatilisation loss of nitrogen

(c) Denitrification loss of nitrogen (d) Run-off loss of nitrogen

252. Use of rock-phosphate is good in : **a** UPPSC Pre-2008

(a) Laterite soils (b) Black cotton soil

(c) Alluvial soils (d) Calcareous soil

253. Various fertilizers are applied to provide plant nutrient. What is the Nitrogen percentage in Ammonium Sulphate? **Ans.: 20.6%** RRB SO-2018

254. Water soluble phosphatic fertilizer is – **4** TN AO-2012

(1) Rock phosphate (2) DAP (3) SSP (4) Orthophosphoric acid

255. What are the nitrogen and P_2O_5 contents in diammonium phosphate respectively in percentage ? **B** IAS Pre-2010

(a) 16 and 35 (b) 20 and 46 (c) 25 and 45 (d) 14 and 46

Explanation:

Diammonium phosphate (DAP) is a widely used fertilizer containing nitrogen and phosphorus. The typical composition of DAP is approximately 18-20% nitrogen (N) and 46-48% phosphorus pentoxide (P_2O_5).

256. What are the two plant nutrients other tha n phosphorous are found in super- **d** TNPSC Agri-

phosphote? 1997

(A) Ca, Fe (B) Ca, F (C) Ca, N (D) Ca, S

257. What is amount of ammonium nitrogen and nitrate nitrogen presence in 25kg of calcium ammonium nitrate (20% N)? **B** IAS Pre-2005

(a) 1.5 kg ammonium nitrogen and 3.5 kg nitrate nitrogen

(b) 2.5 kg ammonium nitrogen and 2.5 kg nitrate nitrogen

(c) 3.5 kg ammonium nitrogen and 1.5 kg nitrate nitrogen

(d) 4.5 kg ammonium nitrogen and 0.5 kg nitrate nitrogen

258. What is chemical formula of urea ? **c** UPPSC Pre-2005

(a) NHCONH (b) $NHCONH_2$ (c) NH_2CONH_2 (d) NH_2CONH_3

259. What is optimum time of application of farmyard manure : **2** RPSC ACF Agri -2011

(a) At the time of sowing (b) One month before sowing of crop

(c) One week after sowing (d) Six months before sowing of crop

260. What is the average physical size range (nm) of Nano Urea particles being manufactured in India? **3** RPSC AAO Ag -2022

(1) 50 – 100 nm (2) 100 – 200 nm (3) 20 – 50 nm (4) 1 -20 nm

261. What is the chemical formula of phosphogypsum : **c** UPPSC Pre-1998

(a) FeS_2 (b) $MgSO_4.7H_2O$ (c) $CaSO_4.2H_2$ (d) None

262. What is the commercial potash fertilizer preferred for tobacco crop ? **B** IAS Pre-2009

(a) K_2SO_4 (b) KCl (c) K_2CO_3 (d) KMn_4

263. What is the effect of application of phosphatic fertilizer to a green manure leguminous crop on the availability of phosphorus to the succeeding crop? **a** IAS Pre-1993

(a)Greater amount of phosphorus is taken up and converted into organic form, which is released on decomposition of green matter

(b) Green manure increases the availability in inorganic form to the nest crop

(c) It does not affect the availability of phoshorus to succeeding crop

(d) it fixes the phosphorus through humus and reduces the availability

264. What is the N : P content is DAP (Diammonium phosphate) fertilizer – **a** Raj JET-2014

(a) 18 : 48% (b) 20 : 50% (c) 46 : 20% (d) 20 : 20%

265. What is the nitrogen content in can fertilizer **a** IBS,AFO-2019

(a) 25 (b) 28 (c) 20.6 (d) 30 (e) 22

266. What is the percentage of Sulphur in agricultural grade pyrite : **a** UPPSC Pre-1998

(a) 18% (b) 22% (c) 25% (d) 28%

267. What is the permissible limit of biuret content in urea for foliar spray and soil application, beyond which it is toxic to plants ? **2** RPSC AO Ag - 2021

(1) 0.3% and 1.096 (2) 0.5% and 1.5% (3) 0.7% and 1.5% (4) 1.0% and 2.0%

268. What is the upper crops tolerable limit of biuret in urea ..? **3** RPSC Pre-1995

(1)0.5% (2)1.0% (3) 1.5% (4) 3%

269. What per cent of Calcium is found is Gypsum ? **1** Raj JET-2018

(1) 29.2 (2) 19.5 (3) 39.5 (4) 26.5

270. What quantity of urea will be required for 10 hectare area at the rate of 120 kg nitrogen per hectare? **4** RPSC ACF Agri -2011

(a) 160 kg (b) 260 kg (c) 520 kg (d) 2600 kg

271. When urea is hydrolysed to ammonium carborate the pH – **2** TNPSC – Ag: 1999

(1) Increases (2) Decreases (3) Remain unchanged (4) None of the above

272. Which among the following fertilizers are fully imported in india ? **c** Delhi PGT-2014

(a) Nitrogenous (b) Phosphatic (c) Potassic (d) sulphur

273. Which among the following is called highly hygroscopic fertilizer ? **A** ADA MP-2015

(A) Urea (B) Ammonium sulphate

(C) Calcium ammonium nitrate (D) Sodium nitrate

274. Which commercial fertilizer contains Mg & Ca as secondary nutrients? **3** MP PG PAT-2016

(1) Epsum (2) Gypsum (3) Both Epsum & Gypsum (4) None of these

275. Which fertilizer contains nutrients other than primary nutrients **c** Agri Pre PG-2013

(a)Urea (b) DAP (c) Ammonium sulphate (d)Ammonium nitrate

276. Which fertilizer is most beneficial for alkali soils ? **C** ADA Guj-2013

(A) Urea (B) . Ammonium nitrate

(C) Ammonium sulphate (D) Calcium ammonium nitrate

277. Which fertilizer shows luxury consumption in plant ? **C** ADA MP-2015

(A) Nitrogen (B) Phosphorus (C) Potassium (D) Zinc

278. Which fertilizers should not be mixed together when applied? **1** RPSC Pre-2003

(1) Basic slag and urea (2) Basic slag and potassium chloride

(3) Basic slag and ammonium sulphate

(4) Basic slag and potassium sulphate

279. Which is not a high analysis fertilizer – **4** Ag Sup JAU 2017

(1) Ammonium Phosphate (2) Urea (3) DAP (4) Sodium Nitrate

280. Which is straight fertilizer ? **c** School Lect. 2019

(a) Diammonium phosphate (b) NPK

(c) Urea (d) Nitrophoska

281. Which is the most commonly used potassium fertilizer ? **c** Delhi PGT-2014

(a) Sulphate of potash (b) Potassium oxide

(c) Muriate of potash (d) Potassium Permanganate

282. Which is the national representative body of all fertilizer manufactures in India? **a** Agri Pre PG-2021

(a) FAI (Fertilizer Association of India) (b) ISSS (c) FCO (d) NBSS & LUP

283. Which material cannot he mixed with superphosphate ? **a** UPPSC Pre-2009

(a) Ammonium sulphate (b) Potassium sulphate

(c) Calcium carbonate (d) Potassium schoenite

284. Which of the fertilizer not produced in India : **4** RPSC Pre-2008

(1) Urea (2)SSP (3) Zinc sulphate (4) Muriate of Potash

285. Which of the following contains highest nutrients? **3** MP PG PAT-2016

(1) FYM (2) Compost

(3) Droppings of sheep & goat (4) None of these

286. Which of the following fertilizer is insoluble in water? **c** MP PAT-2016

1. Single super phosphate 2. Double super phosphate

3. Rock phosphate 4. Triple super phosphate

287. Which of the following Fertilizer is not compatible for using in fertigation with **3** RPSC, AAO-

the potassium sulfate? 2018

(A) Urea (B) Ammonium nitrate

(C) Calcium nitrate (D) Potassium nitrate

288. Which of the following fertilizer/s is/ are not produced in India **3** RPSC, AAO-2018

(A) DAP (B) Urea

(C) Muriate of potash (D) All of these

289. Which of the following fertilizers is the only fertilizer under statutory price control ? **c** BHU UET-2015

(a) Potash (b) Ammonia (c) Urea (d) Phosphate

290. Which of the following fertilizers leaves most acidic effect on soil ? **2** TN PSC Ag-II: 2001

(1) Urea (2) Ammonium sulphate (3) Sodium nitrate (4) None of these

291. Which of the following fertilizers supply nitrogen to the crop ? **3** TN ACF-2012

I. Ammonium sulphate

II. Ammonium chloride

III. Diammonium phosphate

IV. Ammonium phosphate sulphate

of these

(1) I, II and IV (2) I, III and IV (3) I, III and II (4) I, II, III and IV

292. Which of the following is a complex fertilizer ? **c** BHU PET-2015

(a) Single superphosphate (b) Ammonium sulphate nitrate

(c) Ammonium phosphate (d) Calcium ammonium nitrate

293. Which of the following is a nitrification inhibitor **b** Agri Pre PG-2014

(a)Thio urea (b)N-serve

(c) Sulphur coated urea (d)Neem coated urea

294. Which of the following is a nitrification inhibitor? **2** RPSC Pre-2008

(1) Thio urea (2) N-serve

(3) Sulphur coated urea (4) Neem coated urea

295. Which of the following is a non-edible oil cake ? **2** RPSC AAO - 2018

(a) Mustard cake (b) Malmo cake (c) Linseed cake (d) Sesame cake

296. Which of the following is a slow release fertilizer- **4** MP PG PAT-2016

(1) Neem coated urea (2) Nserve

(3) N Thio urea (4) All of these

297. Which of the following is an example of integrated nutrient management (INM) **b** Agri Pre PG-2014

(a) N+ P + K + Zn (b) Urea + FYM + Biofertilizer

(c) Urea + 2,4-D (d) N+ P + Bavistin

298. Which of the following is commonly referred as muriate of potash ? **b** Gujrat AO-2017

(a) Potassium nitrate (b) Potassium chloride

(c) Potassium sulphate (d) Potassium di hydrogen phosphate

299. Which of the following is complex fertilizer? **b** ICAR Gen Agri-2008, 09

(A) Potassium sulphate (B) Urea ammonium Phosphate

(C) Ammonium sulphate (D) Calcium ammonium Nitrate

300. Which of the following is neutral fertilizer? **A** BOM AO-2021

a. CAN b. UREA c. SSP d. Ammonium Sulphate

301. Which of the following is not a Nitrogenous fertilizer? 4 MP PG PAT-2016
(1) Ammonium chloride (2) Anhydrous ammonia
(3) Calcium cyanamide (4) All of these

302. Which of the following is not a straight fertilizer? 3 MP PG PAT-2016
(1) Nitrogen fertilizer (2) Phosphate fertilizer
(3) FYM (4) Potash fertilizer

303. Which of the following nitrogenous fertilizer contains higher percentage of secondary nutrient compared to primary nutrient ? 2 Raj JET-2020
(1) CAN (2) Ammonium sulphate
(3) Ammonium sulphate nitrate (4) Urea

304. Which of the following nitrogenous fertilizer is of amide group? B AO GPSC-2013
(A) Ammonium sulphate (B) Urea (C) CAN (D) Sodium Nitrate

305. Which of the following pairs are correctly matched? c IAS Pre-1999
1. Ammonium sulphate : Acidic
2. Calcium ammonium nitrate : Neutral
3. Potassium nitrate : Basic
Select the correct answer using the codes given below
(a) 1and 2 (b) 2 and 3 (c) 1and 3 (d) 1,2 and 3

306. Which of the following phosphate fertilizer is suitable for acidic soils ? 1 Ag sup 2018
(1) Rock phosphate (2) Ammonium phosphate
(3) Diammonium phosphate (4) Dicalcium phosphate

307. Which of the following potassic fertilizers are soluble in water? c MP PAT-2016
1. KCl 2. K_2SO_4 3. Both of the above 4. None of these

308. Which of the following type of fertilizers mostly exported from our country – 3 Ag sup 2018
(1) Nitrogenous (2) Phosphatic (3) Potashic (4) Zinc

309. Which one is neutral fertilizer? c ICAR gen Agri-2010
(A) CAN (B) Urea (C) DAP (D) SSP

310. Which one is non-edible oil cake? 1 RPSC AAO Ag -2022
(1) Castor cake (2) Rapeseed and mustard cake
(3) Groundnut cake (4) Coconut cake

311. Which one is not an acid forming fertilizer : b UPPSC Pre-1999
(a) Ammonium sulphate (b) Calcium ammonium nitrate
(c) Nitrophosphate (d) Urea

312. Which one is organic nitrogenous fertilizer ? b BHU PET-2014
(a) Ammonium sulphate (b) Urea
(c) Calcium Ammonium Nitrate (d) Ammonium Chloride

313. Which one of the following fertilizer can be top dressed 1 RPSC Pre-2010
(1) Ammonium sulphate (2) Single super phosphate
(3) Diammonium phosphate (4) Muriate of potash

314. Which one of the following fertilizer is suitable and economical to apply under acidic soil condition ? 3 RPSC Pre-1995
(1) DAP (2) Single Super Phosphate
(3) Rock Phosphate (4) Basic Slag

315. Which one of the following fertilizers can be used for foliar spray | 3 | RPSC Pre-2010

(1) Ammonium sulphate (2) Muriate of potash

(3) Urea (4) Diammonium phosphate

316. Which one of the following fertilizers contains sulphur also ? | b | UPPSC Pre-2006

(a) DAP (b) SSP (c) NPK (12:32:16) (d) MOP

317. Which one of the following fertilizers is least hygroscopic ? | d | BHU UET-2013

(a) Urea (b) Ammonium sulphate

(c) Diammonium phosphate (d) Calcium ammonium nitrate

318. Which one of the following fertilizers is least hygroscopic? | c | IAS Pre-1993

(a) Urea (b) Ammonium soleplate

(c) Ammonium phosphate (d) Calcium ammonium nitrate

319. Which one of the following fertilizers is organic in nature – | c | BHU UET-2015

(a) Single superphosphate (b) Diammonium phosphate

(c) Urea (d) Ammonium chloride

320. Which one of the following has th highest iron content (in percentage)? | C | IAS Pre-2008

(a) Ferrous sulphate (b) Ferrous ammonium phosphate

(c) Ferrous oxide (d) Ferrous ammonium sulphate

321. Which one of the following is 1 : type clay mineral ? | c | BHU PET-2017

(a) Vermiculite (b) Illite (c) Nacrite (d) Saponite

322. Which one of the following is a mixed fertilizer – | d | BHU PET-2011

(a) Urea (b) Superphosphate

(c) Calcium ammonium nitrate (d) Amophos

323. Which one of the following is an organic chemical fertillzer? | B | IAS Pre-2006

(a) Calcium ammonium nitrate (b) Urea

(c) Ammonium phosphate (d) Muriate of potash

324. Which one of the following is complex fertilizer? | A | IBPS SO-2017

A.DAP B.CAN C.SSP D.MOP

325. Which one of the following is correct : | b | UPPSC Pre-1996

(a) $P_2O_5 \times 2.29 = P$ (b) $P_2O_5 \times 0.44 = P$ (c) $P_2O_5 \times 1.20 = P$ (d) $P_2O_5 \times 0.83 = P$

326. Which one of the following is not a phosphatic fertilizer – | c | Gujrat AO-2017

(a) DAP (b) KH_2PO_4 (c) KCl (d) Super phosphate

327. Which one of the following is not the advantage of using mixed fertilizers: | 1 | RPSC Pre-1998

(1)Economical (2)require less care

(3) reduce salinity (4) Application easier

328. Which one of the following is the chemical formula of Urea? | C | IAS Pre-2008

(a) $NH_4 H_2 PO_4 (NH_4)_2 SO_4$ (b) $(NH_4)_2 SO_4 NH_4 NO_3$

(c) $CO (NH_2)_2$ (d) $(NH_4)_2 SO_4$

329. Which one of the following pairs is correctly matched ? | a | IAS Pre-1995

Fertilizers	Nutrient content
Urea	42.0 (%N)
Di Ammonium phoshpahe	20.0 (%P)
Ammonium sulphate................	21.5 (%N)
Muriate of potash	47.5 (%K)

330. Which one of the following phosphatic fertilizer contains water- soluble phosphoric acid? **c** MP PAT-2013
(A) Basic slag (B) Rock phosphate
(C) Dicalcium phosphate (D) Ammonium phosphate

331. Which one of the following soil order covers the largest area in India ? **a** Raj JET-2014
(a) Inceptisols (b) Aridisols (c) Entisols (d) Vertisols

332. Which one of the following statements is not correct ? **1** RPSC, AAO-2019
(1) Rock Phosphate is a water soluble fertilizer
(2) Single super phosphate is a water soluble fertilizer
(3) Triple super phosphate is a acid soluble fertilizer
(4) Ammonium phosphate is a water soluble fertilizer

333. Which one of the followings is an organic chemical fertilizer ? **3** RPSC, AAO-2019
(1) Calcium Ammonium Nitrate (CAN)
(2) Di-Ammonium Phosphate (DAP)
(3) Urea (4) None of these

334. Which one of the followings is an organic chemical fertilizer ? **3** RPSC AAO - 2018
(a) Calcium Ammonium Nitrate (CAN) (b) Di-Ammonium Phosphate (DAP)
(c) Urea (d) None of these

335. Which phosphate compound is present in Single Super phosphate ? **c** BHU PET-2014
(a) $CaHPO_4$ (b) $Ca_3(PO_4)_2$ (c) $Ca(H_2PO_4)_2$ (d) H_3PO_4

336. Which soils favour maximum ammonia volatilization losses of fertilizer-N ? **c** BHU PET-2013
(a) Acid Soils (b) Waterlogged Soils
(c) Sodic Soils (d) Saline Soils

337. Whith one of the following statements is not correct ? **1** RPSC AAO - 2018
(a) Rock phosphate is a water soluble fertilizer.
(b) Single super phosphate is a water soluble fertilizer.
(c) Triple super phosphate is a acid soluble fertilizer
(d) Ammonium phosphate is a water soluble fertilizer

338. Zinc Sulphate $(ZnSO)_4$ should not be mixed with : **c** UPPSC Pre-1998
(a) Urea (b) Muriate of potash (c) D.A.P (d) F.Y.M.

339. Zinc sulphate $(ZnSO_4)$ should not be mixed with it : **a** UPPSC Pre-1997
(a) Urea (b) D.A.P. (c) Murate of potash (M.O.P.) (d) F.Y.M.

340. Zinc sulphate should not be mixed with **D** TO MPUAT-2014
(A) Urea (B) FYM
(C) Ammonium Chloride (D) DAP

341. Zinc-coated urea should contain minimum.........% zinc? **d** Agri Pre PG-2022
(a) 9 (b) 14 (c) 7 (d) 2

CHAPTER- 159: INSTRUMENTS PYQ'S

1. A device for measuring percolation and leaching losses from a column of soil under controlled condition is known as : **4** RPSC Pre-2003
   (1) Infiltrometer (2) Evaporimeter (3) Psychrometer (4) Lysimeter
2. A device used to present data using map is called : **1** RPSC ACF Agri -2011
   (a) Cartogram (b) Histogram (c) Pictogram (d) Pie gram
3. By the neutron moisture meter, surface soil moisture (upto 30cm depth) measurement could not be possible, because – **2** RPSC ARO Ag Chem - 2022
   (1) length of instrument is more (2) radiation hazard
   (3) range of moisture does not support in surface soil
   (4) due to soil properties variation
4. Find the incorrect match – **3** TN PSC Ag-I:1999
   (1) Lysimeter - Evapotranspiration
   (2) Leaf water potential - Pressure chameber
   (3) Field capacity - Tensiometer
   (4) Solar radiation - Pyrheliometer
5. Flame photometer is used in the detection of which of the following nutrients(s)? **3** RPSC, AAO-2018
   (A) N and P (B) N and K (C) K (D) P
6. For accurate pH measurement , which of the following is often used **c** BHU PET-2016
   (a) Pocket pH meter (b) Dye solution (c) pH meter (d) Colour chart
7. Gypsum blocks measure the soil moisture tension (atm.) most efficiently within the range of – **b** BHU PET-2010
   (a) 15-31 (b) 1-15 (c) 0.33-15 (d) 0-0.85
8. Identify the correct match – **4** TNPSC – Ag: 1999
   (1) Lysimeter – evapotranspiration (2) Wind vane – wind direction
   (3) Anemometer – wind velocity (4) All the above
9. In Electromagnetic spectrum, the range of near infrared band is. **4** Agri Pre PG-2016
   (1) 0.4 to 0.7μm (2) 730 cm (3) 0.1 to 30 cm (4) 0.7 to 3.o μm
10. In the pressure plate apparatus the ceramic plates are unable to measure pressure beyond – **2** RPSC ARO Ag Chem - 2022
    (1) 15 bar (2) 20 bar (3) 30 bar (4) 50 bar
11. Infrared thermometer is used to measure : **c** UPPSC Pre-2007
    (a) soil temperature (b) air temperature
    (c) crop canopy temperature (d) water temperature
12. Instrument used for estimating soil moisture is – **4** TN PSC Ag-II: 2001
    (1) Gypsum block (2) Tensiometer (3) Neutron probe (4) All of these
13. Lysimeter is used for measurement of **C** HPSC ADO-2022
    (A) transpiration (B) water flow (C) evapotranspiration (D) evaporation
14. Lysimeter is used for measuring – **1** TN AO-2012
    (1) Evapotransiration (2) Evaporation (3) Transpiration (4) Humidity
15. Lysimeter is used for measuring – **2** TN PSC Ag-II: 2001
    (1) Soil moisture (2) Evapotranspiration (3) Soil temperature (4) None of these

16. Match List I (Instrument) with List II (Used to measure) select the correct answer using the cods given below the lists d **IAS Pre-1999**

Lists I	List II
A. Tensiometer	1. Matric suction in the soil
B. Piezometer	2. Temperatue
C. Paychrometer	3. Rate of water entry into the soil
D. Infiltrometer	4. Water pressure in the soil

	A	B	B	D		A	B	C	D
(a)	1	4	2	3	(b)	2	3	1	4
(c)	1	4	3	2	(d)	4	1	2	3

17. Match List I with List II and select the correct answer C **IAS Pre-2001**

List I (Soil parameter)	List II (Apparatus sued)
A. Mechanical composition	1 Atterberg's apparatus
B. Soil aggregation	2. Pycnometer
C. Plasticity	3. Buoyoucos hydrometer
D. Particle density	4. Yoder's apparatus

	A	B	C	D		A	B	C	D
(a)	3	1	4	2	(b)	2	4	3	1
(c)	3	4	1	2	(d)	4	3	1	2

18. Match List-I with List-II and select the correct answer using the code given bellow the Lists : A **IAS Pre-2010**

List-I (Method of measuring soil moisture)	List-II (Useful range kpa)
A. Tensiometer	1. 0 to < – 1500
B. Resistance blocks	2. 50 to < – 10000
C. Neutron scattering	3. – 100 to < – 1500
D. Pressure membrane apparatus	4. 0 to – 85

Code :

	A	B	C	D		A	B	C	D
(a)	2	3	1	4	(b)	4	1	3	2
(c)	4	3	1	2	(d)	2	1	3	4

Explanation:

A. Tensiometer: Measures soil moisture in the range of 0 to -85 kPa. Tensiometers are useful for measuring soil moisture in the wetter range (low tension).

B. Resistance blocks: These are used for measuring soil moisture in the range of -100 to < -1500 kPa. Resistance blocks are often used in drier soils where higher tensions are measured.

C. Neutron scattering: Effective across a wide range, including very dry conditions, so it fits with 0 to < -1500 kPa.

D. Pressure membrane apparatus: Used for measuring soil moisture at very high tensions, from 50 to < -10000 kPa. This method is suitable for measuring moisture in very dry soils.

19. **Pressure plate apparatus is used for measurement of soil moisture tension upto** — c — BHU PET-2016
(a) 4.2 bars (b) 0.33 bars (c) 15 bars (d) 30 bars

20. **Salinity of a soil detected by using –** — 4 — TN PSC Ag-II: 2001
(1) pH meter (2) More than PET (3) Membrane plate apparatus (4) Osmometer
Most correct answer is : EC meter

21. **Soil moisture can be estimated using –** — 4 — TN AO-2008
(1) Anemometers (2) Barometers (3) Hygrometers (4) Tensiomters

22. **Soil moisture is measured by** — A — ADA MP-2015
(A) Hydrometer (B) Tensiometer (C) Peizometer (D) None of above

23. **Soil moisture tension is measured by –** — 3 — TNPSC – Ag: 1999
(1) Hydrometer (2) Infiltrometer (3) Tensiometer (4) Penetrometer

24. **Soil strength is measured by ?** — e — IBS,AFO-2020
(a)Thermometer (b) Dynamometer (c)Tensiometer
(d) Micrometer (e) Penetrometer

25. **Tensiometer is suitable for which type of soil?** — B — HPSC ADO-2022
(A) Clay soil (B) Sandy soil (C) Loamy soil (D) Laterite soil

26. **Tensiometer measures the :** — b — UPPSC Pre-2005
(a) Total soil water potential (b) Total soil moisture tension
(c) Matric potential (d) Total soil moisture suction

27. **Tensiometer used to measure soil moisture content could be used up to which soil moisture tension?** — 2 — RPSC AAO-2022
(1) 3.0 atmosphere tension (2) 0.85 atmosphere tension
(3) 5.0 atmosphere tension (4) 12.0 atmosphere tension

28. **Tensiometer used to measure soil moisture content could be used up to which soil moisture tension?** — 2 — RPSC AAO Ag -2022
(1) 3.0 atmosphere tension (2) 0.85 atmosphere tension
(3) 5.0 atmosphere tension (4) 12.0 atmosphere tension

29. **Tensiometers measure soil moisture tension (bar) only up to –** — c — BHU PET-2014
(a) 30.0 (b) 15.0 (c) 0.85 (d) 0.33

30. **The use of tensiometer is confined up to metric potential of –** — 1 — UPPSC Pre-2003
(1) -0.8 bar (2) – 0.6 bar (3) – 0.4 bar (4) – 0.2 bar

31. **The useful limit of the most of the tensiometer is equal -** — 3 — RPSC ARO Agro-2022
(1) 0.50 atm (2) 0.65 atm (3) 0.85 atm (4) 1.00 atm

32. **Which is a correct match in the following** — b — UPPSC Pre-2000
(a) Particle size analysis – Permeameter of soil
(b) Soil moisture estimation – Neutron scatterometer
(c) Soil moisture retention - Hydrometer (d) Soil bulk density – Picnometer

33. **Which of the following instrument is used for measuring soil moisture?** — d — IBS,AFO-2021
(a) Anemometer (b) Altimeter (c) Crescograph
(d) Tensiometer (e) Auxanometer

CHAPTER- 160 : INSTITUTES SOIL SCIENCE PYQ'S

1. National Bureau of Soil Survey and Land Use Planning is located at : **3** — RPSC ACF Agri -2011

(a) Hyderabad (b) Mau NathBhanjan (c) Nagpur (d) Udaipur

2. In India, National Bureau of soil survey and Land use planning (NBSS & LUP) was d established in the year? **2** — RPSC ARO Ag Chem - 2022

(1) 1975 (2) 1976 (3) 1977 (4) 1978

3. Indian Institute of Soil Science is located at : **d** — UPPSC Pre- 2008

(a)Karrial (b)Nagpur (c)Dehradun (d)Bhopal

4. Headquarter of Central Soil and Water Conservation Research and Training Institute is **b** — UPPSC Pre- 2009

(a) Agra (b) Dehradun (c) Chandigarh (d) Ootakmond

5. Where is the Central Soil and Water Conservation Research and Training Institute (CSWCRTI)situated? **b** — IFFCO T - 2019

(a) Lucknow(b) Dehradun (c) Karnal (d) Bangalore

6. Central Soil Salinity Research Institute is located at : **c** — UPPSC Pre- 1997

(a) Jodhpur (b) Dehradoon (c) Karnal (d) Hyderabad

7. Central Soil & Water Conservation Research & Training Institue, in Gujarat is located at – **c** — Gujrat AO- 2017

(a) Boriavi (b) Kutch (c) Vasad (d) Godhra

8. Indian Institute of Soil Science is located at – **b** — MP PAT- 2013

(A) Hisar (B) Bhopal (C) New Delhi (D) Lucknow

9. Indian Institute of soil science is located at : **3** — RPSC Pre- 1998

(1) Ludhiana (2) Hisar (3) New Delhi (4) Bhopal

10. Indian Institute of Soil Science is located at: **b** — MP PAT- 2016

1. Indore 2. Bhopal 3. Jabalpur 4. Raipur

11. Mark a place where national Bureau of soil survey and Land use planning is located **3** — RPSC Pre- 2007

(1) Hyderabad (2) Udaipur (3) Nagpur (4) Mau Nath Bhanjan

CHAPTER- 161 : SOIL SCIENTITS PYQ'S

1. The phenomenon of Cation Exchange was discovered by - **1** RPSC ARO Ag Chem - 2022
(1) J. Thomas Way (2) Gomez, A. A. (3) Venselow (4) Krishnamoorthy

2. In Cation exchange equations for divalent monovalent ion exchange process, most widely used ion exchange equation is given by - **3** RPSC ARO Ag Chem - 2022
(1) Kerr (1928) (2) Vanselow (1932) (3) Gapon (1933) (4) Jenny (1941)

3. The law of restitution was propounded by :- **4** RPSC, AO-2016
(1) Mitscherlich (2) Spillman (3) Baule (4) J.Von Liebig

4. Match List I (Scientists) with List II (Associated with) and select the correct answer using the codes given below the lists **c** IAS Pre-1999

Lists I	*Lists II*
A. L.D. Baver	1. Crop logging technique
B. H.F. Clements	2. Soil physics
C. E. John Russel	3. Buffer method for determining lime requirement of soils
D. H.E Shoemaker	4. Rothamsted experimental station Harpenden

	A	B	C	D		A	B	C	D
(a)	1	2	3	4	(b)	2	1	3	4
(c)	1	2	4	3	(d)	2	1	4	3

5. Match List I with List II and select the correct answer **A** IAS Pre-2002

List I (Concept)	List II (Scientists)
A. Q/I relationship of K	1. Sorenson
B. Ratio/sssquare root law	2. Beckett
C. 'A' Value	3. Schofield
D. Soil reaction	4. Fried and Dean

	A	B	C	D		A	B	C	D
(a)	2	3	4	1	(b)	2	3	1	4
(c)	3	2	4	1	(d)	3	2	1	4

6. Match List I with List II and select the correct answer **C** IAS Pre-2004

List I (Scientists)	List II (Law/test/hypothesis)
A. Spillman	1. Pressure – flow model
B. Munch	2. Gibberellin isolation
C. Yabuta and Hayashi	3. Concept of Limiting Factor
D. Liebig	4. Law of diminishing returns

	A	B	C	D		A	B	C	D
(a)	4	3	2	1	(b)	2	1	4	3
(c)	4	1	2	3	(d)	2	3	4	1

7. Match List I with List II and select the correct answer using the code given below the lists **B** IAS Pre-2006

List I (Theory)	List II (Scientist)
A. Pressure flow theory of solute translocation	1. Mitchell

B. Cytochrome pump theory of salt uptake — 2. Dixon
C. Chemeosmotic theory of ATP synthesis — 3. Munch
D. Cohesion tension theory of ascent of sap — 4. Lundergarth

	A	B	C	D		A	B	C	D
(a)	1	4	3	2	(b)	2	3	4	1
(c)	2	1	4	3	(d)	2	4	1	3

8. Match List I with List II and select the correct answer using the code given below the lists — **A** — IAS Pre-2008

List I (Scientist)	List II (Area of contribution)
A. Mohr	1. Soil moisture limits
B. Munsell	2. Relative hardness of minerals
C. Atterberg	3. Soil colour chart

	A	B	C		A	B	C
(a)	1	3	2	(b)	2	3	1
(c)	3	2	1	(d)	2	1	3

9. The method of extraction of available P in acid soils was given by — **B** — IAS Pre-2010
(a) Olsen et al. (1954) (b) Bray and Kurtz (1945)
(c) Subbaiah and Asija (1956) (d) Chesnin and Yien (1951)

10. The author of book **'The Nature and Properties of Soils'** is : — **c** — UPPSC Pre-1996
(a) Dr. J.S. Kanwar (b) Wali and Motiramani (c) Dr. NC. Brady (d) I.J. Kune

11. Who proposed the "Inverse yield Nitrogen" law : — **a** — UPPSC Pre-1998
(a) Wilcox 1929 (b) J.V. Biebig 1840 (c) Mitscherlich (d) Macy 1936

12. When plants are supplied with adequate amount of all but one limiting element, their growth is proportional to the amount of limiting element. this law is known as : — **d** — UPPSC Pre-1998
(a) Liebig law of minimum (b) Macy poverty adjustment
(c) Blackman's law of optima and limiting factors
(d) Mitscherlich's law of diminishing return

13. Principle of stokes law is used for : — **b** — UPPSC Pre-2002
(a)Chemical –analysis (b) Mechanical analysis
(c) Microbiological analysis (d)None of these

14. Heat flow in soil is described by : — **c** — UPPSC Pre-2008
(a) Darcy's law (b) Fick's law (c) Fourier's law (d) Ohm's law

15. The essentiality of iron for plants was proved by : — **a** — UPPSC Pre-2010
(a) E. Geis (b) C. Sprengel (c) K. Warington (d) C. B. Lipman

16. Experments on effect of manures on crop were initiated by____ — **a** — NSC MT H-2019
(a) Sir Johan BannetLawes (b) G.J. Mendel (c) Van Helmont (d) Justus Von liebig

17. Weathering stage in soil formation was given by? — **b** — IFFCO T -2019
(a) Jenny (b) Mohr (c) Von barren (d) Dokuchaiev

18. Particle size analysis is based on – — **1** — TN AAO-2019
(1) Stoke's law (2) Darcy's law (3) Poisellieu's law (4) Ohm's law

19. The preparation of farm-yard manure by trench method was given by : — **2** — RPSC ACF

(a) N.S. Subbarao (b) C.N. Acharya (c) T.S. Biswash (d) B. Bear — Agri -2011

20. The adjusted sodium adsorption ratio (Adj SAR) was first proposed by - **4** RPSC ARO Ag Chem - 2022
(1) Eaton (1950) (2) Richards (1954) (3) Bear (1964) (4) Suarez (1981)

21. 'Catena' word introduced first time in soil science by – **4** RPSC ARO Ag Chem - 2022
(1) Jenny (1941) (2) Marbut (1945) (3) Dokuchaev (1900) (4) Milne (1935)

22. The Jenny (1941) formulated the following equation - S = f (Cl, b, r, p, t......) in this equation 'r' stands for - **2** RPSC ARO Ag Chem - 2022
(1) right time (2) topography (3) organism (4) climate

23. Who introduced concept of nutrient index value to describe the fertility status of soil?. **2** RPSC ARO Ag Chem - 2022
(1) Havlin et al. (2) Parker et al. (3) Takkar et al. (4) Sakai et al.

24. The 'A' value concept was given by - ***** RPSC ARO Ag Chem - 2022
(1) Larsen (1967) (2) Russell (1954)
(3) Max Planck (1900) (4) Freud (1964)

25. Who is the father of Indian Soil Science and Agricultural Chemistry? **2** RPSC ARO Ag Chem - 2022
(1) V.V. Dokuchaev (2) LW. Leather (3) J.V. Liebig (4) J. Thomas

26. In Chepil and Woodruff's equation of soil loss calculation for wind erosion, WE = f(ICKLV), here 'I' denotes - **3** RPSC ARO Ag Chem - 2022
(1) Rainfall intensity (2) Surface roughness
(3) Soil erodibility (4) Vegetative cover

27. Who gave the DTPA extraction of micronutrient determination method in soil? **4** RPSC AAO Ag -2022
(1) Berger and Truog (1939) (2) Subbiah and Asija (1956)
(3) Adamus and Hartwing (1982) (4) Linsday and Norvell (1978)

28. Darcy's law is valid for - **1** RPSC ARO Agro-2022
(1) Only saturated flow (2) Only unsaturated flow
(3) Both saturated and unsaturated flow (4) None of the above

CHPATER -162: TITRATION /ANALYSIS PYQ'S

1. 5000 ppm is same as______________% **1** (RPSC (AO)-2009
(1) 0.5 (2) 0.05 (3) 0.005 (4) 0.0005

2. Calculate the sodium adsorption ratio of a soil, if soil analysis revealed that saturated extract contained 20, 10 and 100 meq/liter of Ca^{+2}, Mg^{+2} and Na^{+1}, respectively :- **4** AARO Agro-2016
(1) 34.8 (2) 31.8 (3) 28.8 (4) 25.8

3. one bar equals to.......mega pascal - **3** RPSC, AAO-2018
(1) 1 (2) 10 (3) 0.1 (4) 100

4. The concept of critical soil test level was given by :- **3** RPSC, AO-2016
(1) Muhr (2) Gregory (3) Cate and Nelson (4) Mitscherlich

5. The residual sodium carbonate of a water containing carbonate, bicarbonate, **3** RPSC Pre-

calcium and magnesium ions as 5, 20, 10 and 5 meq/L, respectively, will be : 1998
(1) 0 meq/L (2) 5 meq/L (3) 10 meq/L (4) 20 meq/L

6. When a litre of solution has one gram molecular weight of a substance dissolved in it, is called – a BHU PET-2012
(a) Molar solution (b) Molal solution
(c) Standard solution (d) Normal solution

7. Who gave the DTPA extraction of micronutrient determination method in soil? 4 RPSC AAO-2022
(1) Berger and Truog (1939) (2) Subbiah and Asija (1956)
(3) Adamus and Hartwing (1982) (4) Linsday and Norvell (1978)

8. The osmotic pressure (in atm.) of the soil solution to which plant roots are subjected to at the saturation point on account of salinity is given by a IAS Pre-1997
(a) 0.36 x ECe $x10^3$ (b) 0.036 x ECe x 10^3
(c) 0.36 x ECe x 10^4 (d) 0.036 x ECe x 10^6

9. In order to assess the immediate fertility level of a given soil for potassium, which one of the following forms of potassium present in soil would one test for? a IAS Pre-1993
(a) Total K (b) Exchangeable K
(c) Water soluble K (d) K held in cthe silt

10. Match *List I* (*Nutrients*) with *List II* (*Soil test technique*) and select the correct answer: b IAS Pre-1997

List 1	*List 2*
A. Available N	1. Morgan's method
B. Available P	2. Chromic acid digestion method
C. Available K	3. Olsen's method
D. Organic matter	4. Alkaline permanganate method

	A	B	C	D		A	B	C	D
(a)	4	3	2	1	(b)	3	4	1	2
(c)	4	3	1	2	(c)	3	4	2	1

11. The molarity of 100ml of a solution containing 0.36g of NaOH will be b IAS Pre-1998
(a) 0.009 (b) 0.090 (c) 1.100 (d) 1.440

12. Mechanical analysis of soil makes use of B IAS Pre-2001
(a) Darcy's law (b) Stoke's Law (c) Schofield's Law (d) Ohm's Law

13. Which one of the following is the correct quantity of Zinc sulphate required to prepare 100 litres of 2000 ppm solution for foliar spray ? Quantity of Zinc sulphate required (in gram) C IAS Pre-2001
(a) 20 (b) 100 (c) 200 (d) 2000

14. Which one of the following is NOT a tracer oriented technique in soil fertility evaluation methods? A IAS Pre-2002
(a) K value (b) A value (c) E value (d) L value

15. Match List I with List II and select the correct answer C IAS Pre-2002

List I (Available)	List II (Method of extraction/estimation)
A. Phosphorus	1. Alkaline $KMnO_4$
B. Sulphur	2. 0.s m $NaHCO_3$
C. Nitrogen	3. DTPA

D. Manganese 4. 0.15% $CaCl_2$

	A	B	C	D		A	B	C	D
(a)	2	3	1	4	(b)	1	4	2	3
(c)	2	4	1	3	(d)	1	3	2	4

16. For the estimation of which one of the following si 'Normal Neutral' ammonium acetate solution is used? — D — IAS Pre-2008

(a) Available sulphur in soil
(b) Available phosphorus in soil
(c) Potassium content in pant material
(d) Available potassium content in soil

17. The analysis of a soil sample shows pH = 7.5, EC = 5.0 dSm^{-1} and exchangeable sodium percentage = 12 To — A — IAS Pre-2008

Which one of the following categories does it belong?

(a) Saline soil (b) Alkali soil (c) Saline alkali soil (d) Acid soil

18. Match List I with List II and select the correct answer using the code given below the Lists : — c — IAS Pre-2009

List I (*Available Nutrient*)	List II (*Extractant*)
A. Boron	1. 0.15% $CaCl_2$ solution
B. Nitrogen	2. Hot water
C. Sulphur	3. Alkaline $KMnO_4$

Code :

	A	B	C
(a)	2	1	3
(b)	1	3	2
(c)	2	3	1
(d)	3	2	1

19. The indicator used in determination of organic carbon from soil is — D — AO GPSC-2013

(A) Methylene blue (B) Diphenyl amine
(C) Methyl orange (D) Methyl red

20. Amount of chemical required to prepare 100 ml solution of 4000 ppm is : — (c) — UPPSC Pre-2000

(a) 150 mg (b) 300 mg (c) 400 mg (d) 500 mg

21. In the routine soil testing available nitrogen is estimated Indirectly by determining. — 4 — UPPSC Pre-2003

(1) Total Nitrogen (2) Organic Nitrogen (3) Total Carbon (4) Organic Carbon

22. Methods for estimation of nitrogen are — 3 — RPSC FSO-2019

(1) Dumas and Carius method
(2) Kjeldahl's and Carius method
(3) Dumas and Kjeldahl's method
(4) Carius method

23. Match List-I correctly with List-II and select your answer using the codes given below — c — TNPSC Ag-1995

List-I	List-II
(A) Arc process	(1) Superphosphate

(B) Gypsum process (2) Nitric acid
(C) Dent process (3) Ammonia
(D) Haber's process (4) Ammonia sulphate

Codes

	a	b	c	d
A	3	2	4	1
B	1	3	2	4
C	2	4	1	3
D	4	3	1	2

24. The sulphur status of normal soil as extracted by 0.15% $CaCl_2$ is interpreted medium, when the sulphur content is - 2 RPSC ARO Ag Chem - 2022

(1) 5 —10 mg/kg^{-1} (2) 10 —15 mg/kg^{-1}
(3) 15 — 20 mg/kg^{-1} (4) 20 — 25 mg/kg^{-1}

25. Azomethane —H is used in determination of - 3 RPSC ARO Ag Chem - 2022

(1) Calcium (2) Sulphur (3) Boron (4) Molybdenum

26. Determination of $CaCO_3$ by rapid titrationmethod (Puri,1930), the indicater used is – 4 RPSC ARO Ag Chem - 2022

(1) Bromothymol blue (2) Bromocresol green
(3) Cresol red (4) Both (1) and (2)

27. Which of the following is responsible for the green colour at the end point of the titration in organic carbon determination? 1 RPSC ARO Ag Chem - 2022

(1) Cr^{3+} (2) Cr^{6+} (3) CA^{4-} (4) C^{4+}

28. During the extraction of micronutrient cations by DTPA method (Lindsay and Norvell, 1978), how much TEA is proton ated? 3 RPSC ARO Ag Chem - 2022

(1) 25% (2) 50% (3) 75% (4) 100%

29. In Kjeldahl digestion fo soil for N determination, K_2SO_4 is used to - 1 RPSC ARO Ag Chem - 2022

(1) Increase the temperature of digestion (2) Break triple bond of Nitrogen
(3) Catalysis of the reaction (4) Convert the NH^+_4 to NO^-_3

30. For preparation of 2 liter solution of 1N potassium dicromate, how much quantity of chemical is needed? 4 RPSC ARO Ag Chem - 2022

(1) 24.52 gin (2) 49.04 gm (3) 75.53 gm (4) 98.08 gm

31. In mineralisable N determination mixed indicator is prepared by - 3 RPSC ARO Ag Chem - 2022

(1) methyl red and bromocresol blue (2) methyl orange and bromocresol green
(3) methyl red and bromocresol green (4) methyl yellow and bromocresol purple

32. In determination of available K by neutralnormal ammonium acetate (IN NH_4 OAC,pH 7.0) solution, the proportion of soil :solution ratio is - 3 RPSC ARO Ag Chem - 2022

(1) 1 : 2 (2) 1 : 4 (3) 1 : 5 (4) 1 :10

33. In determination of Ca+Mg by EDTA method, which of the following indicator is used in titration of Ca alone? 4 RPSC ARO Ag Chem - 2022

(1) Phenolphthalein (2) Diphenylamine
(3) Eriochrome black T (4) Calcon

34. Reagent used for the extraction of phosphorus in alkaline soils **c** ICAR Gen Agri-2004

(A) Bray No.1 (B) Bray No.2

(C) Olesensreagent (D) Both A & B

CHAPTER- 163 : IMPORTANT SOIL SCIENCE BOOKS PYQ'S

1. Author of book 'Nature and Properties of soil' is : **a** UPPSC Pre-2002

(a) N.C. Barady (b) J.S. Kanwar (c) F.E. Bear (d) E.W. Russel

2. The book "The Nature and Properties of soils" is written by : **4** RPSC, AAO-2009

(1) D.S. Kler (2) M. Reddy

(3) T.Y. Reddy and G.H.S. Reddy (4) N.C. Brady

3. The book 'Element of Agriculture Chemistry' was published by________ **b** NSC MT H-2019

(a) Justus von Liebig (b) Sir Humphry Davy (c) Van Helmont (d) J.B. Lawes